NEBULAE
AND
GALAXIES

By
GIORGIO ABETTI
and
MARGHERITA HACK

Translated by
V. BAROCAS

THOMAS Y. CROWELL COMPANY ★ NEW YORK

Established 1834

First published as
'Le nebulose e gli universi-isole'
in the series Edizioni Scientifiche Einaude
by Paolo Boringhieri, Turin, Italy
First published
in the United States of America in 1965
Printed in the United States of America

1 2 3 4 5 6 7 8 9 10

Contents

Illustrations

ILLUSTRATIONS

ILLUSTRATIONS

ILLUSTRATIONS

Preface

SINCE early astronomical observations it has been customary to call 'nebulae' those celestial objects which appear like small faint clouds, scattered in various regions of the sky. With the rapid development of methods of observation, it soon appeared, however, that countless other systems existed beyond the boundaries of our Galaxy, which were different in form, size, distance, and could not be identified by the simple and general term of 'nebulae'. It became, therefore, necessary to distinguish between the many types of nebulae and to give to each a suitable name.

There are three groups of celestial objects which are generally called nebulae in astronomy. In this book we have attempted to give a description of these objects as well as some indication of their physical constitution, their dimension, their distance and their possible evolution.

The first of these groups is that of planetary nebulae, so called by early observers probably because they appeared as small round or oval discs of a greenish colour reminiscent of the planets. These objects belong to our Galaxy and we know now their physical constitution and their probable formation.

The second group includes two types of nebulae which differ in appearance, but which are of the same nature. We are referring to those large masses of gas scattered in great numbers, mainly in the plane of the Milky Way. One type is seen as shining, irregular shapes, with some parts much brighter than others and they may cover large areas of the sky. The other type is seen as dark masses of gas which absorb the light of stars within them or situated beyond them. The gas is the same, composed of the same elements in both cases. In the first type the gas is excited by the very hot neighbouring stars and in the second it is in a neutral state and is therefore dark and no stars are visible. All these nebulae belong to our Galaxy. The first

PREFACE

are called 'bright irregular nebulae' and the second 'dark irregular nebulae'.

The third group of nebulae consists of millions of 'external galaxies' or 'island universes'. These nebulae populate the universe, beyond our Galaxy, to its boundaries which cannot be reached by our instruments. They are of various shapes and in different stages of evolution. With the help of modern instruments of increasing power and efficiency, and of modern methods of observation, these objects have become of great interest to astronomers. We must remember, however, that research in this field is still at an early stage both in the observational and in the theoretical field, and that any information on the actual present state of these objects, is likely to be extremely useful.

This is not intended to be a technical book on the subject of nebulae, but rather a book which may be of help and interest to the rapidly increasing number of people interested in celestial phenomena.

G. B.
M. H.

Osservatorio Astrofisico di Arcetri—Firenze.
Osservatorio Astronomico di Merate (Como).

AUTHORS' NOTE

The reader unfamiliar with standard astronomical terminology, will find the terms explained in the Appendix at the end of this book.

CHAPTER I

Nebulae

I.1 Historical background.

THE bright patches in parts of the Milky Way and the faint clouds
mixed with stars attracted the attention of observers of the sky even
before the invention of the telescope. When later Galileo pointed his
telescope to the sky and made his discoveries, he wrote in his *Sidereus
Nuncius*, published in Venice in 1610:

'. . . we observed the essence, that is the material forming the
Milky Way itself. By means of the telescope it is possible to scrutinize
this part of the sky and to settle, by the certain evidence before our
eyes, all the disputes which for many centuries harassed philosophers.
In fact the Galaxy is nothing more than a congeries of numerous
stars, scattered in groups. In whatever region of it we point our
telescope, at once a great multitude of stars is seen. Several appear
large and very distinct, but all the small stars are completely un-
explorable.

'It is not in the Galaxy alone that we note this milky whiteness,
similar to whitish clouds, but in the ether also we see a great number
of small areas of similar colour, which shine with faint light here
and there. If we direct our telescope to them, we will see a thick
conglomeration of stars. Moreover, what is even a greater wonder
is the fact that the stars, which until now have been called nebulae[1]
by some astronomers, are actually groups of small stars distributed
in a wonderful way. Each one of them cannot be seen on account of
its faintness, which is due to its great distance from us, but the
mixing of their rays produces that whiteness which up to now has
been thought to be a denser part of the sky with the capacity of
reflecting the light of the stars or of the sun. We have observed some

[1] In the original text: stellae ab astronomis singulis in hanc usque diem
Nebulosae appellatae.

of these areas and two of them in particular. In the first we have the nebula called "Orion's Head" in which we have counted twenty-one stars. The second contains the nebula called "Praesepe" which consists not of one star only, but of a congeries of more than forty small stars: we have noted thirty-six besides the "Asellos".[1]

The Asellos are the two stars visible to the naked eye: Asellus Borealis (γ Cancri) of fifth magnitude, and Asellus Australis (δ Cancri) of fourth magnitude.

Later, in 'The Assayer', Galileo repeated the same idea:

'We know for certain that a nebula is nothing more than a conglomeration of minute stars, invisible to us. In spite of this, the field occupied by them is not invisible to us, but appears in the likeness of a small whitish patch, which is produced by the joining together of all the rays which surround each small star.' And again in the third day of the 'Dialogue on the Two Chief Systems of the World' Sagredo says: 'Nebulae used to be only little whitish patches, but then with the help of the telescope we have transformed them into little groups of many beautiful and brilliant stars.'

Simon Mayr or Marius, contemporary of Galileo, in 1612 gave a description of the Andromeda Nebula in the preface to *Mundus Jovialis*. This nebula, visible to the naked eye, appeared through his telescope as a cloud consisting of three rays, whitish, irregular and faint, brighter towards the centre.

Later, in 1656, Huygens, who had improved the telescope and had obtained magnifications greater than those used by Galileo, gave a good description and a drawing of Orion Nebula in *Systema Saturnium*: 'Portentum, cui certe simile aliud nunquam apud reliquas fixas potui animadvertere.'[2] Moreover he claims to be the first to have discovered the nature of the nebular material surrounding the stars. In his opinion this is totally different from that in the nebular regions of the Milky Way, the latter consisting of a conglomeration of stars.

In the following century many more observations of nebulae by telescope were obtained, as astronomers became more interested in these objects.

In 1751, Nicolas-Louis de Lacaille, astronomer and mathematician of the 'College Mazarin', was at the Cape of Good Hope for the

---

[1] In the original text: nos, praeter Asellos, trigintasex notavimus.
[2] 'It is a portent to which I have been unable to see anything similar among the remaining fixed stars.'

purpose of determining the solar parallax, and while there he happened to observe two celestial objects, which had already been mentioned by Portuguese and Dutch sailors, and which he called the 'Cape Clouds'. These are the two well-known groups of nebulae which we call 'Magellanic Clouds'. Lacaille gives a very detailed description of these objects in his memoir *Sur les étoiles nébuleuses du ciel austral*.

Some years later, in 1771, Charles Messier, who had been nicknamed by Louis XV *'le furet des comètes'*, because he had discovered fourteen of them, published in the memoir of the Paris Observatory his now well-known *Catalogue des nébuleuses et des amas d'étoiles* which contains the equatorial co-ordinates of 103 objects.

It was left to W. Herschel to add considerably to the knowledge of nebulae. He achieved this with the reflectors that he constructed himself, particularly with his 48-inch (f. l. 40 ft.) which at that time was really a giant telescope.

Herschel, helped by his sister Caroline, published his *Catalogue of one thousand new nebulae and clusters of stars* in the *Philosophical Transactions* in 1786. In it he called attention to the great variety of celestial objects listed. He described the shape of some of them and in particular he mentioned the nebulosity which produces that 'wonderful and inexplicable phenomenon' observed around Orion. Finally he called attention to the appearance of some of the nebulae which showed that they could be resolved into stars.

At this stage the problem to be solved was whether the celestial objects of nebular character observed by Galileo and by his successors, were really conglomerations of stars which could be resolved into single stars, according to the power of the telescope used, or whether these nebulosities were, at least in part, composed of shapeless bright matter. At first Herschel was uncertain of the nature of nebulae and which method of classification to adopt. He was convinced that with the use of more powerful telescopes, it would be possible to resolve all nebulae into stars. He also accepted Kant's hypothesis, according to which some of the nebulae could be systems similar to our Galaxy, namely that they were 'island universes' all contained in the greater universe. However, his later observations convinced him of the existence of a nebulosity mixed with stars which consisted mainly of 'a bright fluid of nature completely unknown to us'. Herschel believed that these 'shining fluids' were essentially very

17

B

different from aggregates of stars, although both were so mixed together as to make it extremely difficult to identify the one from the other.

He classified nebulae in the following six classes:

1. Clusters of stars in which stars could be easily separated and which could be subdivided into two classes; globular clusters and irregular clusters.

2. Nebulae which could be resolved into stars, or which could be resolved at a future date, when more powerful telescopes would be available.

3. Real nebulae in which stars are completely absent and which can be divided into classes according to their brightness and their size.

4. Planetary nebulae.

5. Stellar nebulosity.

6. Nebulous stars.

Herschel had also observed that in the regions of the sky where stars tend to crowd together, such as the Milky Way, there existed much darker areas, as if stars were totally absent and one could look through these gaps into infinite space. In conveying to his faithful assistant, his sister Caroline, the idea that these might well be 'holes' in the sky, Herschel warned her to be on the look out for the presence of nebulae often existing near these 'holes'. Herschel was very struck by the great size of these dark areas, and he observed them with great pains and great care, but did not succeed in reaching a satisfactory explanation of their origin.

William Parsons (Lord Rosse) followed in the footsteps of Herschel in the construction of large reflectors. In 1845 he made a large speculum 72 inches in diameter and 54 ft. focal length. This huge telescope was erected at Birr Castle, Parsonstown in Ireland, and was known as the 'leviathan of Parsonstown'. The tube of the telescope was erected between two walls which limited its movement to an hour angle of only one hour near the meridian. With this unwieldy but powerful telescope, Lord Rosse and his fellow workers were able to observe the structure and the difference between various types of nebulae and stellar clusters, and they were able, moreover, to distinguish between nebulosity and conglomeration of stars.

After three months of observations with this telescope, Lord Rosse discovered that the nebula Messier 51 in the constellation of Canes

Venatici presented a very clear and delicate spiral structure, of almost geometrical precision. Many other nebulae, observed with the same instrument, presented more complicated shapes, but in every case there was a definite suggestion that they belonged to the same type, with spirals which in some cases were perhaps a little wider than others, sometimes sharply defined, and with varied orientations with respect to the line of sight. In a note to the Royal Society Lord Rosse, in June 1850, remarked that generally the details of these objects were very difficult to see even in a night of good seeing and with full aperture of the telescope. In the case of M.51 and a few others, the full aperture showed plenty of details which led him to believe that in a night of good seeing, even a smaller aperture might reveal the various branches of the spiral. Messier had described M.51 as a double nebula without stars, while William Herschel described it as a round, bright nebula, surrounded, at a given distance from the centre, by a halo and having a near companion. John Herschel was able to detect a partial division of the southern end of the ring into two branches. This remarkable discovery revealed the existence of dynamic action in stellar systems which, as Lord Rosse himself commented, had not been taken into account in celestial mechanics.

In 1848, when it was still thought that all nebulae were composed of stars, George Phillips Bond, the second director of Harvard College Observatory, noticed that the Andromeda Nebula had dark bands across it. Lord Rosse, observing M.27, the so-called 'dumbbell nebula', with his 72-inch telescope, discovered the existence of two bright clusters of fairly luminous stars, surrounded by dark bands and faint rings.

This type of observation of nebulae and clusters was continued later by John Herschel, son of William, and by Lord Rosse's son. Nor were the observations limited to Great Britain. Edward Schönfeld at Mannheim, Heinrich Ludwig d'Arrest in Copenhagen and several others continued the visual observations and published catalogues listing an increasing number of these objects. The catalogues of the two Herschels, which were published in the years 1833 and 1847 respectively, were combined in 1864, in the *General Catalogue of Nebulae and Clusters* and published in *Philosophical Transactions*. Ninety per cent of all nebulae in this catalogue had been discovered by the Herschels. The catalogue includes celestial objects of the northern hemisphere and of the southern hemisphere as far as the

South Pole, discovered by John Herschel working with an 18-inch reflector at the Cape.

In Italy, Father Secchi of the observatory of the Collegio romano began the study of nebulae in 1853, and some of his drawings were published in his book *Le Soleil*. In his memoir *Astronomia in Roma nel pontificato di Pio IX*, he wrote:

'. . . From our spectroscopic observations, we can add the dark nebulae, which move in the great universe, to the dark heavenly bodies which have already been shown to revolve around some stars, as for instance Algol . . . In these studies one interesting fact stands out; namely the probable existence of dark masses scattered in space. These dark masses were seen because of the light background on which they are projected. Up to now these masses have been classified as "dark holes". This interpretation is however very improbable, particularly after the discovery of the gaseous nature of the nebular masses. It is more likely that the darkness is the result of a dark nebulosity, which, seen against a lighter background, absorbs its light.' Dealing with his investigations of the nebulae in Sagittarius he continues:

'It was in these regions that we found those totally dark patches, which by being so well defined and sharp, gave us the impression that they were shadows of dark masses, rather than "holes". The probability that this is so, is supported by the fact that many of the nebulae, although having a continuous spectrum, are certainly composed of gaseous matter and therefore could not have large breaks of great linear extension. Now this formation is found in the channels of Andromeda Nebula, a formation which is almost impossible in an expanding mass, since the breaks would soon be filled in.'

Still in the field of visual observations, carried out at about the same time, we could mention Tempel's observations in the years 1876–79. These observations were taken at the Arcetri Observatory with the Amici equatorial constructed in 1840, which is a refractor of 11-inch aperture (28 cm.) and 17 ft. focal length (5·3 m.). With this instrument endowed with an extremely good objective, Tempel made a number of sketches and drawings of the main nebulae, for which he obtained the prize of the Accademia dei Lincei. The drawings, which are still at the Arcetri Observatory, have now been published. They are also very interesting because Tempel reproduces, for comparison, drawings made by other observers such as Herschel, Lord Rosse, Lassel, d'Arrest and Secchi. The difference in the type and power of the instruments used, as well as the difference in the perception and visual acuteness of the various observers, gave rise to notable differences in the observed nebulae. A comparison of these drawings with modern photographs of the same objects could be of great interest.

The use of photography and the application of spectral analysis to the study of celestial objects have increased our knowledge of nebulae in a remarkable way.

In 1850 Bond and his associates at the Harvard College Observatory were among the first to obtain photographs of stars by means of wet plates. The rapid progress in the development of emulsions and of photographic techniques, together with the improvements of fast objectives and mirrors of wide field, made it possible for astronomers in the following years to obtain celestial photographs of increasing value and interest. As a consequence of this, a great number of new celestial objects were discovered. Moreover the photographic observations confirmed many of the visual observations and revealed a wealth of details about the structure of these celestial objects.

In 1919 Edward Emerson Barnard, at the Yerkes Observatory, obtained some excellent photographs of the Galaxy and in a memoir on the dark areas of the sky, he discusses the evidence obtained. He admits that at first he could not believe in the existence in the sky of dark obscuring masses, but that he was convinced later by the evidence given by his photographs as well as by careful visual observations of the regions. From these observations he came to the conclusion that the dark patches were not only due to the absence of stars, but rather to the existence of dark masses nearer to us than the stars. Barnard worked for many years in order to obtain photographs of as many of these objects as possible. He was able to detect that the dark masses appeared to be more common near the bright parts of the Milky Way. That, perhaps, was due to the fact that they could be more easily detected against a luminous background. One of the first to suggest that the dark areas were due to matter scattered in space was Ranyard, who in 1894 published in the magazine *Knowledge*, of which he was editor, a series of articles on the Milky Way and on nebulae. In discussing the dark lane south-east of Ophiuchus, which was clearly visible in a photograph taken at Lick Observatory, he expressed the view that without doubt it was an obscure mass existing in space and blocking the light of nebular or stellar regions beyond it. In this way the presence of dark matter scattered throughout the sky, which had been observed by Bond, Lord Rosse and Secchi, was confirmed.

William Huggins and Father Secchi were pioneers in the field of spectral analysis of nebulae. The former was able, with the help of the spectroscope, to prove, at first visually and later with the aid of photographs on dry plates (he was the first to use them in astrophysics), the gaseous constitution of the third and fourth classes of nebulae observed by W. Herschel. In 1864, he announced the discovery of the gaseous nature of eight planetary nebulae, proving that these could not any longer be considered as other suns, but rather as enormous gaseous masses or *luminous vapours*. Having observed, by means of the spectroscope, that their spectrum consisted of very few emission lines without a continuum, he concluded that the uniformity and the extreme simplicity of the spectra of these nebulae contradicted the theory that this gaseous matter represented the *shining fluid* suggested earlier by W. Herschel, from which new stars were born by condensation. According to Huggins, if that was so, evidence should be found, in this primeval fluid, of all the elements which are found in the stars. Therefore the spectra of planetary nebulae should have a great number of bright lines, in the same way as stellar spectra present dark lines.

Huggins studied the spectrum of thirty chemical elements in the laboratory. When he came to observe the spectrum of the planetary nebulae, he found only one bright line in proximity to one of nitrogen, while the other bright lines of this element were absent. He was inclined to think, therefore, that the presence of that bright line in this type of nebula, indicated the existence of a form of matter more elementary than nitrogen and still unknown to terrestrial analysis; the hypothetical *Nebulium*. Later it was possible to identify in the spectra of gaseous nebulae, the second line of Balmer series $H\beta$ as well as the first $H\alpha$. The latter was identified by Vogel and by Secchi.

Secchi observed that all planetary nebulae had the same spectrum with one very intense principal line since all the light of the nebula was condensed in the few bright lines. These lines are clearly visible in spite of the very faint brightness of the nebula as a whole. Moreover the spectroscope showed too that the Orion Nebula was of a gaseous nature, while the Andromeda Nebula presented a continuous spectrum.

In the field of spectral analysis applied to the study of celestial objects, photography was shortly to provide much information and many discoveries about the physical constitution of various types of nebulae.

After the Messier catalogue and John Herschel's general catalogue of 1864 and the others already mentioned, John Louis Dreyer of Armagh Observatory published, in 1888, a new general catalogue of nebulae and star clusters, intended as a revision, correction and enlargement of John Herschel's catalogue. This new catalogue, usually known as the NGC, gives the equatorial co-ordinates, namely the right ascension and the polar distance, for the epoch 1860, as well as a short description of 7,840 nebulae of various types and star clusters. The *Index Catalogue*, referred to as the IC or NGC II, followed in 1894 and in 1908, and contained a list of a further 5,086 objects. The NGC and both the IC catalogues have been reprinted in 1953 in a single volume by the Royal Astronomical Society.

The number of nebulae of all types visible on photographs increased rapidly with the increasing power of new telescopes. Frederick Seares, in 1925, estimated that 300,000 of these objects could be photographed with the 60-inch reflector of Mt. Wilson, with an exposure of one hour. A number even greater can be seen on the plates of the *Sky Atlas*, obtained with the 48-inch Schmidt of Mt. Palomar.

In the southern hemisphere, the systematic search for nebulae which, as we have seen, was started by John Herschel, lagged behind the discoveries in the northern hemisphere, on account of the lack of observatories and large telescopes. Recently, however, Shapley and his associates have embarked on a vast programme of research at Arequipa (South America) and at Bloemfontein (South Africa), with the purpose of extending our knowledge about the nebulae of the southern hemisphere. To these observations we have to add those obtained at the Radcliffe Observatory in South Africa and at Mt. Stromlo in Australia, so that our knowledge about the nebulae of the southern hemisphere is now rapidly increasing.

As far as the galaxies are concerned, the collecting of data is increasing daily. These data refer to dimension, colour, type, magnitude, spectral type, radial velocity and distribution of luminosity and population.

At present the number of known nebulae has increased considerably, and with the help of the large telescopes available it is proposed to prepare a catalogue which will include objects down to magnitude 15. With the 200-inch telescope the galaxies which are observable are so numerous that they can no longer be counted. Probably there are about one thousand million of them. A thousand million galaxies, each containing a thousand million stars, in a sphere of radius equal to about two thousand million light-years, is as far as our present telescopes can reach.

I.2 Nomenclature.

We leave the historical period of early determination of distance of some fixed stars and their distribution in the Galaxy and, with the increasing help of photography and spectral analysis, we enter what we may call the modern period, in which it has been possible to define clearly the meaning of the term *nebulae* and to classify them according to their various types.

The fundamental fact which has resulted from the modern photographic and spectroscopic investigations, is that we must make a distinction between various types of nebulae. These are: the irregular gaseous clouds, both bright and dark, scattered among the stars; the planetary nebulae; and those which present a well-defined and symmetrical form, either globular or spiral, but which must not be confused with star clusters, also of symmetrical form, but which can be distinguished from the others by the total absence of nebular matter and which, for this reason, are not dealt with in this book.

From the structure of the Galaxy and from direct and indirect measurements of distances, it soon became apparent that both the irregular bright and dark clouds and planetary nebulae belonged to our Galaxy, while the other nebulae were systems apart. Some of these have dimensions and structure similar to our Galaxy, while others are in different stages of a possible evolutionary cycle. Gradually thus, the distinction between galactic nebulae and extra-galactic nebulae became clear. Among the former we have (a) the diffuse nebulae, bright and irregular in shape, scattered about in the Galaxy and which probably would be better named bright irregular nebulae; (b) dark nebulae, namely dark gaseous masses with irregular contours which can be seen in the sky because they absorb, in varying degree, the light of stars which happen to be within or beyond them; (c) planetary nebulae, called erroneously thus, because they present bright discs, similar to a planet, through a telescope of low power.

With higher power and in photographs, they actually appear as masses of gas of small dimension and of a round shape, often with a bright star at the centre.

The so-called extra-galactic nebulae are systems, as we have already explained, which present all the characteristics of our own Galaxy and which therefore must consist of the same components, namely stars of various spectral classes, variable stars, novae and nebulae. It is perhaps more correct to call these objects *external galaxies*, leaving out altogether the term nebula. In the following pages we shall refer to them as *galaxies*, as is the present prevailing custom. We shall see, in due course, how these galaxies can be classified further.

CHAPTER II

Methods of observation and spectral analysis of nebulae

THE spectral analysis of bright nebulae of various types, gives important information about their relationship with the stars embedded in them. In the case of dark nebulae, when there are stars which are bright enough for their light to travel through the matter of the nebulae, it is possible to determine the physical constitution of this dark matter, from the selective absorption observed in the spectrum of such stars.

The manufacture of photographic emulsions and filters has progressed to such an extent that it is now possible to obtain photographs of the sky in very limited regions of the spectrum, extending from the ultra-violet to the infra-red. For instance, by combining a red filter with a panchromatic plate it is possible, with fast cameras and wide field lenses, to obtain photographs of extended nebulae, in radiations centred on $H\alpha$ and 300 Å. wide. Similar arrangements can be used for other spectral regions.

Nowadays, by means of interference filters which isolate narrow regions of the spectrum, we can photograph nebulae in monochromatic light. The work in this field, of Charles Fabry and Henry Buisson (1914) with the Fabry–Perot interferometer, is considered of fundamental value. Using an interferometer at the focus of the 31·5-inch (80-cm.) reflector at the Marseilles Observatory they were able, by comparing the interference ring produced by the Orion Nebula with those produced by a mercury lamp, to determine photographically the wavelength of the two lines of the hypothetical *Nebulium* in the violet, as well as other lines. They were also able to determine the radial velocity at different points of the nebula and to set an upper limit of 15,000°K. for its temperature.

After the early spectroscopic work of Huggins, spectrographs which had been considerably improved were increasingly used for extended nebulae, for planetary nebulae and for galaxies, up to the limit imposed by the power of the telescopes used. Since nebulae generally are faint objects, it is necessary to use telescopes and spectrographs with high photographic speed. As far as the focal length of the telescope is concerned, its choice is dictated by the apparent dimension of the nebula as a whole or of the part of it, whichever is to be studied. The dispersion will have to be as high as possible, in order that the spectral lines should be clearly resolved.

Generally a spectrograph has a narrow slit on which falls the light from the source which is to be analysed. The spectrograph has also a collimator, that is a lens placed in such a position that the slit is at its focus. In this way the rays from the slit are rendered parallel by the collimator and this parallel beam falls on the prism or grating which is in a position to give images affected as little as possible by aberrations. The beam is then divided into a number of rays of monochromatic radiations which are focused by a second lens onto the photographic plate. On this we record the spectrum of the source of light which will consist of a number of monochromatic images of the slit.

The slit is essential when the spectrum to be studied is that of an extended source such as the Sun or even of an ordinary lamp, which produces a continuous spectrum. Should the slit be omitted, we then would have on the plate a series of monochromatic images of the source. As these images have a measurable size, they would partially overlap and thereby produce a white image of the source, surrounded by colours at the edge. When dealing with stars, however, the slit is not indispensable. Stars are point sources, and it is our atmosphere which, behaving like an agitated ocean of air, introduces distortions, producing seeing discs of very small dimensions, but nevertheless measurable. Therefore a stellar spectrum, obtained by a slitless spectrograph, will present less detailed features than the one obtained by a spectrograph with a slit.

In the particular case of planetaries, we are dealing with extended objects, which are generally very faint and which have a bright line spectrum. If we photograph the spectrum with a slitless spectrograph, we obtain a number of monochromatic images of the nebula with very little overlap, since the continuum is extremely faint and is practically non-existent. In this way, besides the spectrum, it will be possible to study the form and dimensions of the nebula, as well as the intensity distribution of the monochromatic radiation in the various parts of the nebula.

At present the technique of interference filters is developing rapidly. These filters can isolate a narrow region in the neighbourhood of the most intense emission lines of the nebular spectrum. It is therefore possible to obtain a series of photographs of the nebula in the light of some of its spectral lines. Interference filters when compared with slitless spectrographs, have the advantage that a photograph of a nebula can be obtained either in the light of some of its spectral lines or in the visual or ultra-violet continuum. It is then possible to compare the intensity of the various monochromatic radiations with that of the continuum.

The system used by Ira Bowen, director of the Mt. Wilson and Mt. Palomar Observatories, is of great interest and has contributed greatly to the study of planetary nebulae—the most important contribution being the identification of the nebulium lines. Bowen made use of an ordinary stellar spectrograph to which had been added a simple optical device, called the *image slicer*. This serves the purpose of changing the form of the image of the planetary which is on the plane of the slit, without altering in any way its area. By means of this optical device all the radiation enters the spectrograph without being scattered in the plane of the slit. The image of the planetary, whether round or elliptical, is sliced into long and narrow strips of the width of the slit and added end to end along the slit. The principle of this slicer is very simple. A small mirror $ABCD$ (fig. 1) is tilted at an angle of 45° to the plane of the slit and its surface is covered by the image of the planetary. This mirror reflects the image on a series of small mirrors 1, 2, 3, . . . n which are also tilted at an angle of 45° to the plane of the slit. Each of these mirrors has the same width as the slit and each one intercepts a narrow strip of the image of the planetary and reflects it into the slit. By this means we can photograph the spectrum of the whole disc of the planetary with a greater probability of discovering very weak lines, which would otherwise not be visible if only a narrow strip of the planetary was used.

A great variety of combinations for the construction of spectrographs particularly well suited for the spectrographic study of nebulae is possible with the 200-inch telescope of Mt. Palomar, Schmidt cameras and diffraction gratings, which concentrate a great part of the diffracted light in a given order of the spectrum.

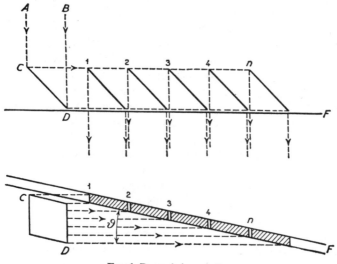

Fig. 1. Bowen's image slicer

For the study of fainter objects, as for instance the very remote galaxies, a special spectrograph has been constructed for the 200-inch Hale telescope. This spectrograph, when required, can be mounted at the prime focus of the large mirror. The dispersive element consists of two gratings, one of 300 lines/mm. and the other of 600 lines/mm., which are coupled with two Schmidt cameras working at ƒ0·47 and ƒ0·95. Dispersions ranging from 430 Å./mm. to 105 Å./mm. can be obtained, according to the combination used. For brighter objects other combinations have been constructed, which can be mounted at the coudé focus of the large telescope. This coudé focus is formed by means of secondary mirrors placed at the south end of the polar axis, where a multiple spectrograph is situated. The dispersive element of this spectrograph consists of a composite grating made of four gratings which operate as one with a ruled surface of 28 × 36 cm. The gratings have 400 lines/mm. with approximately 65% of the light concentrated in the third order violet and in the second order red. The composite grating can be used in conjunction with five different cameras with a focal length varying between 365 and 21 cm. and gives a dispersion which can be varied between

2·3 Å./mm. and 40 Å./mm. respectively. It is easy to see how by means of these various combinations spectra of considerable dispersion, of various types of nebulae, from the brightest to the faintest, can be studied.

Another type of spectrograph, recently (1956) constructed for the 60-inch Mt. Wilson reflector, can be used with any one of three gratings and the light concentrated in the different orders makes it possible to photograph various regions of the spectrum from the violet to the infra-red. For the 40-inch (1 m.) reflector of the Merate Observatory (Italy), a spectrograph has been constructed with a grating which enables the spectrum of nebulae to be obtained from the violet to the infra-red.

For the study of small gaseous nebulae, particularly planetaries, a slitless spectrograph has been used successfully at Lick Observatory. The converging beam of light from the primary mirror of the reflector is transformed into a parallel beam by a concave lens. This light falls first on a prism and then on a convex lens. The spectrum of the planetary nebula is recorded on a plate and consists of as many monochromatic images as there are emission lines. For the observation of spectra of bright nebulae which are extended and faint, Struve and his associates, at the McDonald Observatory

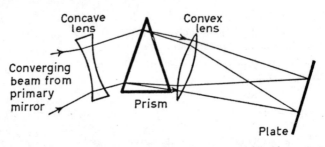

FIG. 2. Schematic diagram of slitless spectrograph of Lick Observatory

(Texas), made use of a slitless spectrograph. This spectrograph consisted of two plane mirrors suitably mounted and placed at a distance of approximately 75 ft. (23 m.) from each other. The mirrors reflected the light of the nebula onto two quartz prisms and a Schmidt camera of 4-inch (94 mm.) aperture and focal length which were placed 75 ft. (23 m.) from the second mirror. With this arrangement, emission spectra of faint and diffuse nebulae of the Milky Way were obtained.

METHODS OF OBSERVATION

In this type of spectroscopic investigation there is the added difficulty of the spectrum produced by the light of the night sky, which may confuse or even, in some cases, cover completely the spectrum of the nebula under investigation. The situation is even worse when the spectrum of the aurora is also present. In such cases it is only possible to observe the most intense bright lines in the spectrum of faint nebulae. The other lines are lost in the background light of the night sky, of the zodiacal light or of the light of faint stars.

The problem of determining visually or photographically the intensity of nebulae of various types is not one which can be easily solved. Some progress has been made by using photo-electric cells. It is possible to determine the surface brightness of nebulae, express this value in stellar magnitudes and compare it with reference stars photographed out of focus. For theoretical discussion it is necessary to know the surface brightness of the nebula in a particular radiation, for instance in that of the hydrogen lines. This quantity can be expressed in erg/cm^2. Apart from the total amount of energy radiated in various wavelengths, it is important to know also the distribution of energy in the various regions of the nebula. This is generally done by determining *isophotic contours*[1] of the nebula, drawn at equal steps in intensity. There are several ways in which these contours can be drawn. If the photographic method is used, then it is necessary to calibrate the plates on which the images of the nebula are recorded. A step filter can be used of which the transmission for each step is known. By means of a microphotometer the degree of darkening given by the filter and by the nebula can be measured and, in this way, the intensity in the various parts of the nebula can be given in a suitable unit. If the photo-electric method is used, then the plate with the spectrum of the nebula is moved slowly in front of a slit, behind which the photo-cell is placed. This method has been used at Mt. Wilson for the measurement of the intensity of planetaries.

Strömgren and Hiltner, at the McDonald Observatory, made a study of the diffuse nebulae with the 82-inch reflector, by using interference filters and a photo-electric photometer. One filter was used to isolate a region 150 Å. wide centred near $H\beta$; for comparison the other was used in a region also 150 Å. wide, near λ 4600 Å. Using these filters of known characteristics, Strömgren and Hiltner determined the intensity in absolute units of these nebulae which are

[1] Isophotic contours are lines obtained by joining points of equal brightness.

31

mostly composed of bright hydrogen, by comparing them with stars of known colour and magnitude. From these values, the number of excited atoms in the mass of gas can be determined.

The interpretation of photo-electric and photographic measurements of magnitude and surface brightness of nebulae, requires also a knowledge of the energy distribution in their spectra, that is the relative intensity in the various emission lines and in the continuum.

After the early spectrophotometric investigations carried out visually by Wilsing and Scheiner (1902), various photographic and photo-electric methods were introduced. One of these methods consists in choosing the spectrum of a source of known energy distribution. This is usually the spectrum of comparison stars, the energy distribution of which is well known from the many measurements existing, up to the limit of transmission of the earth's atmosphere in the ultra-violet. Spectrophotometric research on gaseous nebulae has been made both with slitless and slit spectrographs. There remains the difficulty of establishing a comparison between the stellar discs and the extended surface of nebulae. As the intensity of the emission lines cannot be referred to the continuum, as in the case of stars, the nebular line intensities are generally referred to a spectral line chosen as standard, i.e. $H\beta$.

The study of the shape, of the distortions and of the displacements of the emission lines of planetaries, enables us to determine their internal motions, and their radial velocities, thereby expanding the work originally started by Fabry and Buisson. With high dispersion spectrographs and fast cameras, research has been carried out on the turbulence and the large-scale motions which take place in the extended bright nebulae. In the case of dark clouds of neutral hydrogen, important data for the determination of their motions have been obtained from radio-astronomical observations of the 21-cm. line, and further data on the density fluctuation, temperature and velocity of the gas will be obtained.

CHAPTER III

Planetary nebulae

III.1 Introduction.

PLANETARY nebulae generally appear as irregular discs of a greenish colour. Among them some are found in the shape of a ring, like the well-known Ring Nebula in Lyra, and others with a double ring like NGC 3242. Others have forms which are more complicated and irregular. When observed with a suitable magnification, all present a filamentary structure. In several of these planetaries, one or two faint stars can be distinguished at the centre. The planetary nebulae, like the irregular diffuse, bright nebulae, are part of our galactic system.

Let us pause to consider the similarities and the differences which distinguish these two types of galactic nebulae. The most obvious difference is that of their form. Diffuse nebulae have no regular geometric form and differ from each other on account of their varied shapes, while planetary nebulae generally present a spherical symmetry. The former have no clearly defined limits, while the latter have a definite outline.

As far as dimensions are concerned, those of irregular nebulae vary over a wide range and are, in general, much greater than those of planetaries. On average these latter have diameters of approximately 0·15 parsec[1] and may reach as much as 5 parsecs. Irregular nebulae, on the other hand, have diameters which vary between 5 and 10 parsecs, but some exist with very small diameters of about 0·05 parsec, while at the other end of the scale, large ones are known with diameters of 140 parsecs.

Some irregular nebulae have certain similarities with the planetaries, as far as their physical composition is concerned. Both types have spectra with bright lines, due to the excitation of the gas of

[1] A parsec is equal to 3·26 light-years (see Appendix).

which the nebula is composed. This excitation is produced by the star or stars, which have a high surface temperature and are embedded in the gas. While all planetary nebulae have this type of spectrum, indicating that all of them are composed only of tenuous gases, many of the diffuse nebulae have also a continuous spectrum with absorption lines, showing that the matter of which they are composed reflects the light of neighbouring stars. This matter, therefore, is composed of solid particles as well as gas. The density of planetary nebulae is about a thousand times greater than that of diffuse nebulae. Unlike the latter, which can be considered as nothing more than denser regions of interstellar space, the planetary nebulae are well-defined objects, probably representing a definite phase in stellar evolution.

We shall see later that the position occupied in the Galaxy by these two types of nebulae is very different. Irregular nebulae tend to congregate towards the galactic plane and in the spiral arms, and nowadays it is thought that in them, new stars are formed. Planetary nebulae, on the other hand, congregate towards the galactic centre, and many of them are found at a great distance from the galactic plane. Their distribution in space is typical of those stars belonging to population II, which are thought to be old stars. Thus the planetary nebula phase could well represent the old age, as it were, in the life of a star.

III.2 Space distribution.

At present, about 500 planetary nebulae are known. Of these about a hundred have been discovered by Henize in the southern hemisphere, and as many as 216 have recently been discovered by Minkowski, who has carried out a systematic search on photographs taken with a 10-inch telescope and the 18-inch Schmidt of Mt. Wilson, both equipped with a prism objective. These observations enabled Minkowski to reach some extremely interesting conclusions. Points representing 371 nebulae, plotted in a graph having galactic longitude for abscissae and galactic latitude for ordinates, show the existence of a strong concentration near the galactic centre (galactic longitude 328° and galactic latitude 0°)[1] and of a moderate concentration along the galactic plane (see fig. 3). A comparison with a similar graph (fig. 4) relating to the 155 planetary nebulae which

[1] See Appendix.

34

were known before Minkowski's investigation, shows clearly that all the new planetary nebulae since discovered are situated in the direction of the galactic centre and in the neighbourhood of the galactic plane. These objects are, therefore, extremely difficult to see, because they are partially hidden and their light weakened, by interstellar matter. It is conceivable that all, or almost all, the nebulae which are at a great distance from the galactic plane, have been detected, whereas many of those lying on the galactic plane and in the direction of the galactic centre are almost completely hidden from us. On the other hand, the well-marked concentration in the direction of the galactic centre would indicate that these objects are not only in the direction of the galactic centre, but are actually grouped together there.

From the study of their position in space we can also obtain some information on the distribution of dark matter and on the number of objects hidden by it. In fig. 5 the ordinates represent the number of planetary nebulae per square degree, between $-10°$ and $+10°$ galactic latitudes, and the abscissae represent the galactic longitude. The steep maximum at 328° is an indication of the strong concentration of these objects towards the galactic centre. The broken line denotes the distribution of planetaries one might expect in the absence of obscuring matter. Hence the deficiency of planetaries in the neighbourhood of longitude 10° and 310°, immediately preceding the maximum, is an indication of the presence of obscuring matter, which hides a great number of objects from view.

Minkowski compares also the galactic distribution of planetary nebulae with that of a group of stars of type Be, which are typical

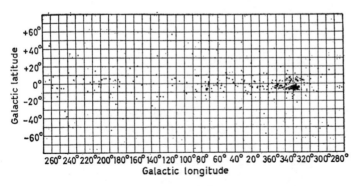

FIG. 3. Galactic distribution of 371 planetary nebulae

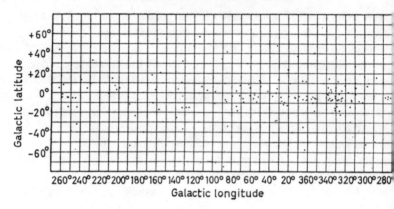

FIG. 4. Galactic distribution of the 155 planetary nebulae known before Minkowski's investigations

stars of population I, namely stars which are found in the arms of the Galaxy.

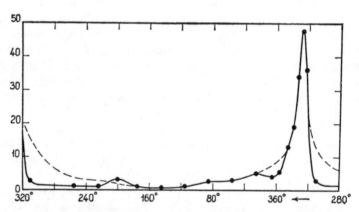

FIG. 5. Concentration of planetary nebulae between −10° and +10° galactic latitude as a function of galactic longitude. (Vertical: No. per 100 sq. deg. Horizontal: galactic longitude)

Be stars are stars of very high surface temperature (20,000° to 25,000° K) and blue in colour. Their spectrum has the same characteristics as that of ordinary B stars, in which absorption lines of neutral hydrogen and neutral helium predominate. In addition, the spectrum of Be stars has a few bright lines, such as the brightest hydrogen line $H\alpha$ and sometimes also the $H\beta$ and $H\gamma$. In exceptional cases almost all the Balmer lines, or some of the lines of HeI, FeII and MgII can be present.

From fig. 6 it appears that Be stars do not show any special concentration at the galactic centre, and their concentration on the galactic plane is definitely greater than that of planetary nebulae.

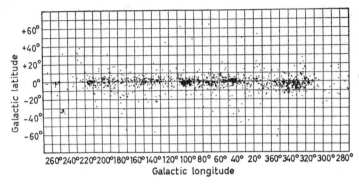

Fig. 6. Galactic distribution of Be stars; typical stars of population I

This noticeable difference in space distribution is a strong argument in favour of the suggestion that planetary nebulae belong to population II, namely the population of the centre of the galactic system.

Further proof of this is found if we compare the space distribution of planetary nebulae and RR Lyrae stars. This type of star is very common in globular clusters which are typical examples of population II. Those RR Lyrae stars belonging to the galactic system (and not to globular clusters which are almost satellites of the Galaxy) have a spatial distribution very similar to that of planetary nebulae. There is also one planetary, NGC 7078, which is known to belong to a globular cluster. The fact that out of nearly ten million stars forming globular clusters, only one object of this type exists, leads us to believe that the planetary stage must be very short. Moreover some planetary nebulae have a high space velocity. Now according to the usual galactic model, objects of the spiral arms (that is, objects of population I) describe orbits which are in the plane of the spiral arms, and which have, therefore, little inclination to the galactic plane and are almost circular, whereas stars of the nucleus that is, stars of population II) describe orbits which may have any inclination and eccentricity. Stars of high velocity are those with orbits of large eccentricity with respect to the galactic plane, and they have a high velocity compared with stars which describe circular orbits. This means that high space velocity is a sufficient condition, but not a necessary one, for belonging to population II.

III.3 Distances and dimensions.

The direct observation of celestial objects, and of planetary nebulae in particular, enables us to determine, by ordinary methods, only the angular diameter a, when this is not too small to be measured, as is the case for the majority of stars. If, however, the distance r of the object from us is known, it is easy to obtain its linear diameter d. Since 1 rad = 206,265″

$$a = d/r \; rad = d \, 206,265''/r$$

In the case of planetary nebulae, the angular diameter a (in seconds of arc) can easily be measured, because of the large dimensions of the disc and the very well defined outline that they have. The most difficult problem, however, is that of determining the distances of these objects.

Planetary nebulae are very remote from us, and all the attempts to measure directly the trigonometrical parallaxes have failed, since they are of the order of, or even smaller than, the errors of observation. In some cases negative values are obtained which obviously have no physical meaning. They only confirm the fact that the distance of planetaries is so great, that the apparent parallactic displacement on the celestial sphere (due to the displacement of the observer on account of the movement of the earth in its orbit) is too small to be measured. Only in the case of NGC 7293 is the value of the trigonometrical parallax (determined by Adriaan van Maanen) slightly larger than the mean error. In order, therefore, to estimate the distance of planetary nebulae, it has been necessary to adopt indirect methods. Some of these are statistical methods based on the components of their proper motion, or their apparent size and magnitude.

The proper motion method is based on the following principle. We are able to observe the displacement of a star in the sky either because of its own real motion or because the Sun itself, with its planets, moves among the stars, so that our position, from which observations are taken, changes. If we consider the proper motion of a great number of objects, and if we assume that their real motions are distributed at random, then the sum of all these motions will be zero, so that the mean proper motion will be equal to the mean parallactic displacement due to the displacement of the Sun. The smaller the average distance of the group under consideration, the greater is the parallactic displacement. Therefore from the average of the proper motion observed, we can obtain the mean parallax of the group. Van Maanen and Andersen, using this method, have found parallaxes of the order of 0·0007″, which are equivalent to distances of 1,400 parsecs or 4,600 light-years.

Another statistical method has been used by Minkowski in his recent study of planetaries. The angular diameter which can be directly observed is used as a criterion for the determination of distances, assuming that, on average, the dimensions of planetaries are almost the same in all parts of the galactic system. If this hypothesis is permissible, then it follows that planetaries which are farther away have smaller angular diameters. Minkowski plotted the mean apparent diameter of planetaries as a function of galactic longitude, and he obtained the graph of fig. 7. In this we see that the mean diameter is a minimum between 320° and 340°, thus confirming the hypothesis that the great number of objects which can be observed in this direction, which is the direction of the galactic centre, is really situated in the neighbourhood of the centre, and therefore at a great distance away from us.

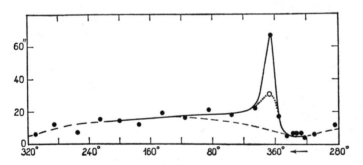

FIG. 7. Mean apparent diameter of planetary nebulae as a function of galactic longitude. (Horizontal: galactic longitude. Vertical: Diameter in seconds of arc)

A maximum for the average diameter is observed at 5° of galactic longitude. Even if we omit from the average a nebula having an apparent diameter which is exceptionally large, the maximum is unchanged, as can be seen in the dotted part of the curve in fig. 7.

PLANETARY NEBULAE

Reverting to fig. 5, it will be seen that at 5° there is a minimum in the number of nebulae which can be observed. Probably the best interpretation of the two curves is that in the direction of 5° galactic longitude, there exist clouds of absorbing matter which allow the observation only of the few nearer planetaries.

Since observations seem to indicate that the planetaries which are visible in the direction of the galactic centre, are actually situated in the centre, their distance can be estimated as being equal to that of the Sun from the galactic centre. This distance is 9,000 parsecs and corresponds to a parallax of 0·00011″, approximately seven times smaller than that determined by the method of proper motions. We must however remember that in this case we have included also giant planetaries, which presumably are nearer to us.

Among the methods which attempt the determination of the distance of single objects, that of Berman should be mentioned. Berman made use of all the available information relevant to the determination of the distances of planetaries, namely mean parallaxes, based on proper motions; angular diameters; radial velocities studied according to the theory of galactic rotation and also the apparent magnitude of the nebulae and of their central star. He also considered the effect of interstellar absorption. The several steps of his method can be summarized as follows: statistical relations between the apparent mean diameters and the corresponding mean parallaxes obtained from proper motions (assuming the linear diameters to be almost constant) give a first scale of distances by means of which the planetaries are subdivided in five homogeneous groups of distances. Radial velocities give information about the galactic rotation of planetaries. The mean nebular magnitudes of the various groups of distances, together with the average distances obtained from the average parallaxes and from the data about the galactic rotation, make it possible to obtain the interstellar absorption. Once this absorption is known the nebular magnitude can be corrected and hence the individual distances of the nebulae can be calculated.

As a result of this investigation it was found that of the 126 nebulae studied, that is all those known before the work of Minkowski and Henize, 49 had diameters between 0·13 and 0·30 parsec. The smallest had diameters of the order of 0·02 parsec, and the largest had diameters up to 5 parsecs. Table 1 gives the distribution of the observed nebulae, according to their diameters.

PLANETARY NEBULAE

TABLE 1

Diameter (parsec)	Number of objects	Diameter (parsec)	Number of objects
0·02 – 0·03	3	0·31 – 0·50	8
0·03 – 0·05	6	0·50 – 0·80	9
0·05 – 0·08	10	0·80 – 1·3	5
0·08 – 0·13	10	1·3 – 2·0	10
0·13 – 0·20	26	2·0 – 3·1	4
0·20 – 0·31	23	3·1 – 5·0	4

In spite of the considerable advance in knowledge in the scale of distances of planetaries made possible by Berman's work, there is still a great deal of uncertainty in this field. Several objections may be raised against some of the hypotheses introduced by Berman. Oort, for instance, criticizes the assumption that the absolute magnitude and the size of both bright and faint nebulae, are equal. Probably different planetaries are at different stages of their evolution, to which different brightness and different size may correspond, as is the case for the stars. Moreover, an average coefficient of absorption for interstellar matter is meaningless, since the matter is distributed in a very irregular manner.

Another method for the determination of distances of planetaries was put forward by Menzel in 1931. This method is particularly interesting since it is mainly based on astrophysical principles, and does not even require preliminary calibration of the method by means of trigonometric parallaxes as is the case for the spectroscopic parallaxes. We do no more than mention Menzel's method since a complete description would require first a description of the spectrum of a planetary and of the physical mechanism which produces it. Further on in the chapter, when dealing with the problem of the origin and development of nebulae, mention is made of the more recent method of Šklovskij, which is also based on astrophysical principles.

III.4 Spectra of planetary nebulae.

The majority of celestial objects, stars, planets and galaxies, have spectra which generally consist of a continuous spectrum upon which are superimposed a number of absorption lines. The planetaries on the other hand, can be distinguished by their characteristic spectrum. The continuum is generally very faint or even non-existent, and many strong emission lines are present. Another peculiarity of the spectrum of planetaries, which for a long time made these spectra very difficult to interpret, is that besides the well-known lines of hydrogen and helium neutral and ionized, there are present strong lines of OIII and NIII. These lines are either very faint or not visible when produced in a laboratory, while some other lines, which are quite strong in a laboratory, are completely absent in the spectra of planetaries.

Two lines, λ 5007 Å. and λ 4959 Å. of OIII, dominate the spectrum to such an extent as to produce the greenish colour of planetaries. These are the *forbidden lines* which cannot be observed in a laboratory and therefore for a long time were not identified. Astronomers thought that they were due to a hypothetical gas, *nebulium*, unknown on Earth.

Spectra with emission lines, very similar to those of the planetaries, are also produced by some bright irregular nebulae. In both cases the interpretation of the spectrum is the same, therefore much of what we are going to say about planetaries will also apply to diffuse nebulae.

III.5 Interpretation of the spectra of nebulae.

The spectrum of a planetary consists of a series of monochromatic discs or rings of various dimensions and intensities. At the centre a very thin line appears which is the spectrum of the central star and consists of a continuous spectrum upon which are superimposed absorption lines (Plate 1).

The interpretation of these spectra presented difficult problems. First of all there was the question of the identification of several lines which were attributed to one or more gases unknown on Earth. The second difficulty was to find an explanation of the behaviour of some lines of a given element which were always weak when produced in the laboratory but appeared intense in the nebular spectrum, while other lines, of the same element, which were among the strongest in a laboratory spectrum, appeared so weak or were missing altogether in the nebular spectrum. Finally it had to be explained why the monochromatic images of the planetary were not all of the same dimension.

PLANETARY NEBULAE

The greatest contribution towards the solution of these problems was made by Fowler and Russell, and by Croze and Mihul. It was, however, Bowen, in a memoir published in the *Astrophysical Journal* in 1928, who gave an explanation of the mysterious green lines which had been attributed to the nebulium.

Let us follow Bowen's reasoning, which excluded the existence of nebulium and led him to a final identification of these lines.

All the lines in the nebular spectra, which had been so far identified, belonged to the light elements (H, He, C, N, O), therefore it was reasonable to suppose that the other lines too belonged to elements of low atomic weight. The Periodic Table of the elements showed that no empty space existed among the light elements, and therefore the hypothesis of the existence of a new gas, nebulium, was unacceptable. Wright, who had measured the relative intensity of lines in many nebular spectra, found that the unknown lines behaved so differently from the others that it did not seem possible that they should all be produced by the same element. As a consequence of this it would not have been sufficient to postulate the existence of one gas only, but rather of a number of gases.

The suggestion put forward by Russell was however much more acceptable. Russell suggested that the mysterious lines were not produced by unknown atoms, but rather by known atoms radiating in conditions with which we were not familiar. He further suggested that this unusual condition of the atom could be an extremely low density.

Before going any further it might be useful to remind the reader of some basic facts of spectroscopy.

In order that an atom may be able to emit a line it is necessary that it should first absorb some energy from outside. The electron is then raised to a higher orbit, further from the nucleus, that is to an orbit which is not that in which the electron is normally found. After an extremely short time, about 10^{-8} s., the electron emits radiation, returning the energy absorbed and falling back to its original orbit. This return to the original state can take place in several ways. The electron may jump back from the new energy level to its original, performing the same transition in the opposite direction; in doing this it would emit a radiation of a frequency identical to that absorbed. Or it may cascade from the new level to the original one in successive transitions thereby giving rise to radiations of different frequencies.

Whichever way is followed, when the electron has returned to the original state, the total energy radiated will be the same as the energy absorbed. The transitions which may occur can be predicted by taking all the possible combinations for the various levels, but they are not all equally probable. Some of the transitions have never been observed and the *selection principle* explains the reason why jumps between certain levels are forbidden, or, as we should say, have a zero probability of happening. Some states are more probable than others.

Although the electron generally is in an excited state for a time of the order of 10^{-8} s., there are some states in which the electron can stay for a much longer time up to 1 second or more. These states are called *metastable*. If the electron happens to be in a metastable state, in conditions of normal density the chances are that a collision will occur which will raise it to a higher level, before the electron has had time to reach its ground level. In the laboratory, where the average free path is of the order of 10^{-3} s., it will be therefore impossible to observe the emission of a line produced by the electron which is moving from its metastable state to the ground level. If, however, the density of the medium is very low, as is the case in nebulae where collisions occur every 10^4 to 10^7 s., then the electron will have ample time to fall of its own accord, to the lowest orbit.

Bowen, in his memoir, identified eight nebular lines with the lines of NII, OII and OIII. These lines are produced by the electron falling from a metastable state. Among these lines the λ 5007 Å. and λ 4959 Å. of OIII (sometimes referred to as N_1 and N_2) are by far the brightest of the lines in the spectrum of planetaries. These lines are referred to as forbidden lines because the probability of their occurring in the laboratory is nil. Fig. 8 shows schematically how these forbidden lines are produced.

Even if the most difficult problem connected with the nebular spectrum had been solved, there remained a number of other questions to solve. We cannot do better than follow again Bowen's original memoirs which have led to the understanding of the mechanism producing the nebular spectrum and, indirectly, to the understanding of the physical and chemical composition of both the nebular matter and the central star.

The majority of the lines observed in the spectrum of planetaries are due to H, HeI and HeII as well as to CII, CIII, NII, NIII and

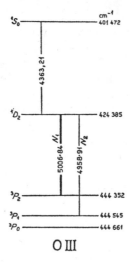

O III

FIG. 8. Transition schemes for the forbidden lines N_1 N_2 and the auroral line λ 4363 Å. of OIII

OII, OIII. The excitation potentials of these lines are all rather high, from 13 eV. for the hydrogen to 54 eV. for the HeII. The excitation potential is the energy required to place an electron on a higher level from which, in falling to another level, it produces a line. All the forbidden lines have very low excitation potentials, less than 5 eV. How can we explain the emission of lines in a gas so highly rarefied as that of planetaries, and what is the source of energy which enables the electrons to leave their ground level first and then, in returning to it, produce the observed spectrum? If lines are observed originating at levels where the excitation potential is between 13 eV. and 54 eV., it follows that the electron originally in its ground level, must absorb a quantity of energy between 13 eV. and 54 eV., which will raise it to the level from which the line originates.

Since a photon of frequency ν has energy $h\nu$ (where h is Planck constant) a relation of equivalence between energy and frequency follows. The relation is:

$$E = 1 \cdot 234 \times 10^{-4}/\lambda$$

where E is expressed in eV and λ in cm.

From the above relation it follows that in order to be raised to a level of potential 13·5 eV., an electron must absorb a photon of

45

wavelength $\lambda = 1\cdot234 \times 10^{-4}/13\cdot5 = 911 \times 10^{-8}$ cm. $= 911$ Å. If the electron is raised to a level of potential 54 eV., then it must absorb a photon of greater energy and therefore of higher frequency, or, in terms of wavelength, a lower wavelength; 225 Å. The very fact of the existence of lines of high excitation potential in the spectrum of the nebulae, requires the existence of radiations rich in ultra-violet quanta, capable of exciting the atoms. The source of this energy is obviously the central star. This must have a very high temperature in order to account for the quantity of ultra-violet radiation required.

Let us now look closer at the origin of the emission lines in a nebular spectrum. There are two different mechanisms, a primary and a secondary.

PRIMARY MECHANISM. Whenever an atom absorbs one of the photons which are emitted by the star with sufficient energy to tear away an electron from the nucleus, we say that the atom is ionized. Every ionization is followed by a recombination. The positive ion (that is the atom which has lost the electron) will capture a free electron, and this electron in its transition from the external orbits down to the lowest orbit, will emit the spectrum of the particular element. This mechanism of photo-ionization is called primary because it makes direct use of photons with sufficient energy which are emitted by the star.

SECONDARY MECHANISM. The secondary mechanism takes place by photo-ionization or by photo-excitation. The electron which following the primary mechanism is returning to the ground level, in its last transition towards the inner level, will emit lines in the extreme ultra-violet. This emission may have enough energy to ionize or excite other atoms and, while returning to the ground level, may produce new emissions. The excitation, however, can also take place by collision of electrons. An electron, after escaping the attraction of the nucleus and absorbing a photon, will have a kinetic energy which is equal to the difference between the energy of the absorbed photon and that required for ionizing the atom. This kinetic energy will be sufficient to excite other atoms by collision. All these mechanisms are called secondary because either the ionizing or exciting photon, or the free electron, derives its energy from a previous absorption of a photon originally emitted by the star.

Some examples will make this clear and at the same time will explain many peculiarities.

FIRST EXAMPLE. From the excitation potential of the observed lines, we can make the first deduction that the exciting star must be rich in quanta of wavelength between λ 911 Å. and λ 225 Å. Let us assume for such a star a surface temperature of about 150,000° K. This means that the radiation from its surface is very similar to that emitted by a black body at the same temperature. Planck's law makes it possible for us to predict the distribution of the intensity of the emitted radiation as a function of the wavelength. From this we find that at the temperature of 150,000° K. the maximum of intensity of the curve is between λ 911 Å. and λ 400 Å. and that there are still many quanta in the neighbourhood of λ 225 Å. Moreover we find that the radiation of wavelength near λ 160 Å. is also quite appreciable. All these high energy photons which are emitted by the star will be absorbed by the atoms of the nebular gas. Since their frequency corresponds to an energy higher than that necessary to detach the electron from the nucleus, the atoms will be ionized and the primary mechanism can take place when an ion captures an electron. It must be remembered that the ionization potential for H is 13·15 eV., to which corresponds a wavelength of λ 911 Å., and that the ionization potential for ionized helium (that is the energy required to detach also the second electron) is 54 eV., corresponding to λ 225 Å.

Let us now follow step by step what happens, for example, to the oxygen atoms which are subjected to the ultra-violet radiation from the star. Because of the great number of quanta of a wavelength less than λ 160 Å. which are capable of ionizing atoms the ionization potential of which is 77 eV., oxygen cannot exist except in the form of an ion four times ionized (OV). It may well happen that an OV ion recaptures an electron, and this falling by successive steps to the ground level will give rise to the emission spectrum of OIV. This recombination will be followed immediately by a new ionization, since there are many photons of frequency high enough to produce it. Therefore a continuous return of electrons to the OV ion can be observed followed immediately by a new expulsion which requires the absorption of several photons of a wavelength smaller than λ 160 Å. Hence, provided a sphere of radius large enough is considered, the number of OIV ions which are transformed into OV ions will be sufficient to absorb completely the stellar radiation of a wavelength smaller than λ 160 Å.

Since the radiation capable of ionizing the OIV ions is extinct at greater distances from the star, the OIV ions will be able to survive, and in recombining with an electron, will produce the spectrum of OIII. In order to ionize OIII, which has an ionization potential of 55 eV., a radiation of a wavelength less than λ 225 Å. is required. The quanta of a wavelength smaller than λ 160 Å. are absorbed by OIV and therefore the radiation between λ 160 Å. and λ 225 Å. will ionize continuously all the OIII ions transforming them again into OIV. Similarly, within a given thickness of a nebula, there will exist a sufficient number of atoms of OIII to absorb the whole radiation between λ 160 Å. and λ 225 Å. Therefore at even greater distances from the star, OIII will be found, which, in recombining with an electron, will produce the spectrum of OII. This mechanism explains the reason for the different dimensions of the monochromatic images of the nebula. The radius of these images increases as the ionization potential decreases.

What we have described is only the primary mechanism by which an ion in recombining with an electron emits a spectrum following the return of the electron to the ground level. If this were the only mechanism producing the emission spectrum, it would be extremely simple to predict the intensity of the lines from the knowledge of the temperature of the central star. Conversely, from the intensity of the lines it would be possible to evaluate the temperature of the star. Unfortunately complications arise from the many secondary mechanisms which intervene.

Although the mystery of the nebulium lines and the reason for the difference in size of the monochromatic images of the nebulae had been solved, the reason still remained to be discovered why certain lines were so abnormally intense. We have to explain why, for instance, the permitted lines of OIII and of NII are generally weak while the forbidden lines are intense. This would lead us to think that the two different types of lines are formed by mechanisms which are totally different. The permitted lines are produced by the primary mechanism which we have already described, namely by the recombination of an electron with an ion. If the forbidden lines too were produced by the same mechanism, that is the capture of free electrons in the metastable levels, there would be no reason to think that similar captures would not occur also in other normal higher levels. Permitted and forbidden lines should have, therefore, approximately the same intensity.

Faced with this question, Bowen thought of the possibility of another mechanism. Since the excitation potentials of the forbidden lines are rather low (between 1·8 eV. and 5·3 eV.), these lines may be excited by collision of electrons having low speeds, which correspond to an acceleration produced by a potential difference smaller or equal to 5·3 eV. Many electrons with low velocity are present in nebulae. In fact an electron expelled from an atom will have a velocity between 0 (when the photon has the energy just necessary to ionize the atom) and the velocity corresponding to a number of eV. equal to the difference between two successive ionization potentials. Since this difference is approximately 20 eV., there will be many electrons which have a velocity between 0 and 20 eV. and which will make use of this energy in order to bring the electron directly from the ground level to the metastable level immediately above. In every collision these electrons will lose their velocity until they themselves will be recaptured and produce a spectrum of recombination.

In conclusion, we can say that the greater intensity of the forbidden lines compared with the permitted lines is due to the fact that while the permitted lines can be produced only as recombination following photo-ionization, the forbidden lines can be excited by collision of the many free electrons having a velocity smaller than 20 eV. Free electrons, however, which have the necessary velocity to excite atoms of H, HeI and HeII, are not available in sufficient numbers. Since the mechanisms producing the permitted lines of H and He and the forbidden lines of O and N are so different from each other, the comparison of the intensity of the lines does not give a reliable indication of the abundance of O and N as in the case of the more abundant atoms of H and He.

SECOND EXAMPLE. For the second example we shall take the mechanism of ionization by secondary radiation.

Let us suppose that ionized helium were to lose a second electron by photo-ionization. When recombination takes place and the electron falling to the ground level gives rise to the spectrum of HeII, it will, at the end, emit a series of lines in the extreme ultra-violet ($\lambda\lambda$ 304 Å., 256 Å., 243 Å.), which are produced in the transitions from the more internal to the lower orbit. Since these lines have a frequency higher than that necessary for ionizing neutral hydrogen and neutral helium, they will be able to produce ionization of these atoms and, as a consequence, a spectrum of recombination will be produced.

The mechanism of excitation by secondary radiation is as follows. An atom of ionized helium, for instance, absorbs to a high degree the radiations which are emitted by another atom of HeII as the electron falls from an excited state to the normal state. When this takes place the absorbing atom will be transferred to the same excited state in which the emitting atom was. From this state the atom will either emit again the same quantum, or it will emit a line of longer wavelength followed by an ultra-violet line. In this manner all the ultra-violet quanta of the recombination spectra can finally be changed into both quanta of longer wavelength, which cannot be absorbed by other atoms, but can leave the nebula and be observed, and into ultra-violet quanta which can ionize or excite other atoms.

We ought here to mention a particular case of the mechanism of excitation by a secondary radiation, which explains why some permitted lines of OIII and NIII are very intense, while other lines, which when produced in a laboratory present similar or higher intensity, are either extremely weak or not observable in nebular spectra. This is due to a coincidence. When an atom of HeII returns to the ground level, after having emitted a number of lines of observable wavelength, it will emit a quantum of wavelength λ 304 Å. It happens that OIII is capable of emitting or absorbing a line of the same wavelength, namely λ 304 Å., corresponding to the transition of the electron from the lower orbit to a higher orbit. From this level the electron can either return directly to the ground level, or reach it gradually by steps, passing through the intermediate levels. In this latter case it may emit ten permitted lines in the observable ultra-violet plus one in the extreme ultra-violet (λ 374 Å.). These ten lines are the only ones of the spectrum of OIII which have an appreciable intensity in the nebular spectra. Other lines which when produced in a laboratory have similar or greater intensity, are either weak or absent in nebular spectra. The coincidence, however, does not end here. The wavelength of the line in the extreme ultra-violet (λ 374 Å) is the same as that of a line that the atom of NIII can emit or absorb. Therefore, the photon λ 374 Å. emitted by the atom of OIII can place an atom of NIII into an excited state, from which it can return to the normal state emitting five lines in the visible region of the spectrum (the only permitted lines of NIII which are observed in the spectrum of nebulae) and one line in the extreme ultra-violet. The intensity of these lines of NIII and of OIII will not give a real indication of the abundance of these elements. It will depend on the number of quanta λ 304 Å. which can be used and hence, indirectly, on the abundance of He (fig. 9).

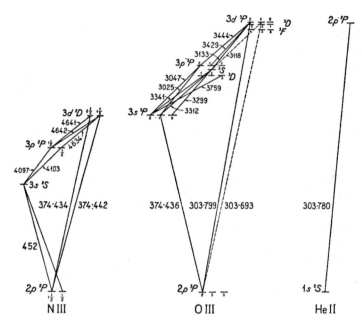

FIG. 9. Secondary mechanism of excitation of OIII and NIII atoms by an atom of HeII. Wavelengths are given in Ångstrom

Of the two secondary mechanisms of ionization and excitation, the second is much more important than the first. Atoms have the ability to absorb much more strongly the radiation corresponding to one of their own frequencies than to a frequency greater than the minimum frequency necessary for their ionization. This mechanism, therefore, is capable of greatly modifying the intensities of the permitted lines from that which would be observed if only the primary mechanism was at work.

III.6   The continuous spectrum of planetaries.

We have stated that the main characteristic of planetaries is a spectrum which consists only of emission lines and without a continuum. This statement, however, requires qualification.

Among the emission lines there are many (particularly those of H and the two nebular lines λ 5007 Å. and λ 4959 Å.) which are so intense that they constitute the dominant feature of the spectrum. The presence of a weak continuum becomes of secondary importance and indeed for a long time astronomers did not pay much attention to it. The main reason for this is that the intensity and the concentration of the light in a rather narrow band of wavelengths, as is the case for the emission lines, requires photographic exposures much shorter than those required to photograph the continuum, which therefore is hardly visible on spectrograms. When the continuum is more intense, as, for instance, in the nebulae NGC 7662 and NGC 6828, or when the exposure is longer in order to obtain the weaker lines, then the continuum appears.

The origin of this continuous spectrum has been explained only partially. One of the causes of emission of the continuum is the recombination of a free electron of any kinetic energy with a proton. In the transition of the electron from an unquantized state, that is from a state in which the electron can have any kinetic energy, to a quantized state of definite energy, there is an output of energy accompanied by an emission of any frequency between infinity and that value corresponding to the minimum energy necessary to ionize the atom of the quantized state in which the electron has arrived. The maximum emission corresponds to a minimum jump, that is the capture of the electron is more probable when its velocity is almost zero; after that the intensity of the continuum decreases rapidly.

In the photographic region there exists a continuous spectrum at the limit of the Balmer series, which corresponds to the recapture of a free electron in the second quantized state. This region theoretically extends from λ 3647 Å. to a wavelength equal to zero; its intensity decreases as the frequency increases and it depends also on the temperature. The continuum extends also into the visual region and it is here that there are difficulties of interpretation. There are two possible explanations for the existence of the continuum, but both appear inadequate when compared with the data of observation. First let us consider the Paschen continuum which, like the Balmer continuum, is produced when the electron recaptured by the proton falls directly into the third orbit. The intensity is a maximum at the limit of the series at λ 8206 Å. At λ 3900 Å., however, the Paschen continuum can contribute only 5% of the continuum observed. Observations, however, give for the continuum an intensity that is almost constant along the whole of the visible and photographic region.

The other possible cause of absorption is due to the hydrogen ion, that is an atom of hydrogen which has captured a second electron. At the time of the capture of the electron, emission takes place in the visible region of the spectrum but it is far too weak to satisfy the requirements of the observations. Other theories have been put forward, but none so far has been completely satisfactory. On the other hand observations are rather few and very difficult to obtain. If the slit of the spectrograph is widened enough to obtain sufficient light, the weak nebular lines can be masked and indeed confused with the continuum, thereby giving a false distribution. When the slit is kept very narrow it is true that spectra of very high purity are obtained, but the small amount of light gathered limits considerably the number of objects which can be observed.

It is to Page that we owe the greatest number of observations of the continuum of planetaries. From his investigations it would appear that the visible continuum between $\lambda\lambda$ 4400 Å. and 5000 Å. has the same intensity as $H\delta$. Page also estimates that the whole continuum is practically constant at all the various wavelengths.

Knowledge of the intensity distribution in the Balmer continuum and the ratio between the intensity of the continuum and that of the lines of the Balmer series, as Page remarks, can give extremely useful information on the physical state of the nebular matter such as temperature and density. We shall have the opportunity of returning to this subject later on.

III.7 Classification of nebular spectra.

From the early observations of nebular spectra, it was obvious that differences existed between spectra of various nebulae and that the relative intensity of the strongest emission lines did not always present the same ratio. In some cases the two green lines character- istic of the nebular spectrum were weaker than $H\beta$, in others they were as much as ten times more intense. When investigating which of the lines are present in various spectra, it appears that in some nebulae, the line of ions having fairly low ionization potential are strongest, while in others the strongest lines are those of ions having a high ionization potential. In some cases, as for example in NGC 7027, lines both of OI and of NeV can be observed. The presence of OI lines requires that the physical conditions of the nebula should be such as to permit the existence of a sufficient number of oxygen atoms the first excitation potential of which is 13·6 eV. The presence of NeV lines requires the existence of a large number of NeV atoms of sufficient energy to allow the electron to overcome a potential barrier of 97 eV., as this is the fourth ionization potential for Ne. It follows, therefore, that in the same nebula various physical conditions must exist. Such a variety of conditions could be explained, for instance, by assuming that NeV lines are formed in layers which are nearer to the exciting star, and that the OI lines originate in more external layers, which are not reached by the stellar radiation in the extreme ultra-violet, since such radiation would already have been absorbed by the gaseous layers nearer the star.

These differences in the various spectra suggested a classification based on the degree of excitation, by comparing the intensities of the lines of neutral atoms with those of ions several times ionized. The last and most complete of these classifications is that introduced by Aller. He selects the ratio between the intensity of the two nebular lines of OIII and the intensity of $H\beta$ as a criterion to determine the degree of excitation of a nebula. He then considers the ratio of intensity between several pairs of lines such as the line λ 3727 Å. of OII and λ 4959 Å. of OIII, the ionization potential of which are 13·6 eV. and 35·1 eV. respectively; between the line λ 4686 Å. of HeII, ionization potential 24·6 eV., and $H\beta$; between the lines of NeV and $H\beta$ and between the lines of NeV and those of NeIII. The values of these ratios, measured for various nebulae having a different degree of excitation, are given in Table 2. Aller subdivides them in ten classes from 1 to 10, in order of increasing excitation. In Table 2 an example of class 1 is missing. This class should group together the planetaries which in their spectra show no evidence of the characteristic nebular lines of OIII. It is very interesting to study how the ratio between the nebular lines and $H\beta$ varies. The intensity of the two lines of OIII which in class 2 is only $\frac{1}{5}$ of $H\beta$ grows rapidly with the degree of excitation, reaching values 10 to 20 times greater in nebulae of higher excitation. On the other hand the ratio of intensity

PLANETARY NEBULAE

between λ 3727 Å. of OII and λ 4959 Å. of OIII is considerably greater in nebulae of class 2. Here the line of OII is 32 times more intense than the line λ 4959 Å., then, while the former decreases, the latter increases and the ratio from 32 becomes 0·02 or 0·03 in classes 9 and 10. It is also worth noting that in the classes of low excitation

TABLE 2

Criterion	Anon. 18h 15m	IC 418	IC 2149	IC 4634	NGC 7026	J 900	NGC 6309	IC 2165	Anon. 21h 31m
$(N_1+N_2)/H\beta$	0·21	1·09	5·5	10·6	12·4	16·7	14·1	18·1	10·4
λλ 3727/4959	32	3·1	0·20	0·03	0·04	0·03	0·03	0·02	0·04
λ 4686/$H\beta$	—	—	—	—	0·13	0·47	0·77	0·6	0·9
NeV/$H\beta$	—	—	—	—	—	0·28	0·5	0·8	2·4
NeV/λ 3869	—	—	—	—	—	0·38	0·5	0·95	3·8
Class	2	3	4	5	6	7	8	9	10

(from class 1 to class 5 or 6) the lines of HeII and NeV are not measurable and that their intensity grows rapidly from class 6 to 10.

The continuum too depends on the degree of excitation of the nebula. According to Page, both the Balmer continuum and the visible continuum are generally stronger in nebulae of a low degree of excitation.

Minkowski, in studying the spectra of several nebulae of low surface brightness, has found that there are several important differences between spectra of planetaries of low surface brightness and those of high surface brightness. Faint nebulae very frequently have spectra in which the line λ 3727 Å. of OII is stronger than $H\beta$ and the line λ 4686 Å. of HeII is very intense. These same peculiarities are very much rarer in spectra of very bright nebulae. It is quite obvious that there should be a strict correlation between the spectrum and the other physical conditions of a nebula, since after all the spectrum is purely a manifestation of these physical conditions. Mayall's work, for instance, shows that spectra of nebulae are very similar if the nebulae have a similar appearance, namely brightness and form.

III.8 Chemical composition and physical conditions.

So far we have described the appearance of the nebular spectra and we have tried to explain the various mechanisms which produce

55

them. All this is of help in the understanding of the physical condition of nebulae, indeed our knowledge of it has reached a point which could not have been thought possible before the developments which have taken place in spectroscopy.

Since the spectrum of a luminous source depends on the atoms of which the source is made and on the physical conditions, such as temperature and density, of the same atoms, the spectrum will give us information on the chemical composition as well as on the temperature and density of the source.

CHEMICAL COMPOSITION. The intensity of a line depends on the number of atoms of the element which are in a position to produce it. On account of the various mechanisms which produce the lines of the nebular spectrum, reliable information on the chemical composition can be obtained by comparing the permitted lines among themselves, produced either by primary mechanism or by recombination. Another source of information is the comparison of the forbidden lines, all produced by the same excitation mechanism of electron collision.

At first only the strongest lines could be photographed. As all these lines belonged to light atoms (H, He, C, N, O), it was assumed that the chemical composition of planetaries was very different from that of the Sun and other stars because of the scarcity of metals. More recently, however, photographs with exposure times ranging from a few minutes up to 19 hours have been taken by Bowen, Wyse, Minkowski and Aller in order to record both weak and strong lines. As a result of these observations several lines belonging to metallic ions were identified and it was possible to establish that in fact the chemical composition of the planetaries is very similar to that of the Sun and other celestial objects. Several lines of atoms and ions were identified with certainty in a great number of planetaries. Lines of HI, HeI, HeII, CII, CIII, CIV, NII, NIII, OI, OII, OIII, OIV, OV, FIV, NeIII, NeIV, NeV, MgI, SiII, SiIII, SI, SII, SIII, ClIII, ClIV, AlII, AlV, AV, KIV, KV, KVI, CaV, CaVII, MnV, MnVI, FeIII, FeV, FeVI, FeVII. Less positive identifications suggested the possible existence of many other elements, the lines of which are present in stellar spectra.

Let us compare the abundance of the elements as determined by Bowen and Wyse for three nebulae, with the latest results of quantitative analysis of the solar atmosphere. In Table 3 the second column

TABLE 3

Element	Number of atoms in NGC 7027	Number of atoms in the Sun
H	100	100
He	10	16
Li	<0·1	1×10^{-9}
Be	<0·1	4×10^{-8}
B	<1	—
C	1	0·01
N	1	0·02
O	1	0·07
F	≤0·001	0·0001
Ne	<0·01	—
Na	0·1	0·0001
Mg	0·01	0·005
Al	<0·1	0·0001
Si	≤1	0·0016
P	<0·1*	0·00004
S	0·1	0·001
Cl	0·01	—
A	0·01	—
K	0·001	0·00001
Ca	0·01	0·0001
Sc	<0·001	6×10^{-8}
Ti	<0·01	0·000004
V	<0·1	0·0000006
Cr	<0·01	0·00002
Mn	<0·01	0·00002
Fe	0·01	0·0008

represents the number of atoms of an element for every 100 atoms of H in the nebula, while the third column gives similar data for the Sun. What is of interest to us is the relative abundance, and to find whether the ratio of the various elements to an element taken as reference (in our case hydrogen) is the same both in the Sun and in the nebula.

Given the uncertainty of these measurements of abundance, and the fact that the knowledge of the physical conditions (temperature and density of the nebula) are based on hypotheses, we cannot say

with certainty that there exists a difference in the chemical composition of the Sun and nebula. What we can say is that in the nebulae
there is no deficiency of metals as compared with the Sun.

Wyse, after his research work with Bowen, has carried out an
investigation on a larger number of nebulae. He wished to find out
whether the chemical composition of NGC 7027, already studied,
should be considered as common to all nebulae and whether there
were differences in the chemical composition between planetaries and
diffuse nebulae. He also investigated the question of whether planetaries could be subdivided into two groups, one with a greater
percentage of carbon and the other with a greater percentage of
nitrogen, as can be done with the Wolf-Rayet stars, which have a
temperature and a spectral type similar to those of the existing stars
of the planetaries. At the end of his investigations, Wyse was able to
show that planetaries and the diffuse nebula in Orion have the same
chemical composition, and that this composition is not very different
from that of the Sun.

ELECTRON DENSITY AND ELECTRON TEMPERATURE. The electron
density, which is defined as the number of free electrons per cubic
centimetre, is a very important physical datum since it is closely
related to the density of the matter which forms the nebula. This is
evident from the following reasoning. The most prominent element
is hydrogen, and since this is subjected to the ultra-violet radiation
of the exciting star, it can be assumed that it is all ionized. The total
number of free particles per cubic centimetre, neglecting the other
elements, will be the protons and the electrons present in the unit
volume. Since for every proton there is an electron, the density of
matter will be double the electron density. It is important therefore
to explain how it is possible to determine the electron density from
the study of the spectrum.

The continuum which can be observed where the Balmer series
ends and which depends on the capture of free electrons in the
second level, will have an intensity proportional to the number of
free electrons and protons and inversely proportional to the electron
temperature.

At this point we ought perhaps to remind the reader of the meaning of electron temperature.

According to the kinetics of gases the temperature is closely related to the velocity of particles, so that their thermal agitation can be taken as a measure of the temperature of the gas. Hence the electron temperature is simply the kinetic temperature related to the velocity of free electrons. Since the capture of an electron is much easier if its velocity is not too high, it is clear that the intensity of the Balmer continuum is inversely proportional to the electron temperature.

The energy emitted in a given interval of the spectrum of the Balmer continuum can be determined directly from the spectrum, provided the dimensions of the nebula are known. If the electron temperature is determined by other means we shall then have an equation where the unknown quantities are the number of free protons and electrons. Since these quantities are practically equal, we are left with only one unknown in our equation and the electron density can thus be determined. Unfortunately the diameters of nebulae are not known with sufficient accuracy because, as we already mentioned earlier on, their distances are known only approximately. There are, however, some methods which can be used to determine the electron temperature. The electron density N_e is:

$$N_e = K T_e^{\frac{3}{2}} S^{\frac{1}{2}} R^{-\frac{1}{2}}$$

where K is a constant, S is the surface brightness of the nebula in an interval of a given wavelength within the Balmer continuum. This quantity does not depend on the distance and can be obtained directly from spectrophotometric observations. T_e is the electron temperature and R the radius of the nebula. The fact that the square root of R appears in the above equation means that the uncertainty of R will have a smaller effect on the actual determination of N_e.

Menzel and Aller have given the results of observations for eight nebulae. According to these the electron density is of the order of 10,000 free electrons per cubic centimetre, a very low density when we consider that in the atmosphere of even the most rarefied stars the electron density is 10 million times larger. That planetaries are more rarefied than stars is proved by the fact that they are transparent. The whole of the nebula as well as the central star is visible. Stellar gases, on the other hand, are very opaque and the only thing that we can observe is a layer near the surface. Take, for instance, the Sun, at a depth of $\frac{1}{1000}$ of its radius, the gaseous mass is already completely opaque and all our direct knowledge is limited to a very thin layer 370 miles thick.

Once the diameter of a nebula has been approximately evaluated we can obtain its mass from the density. The masses obtained are of the order of $\frac{1}{10}$ of that of the Sun. These determinations of the density of matter are based on the assumption that the whole of the hydrogen present is ionized and therefore that the number of protons is equal to that of the electrons. There will exist, however, an external envelope which cannot be reached by the stellar radiation of wavelength less than λ 911 Å. because this radiation is already absorbed by the gaseous mass which is nearer to the star and which consists of neutral hydrogen atoms. The gaseous mass of a nebula can therefore be greater than $\frac{1}{10}$ of the solar mass and probably is as high as $\frac{1}{5}$ of the solar mass. Even this mass is still rather small when the dimensions of the nebula are considered. The diameter of the Sun is 864,000 miles, while that of a planetary can be from 1 to 10 million times greater.

Let us now see how the electron temperature can be determined.

All the characteristics of a nebular spectrum depend on the velocity of the free electrons, as we have already had the opportunity of mentioning when discussing the primary and secondary mechanisms. This means that these characteristics of the spectrum will enable us to obtain the electron temperature. There are several methods which can be used: (1) the study of the energy distribution with respect to wavelengths, in the Balmer continuum; (2) the relative intensity of the auroral and nebular lines of OIII; (3) the profiles of the emission lines; and (4) the magnitude of Balmer's discontinuity.

In the first method use is made of the same equation already mentioned in connection with the calculation of the electron density. When the latter is known we can obtain the value of T_e from the equation. In practice, however, unless one of the two unknowns N_e or T_e can be determined by some other means, it is permissible to make certain assumptions either for the one or the other. The other methods, too, require that the electron density should be known even if only approximately. It is possible to proceed by successive approximations starting for instance in the equation which gives the electron density, with a value of T_e which is very probable. Once a value for the electron density is obtained, this can be used to obtain T_e. In its turn this T_e can be used to obtain a more approximate value of N_e and so on.

The second method is particularly useful because it is easy to measure experimentally the intensity of the strong nebular lines λ 5007 Å. and λ 4959 Å. as well as that of the auroral line λ 4363 Å. All three are forbidden lines of OIII, due to transitions from the metastable to the ground level. The ratio of their intensities is a function of temperature as we know from the mechanism of formation of the forbidden lines. The atoms are excited by collisions with free electrons and the electron is raised to a metastable level of a low excitation potential until it falls back spontaneously and emits a line. These are the transitions which give rise to the forbidden lines in question (fig. 8). Since the probability that an electron should be raised to the level $^1D_2$ or to the level $^1S_0$ is a function of temperature, it is clear that from the relative intensity of the line λ 4363 Å. and of the two nebular lines it is possible to obtain the temperature. In order that the electron should be raised to the level $^1S_0$, which is a higher level than $^1D_2$, it must absorb, by collision, a larger energy. The intensity of the line λ 4363 Å., compared with that of the two nebular lines, will tend to increase with increasing temperature. If we denote with I the intensity of the lines in question, an intensity which can be measured in the spectrum, we have:

$$\frac{I_{\lambda\lambda\ 5007\ +\ 4959}}{I_{\lambda\ 4363}} = 4\cdot4 \times \exp\,(33{,}000/T_e) + 0\cdot75$$

We can see from the above that the smaller the electron temperature is, the greater is the ratio.

Observations carried out on 30 planetaries show that the electron temperatures are between 6,000° and 30,000° K. The majority of nebulae have a temperature between 8,000° and 12,000° K.

III.9   The central stars.

So far we have been dealing with the spectra, the physical conditions and the chemical composition of the planetaries themselves, that is to say the gaseous mass of very low density which surrounds the central star. Let us now consider the nature of these central stars the radiation of which excites the nebular gas and produces the emission spectrum.

Not only planetaries but also diffuse nebulae derive their energy from neighbouring stars or from stars embedded in them. Hubble had observed that when these stars have a high surface temperature, 15,000° to 20,000° K., they appear blue in colour and they belong to classes O to B2. The diffuse nebulae too have emission spectra similar to that of the planetaries. If the stars embedded in the nebular gas are less hot, the number of high energy protons, which can produce photo-ionization of the atoms, is too low and in this case the gas simply reflects the radiation emitted by the star. This behaviour, however, is not general and there exist nebulosities, for instance, which surround stars of class G (that is with surface temperature lower than 6,000° K.) which are sufficiently excited to produce an emission spectrum.

The main difference between stars of high temperature which excite the diffuse nebulae, and the central star of planetaries, lies in their absolute magnitude. Stars which excite the diffuse nebulae are stars of great brightness, of an absolute magnitude between −5 and −7 occupying a position in the Russell diagram characteristic of population I, to which they belong together with the diffuse nebulae. The nuclei of planetaries have magnitudes which, in spite of the fact that their distances and hence their absolute magnitudes are not accurately known, are estimated to be between 0 and −1, and indeed there are some even less bright than that. Their position in the Russell diagram is found by moving to the left along the horizontal branch, where are the variables typical of clusters, namely the RR Lyrae stars. This position is that of Baade's population II to which the planetaries belong.

There are two methods which we can follow in order to obtain information about the physical conditions of the central stars of planetaries. The first is the one normally used to gain knowledge of the physical conditions and chemical composition of all celestial objects, namely the study of their spectra. The second is based on the following idea originally put forward by Zanstra. Since the bright lines of the spectrum of the nebula are due to the excitation produced by the ultra-violet radiation of the central star, the study of their intensity will give us information about the energy emitted by the star itself in the extreme ultra-violet which cannot be observed directly.

Zanstra assumes that when compared with hydrogen all the other elements which compose the nebula represent a negligible percentage of the whole. In the unit of time the star emits a given number N of photons with a frequency higher than the one necessary to ionize a hydrogen atom, therefore there will be N photo-ionizations. After each photo-ionization there follows a recombination, thus there will be also N recombinations. Each recombination can produce either a re-emission in the Lyman continuum, if the electron is recaptured in the original orbit, or one or more lines of one of the infra-red and visible series and it can also produce a line of the Lyman series (fig. 10). Therefore for every photon emitted by the star in the extreme ultra-violet, there will be an emission in the nebula of a photon either in the Lyman continuum or in the Lyman series. If

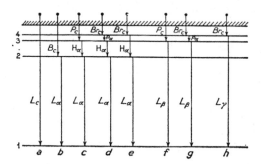

Fɪɢ. 10. Re-combination of an electron and a proton

we denote with L_c and L the total number of photons emitted by the nebula in the continuum and in the series respectively, we have:

$$N = L + L_c$$

None of the L and L_c photons is observable. Because of their high frequency the photons corresponding to the lines of the Lyman series $L\beta$, $L\gamma$ etc. will be immediately reabsorbed as soon as they are emitted, thereby raising other hydrogen atoms to excited states. We can assume that after a number of absorptions and re-emissions, each photon of frequency corresponding to a line of the Lyman series is re-emitted by means of a series of jumps, the last of which corresponds to the emission of $L\alpha$. In practice, therefore, we can assume that $L = L(\alpha)$ where $L(\alpha)$ is the number of photons $L\alpha$ emitted by the nebula. Each emission of $L\alpha$, however, will also be preceded by an emission in the continuum and in the Balmer series and therefore:

$$L(\alpha) = B + B_c$$

where $B + B_c$ will have a similar meaning to $L + L_c$ but will of course refer to the Balmer series. Finally we will have:

$$N = B + B_c + L_c$$

Since the number of photons of the Lyman continuum which emerges from the nebula must be very small, because the majority of them will have been absorbed before that, we can write:

$$N = B + B_c$$

Therefore from the measurement of the intensity of the lines and of the Balmer continuum, which can be observed, we can obtain indirectly the number of photons N which the star emits, per square centimetre, in the ultra-violet. If the star is radiating like a black body, this number N will depend on the temperature and this latter can be calculated. If however the star does not radiate exactly like a black body, and this is the real case, the temperatures obtained in this way will be affected by an error, and the greater the departure from the ideal behaviour of a black body, the larger will be the error.

A similar method has been suggested by Stoy. In the mechanism of excitation of the forbidden lines, a photon of frequency higher than the one necessary to ionize a hydrogen atom, ejects the electron with a given velocity. The kinetic energy of the free electron is used in the excitation of another atom and in doing so it carries its electron to a metastable state of low excitation potential. If P represents the intensity of all the forbidden lines, and E_c the kinetic energy of the electrons ejected from the hydrogen atom, then:

$$P = E_c = E_0 - h\nu N$$

where E_0 is the energy radiated by the star and $h\nu N$ the energy used in ionizing the hydrogen atoms. When we compare the intensity of all the forbidden lines with that of all the lines and the Balmer continuum we shall obtain

$$\frac{P}{H/(h\nu)} = \frac{E_0 - h\nu N}{N}$$

From this we can see that the ratio between the total intensity P of all the forbidden lines and the number of photons $H/(h\nu)$ emitted in the lines and Balmer continuum, is equal to the ratio between the kinetic energy of the free electrons and the number of photons N with frequencies higher than the limit of the Lyman series, emitted by the star. Since the left-hand expression can be determined from the observation of the intensity of the forbidden lines and of the lines and Balmer continuum and since the right-hand expression can be calculated for various values of the temperature, it will be possible, by successive attempts, to find what is the value of the temperature which will make the second term equal to the first. This is true only if we assume that the star radiates like a black body.

Other similar methods based on the same principles have been developed and used by Zanstra. We shall not describe them here because we are interested in the principles which led to the two methods described above, rather than in the practical details.

III.10 Spectroscopic analysis of the nuclei of planetaries.

The direct method for the determination of the physical conditions of the nucleus based on the study of the stellar spectrum presents considerable practical difficulties. The nebular spectrum with its very intense bright lines, hides partially the continuum as well as the dark lines of the central star. In order to eliminate this disadvantage it would be desirable to have high dispersion spectra; this, however, is difficult because of the faint brightness of the objects to be photographed. Only in the case of brighter nuclei has it been possible to study accurately the spectrum.

Aller was able to study a number of them and he reached the following conclusions. The spectra of the nuclei of planetaries can be divided into four classes: (1) Wolf-Rayet class; (2) class Of with bright and dark lines; (3) class O with only dark lines; (4) spectra devoid of any trace of bright or dark lines.

The stars of the Wolf-Rayet class, among which there are both stars of population I and II, present a continuum with strong radiation in the ultra-violet, which indicates a very high surface temperature, higher than 30,000° K. Superimposed on this spectrum are found broad, bright lines of HeII, CII, NII and OII. The nuclei of some planetaries are typical of Wolf-Rayet stars of population II. These, as far as the spectra are concerned, are very similar to the Wolf-Rayet stars of population I but their absolute magnitude is different.

In the class Of are to be found stars of population I while the nuclei of some planetaries belong to population II. Their spectra are more or less those of ordinary stars of class O, namely blue stars of high surface temperature, in the region of 25,000° to 30,000° K. They can be distinguished from the Wolf-Rayet stars by the absence of the broad, bright lines. Their spectra also contain some bright lines apart from the dark lines of ordinary stars of class O.

Stars of class O, like the Wolf-Rayet and stars of class Of, are predominantly of population I, but there are also a few of population II among the nuclei of the planetaries.

The most extraordinary objects are the nuclei, which present a continuum without any trace of absorption or emission, or if these exist they must be extremely faint and completely overshadowed by the nebular emission. From the analysis of nebular spectra, Aller was able to reach the following conclusions on their physical conditions and chemical composition.

The temperatures were evaluated from the spectral type bearing in mind the variation of the ratio between the intensity of the hydrogen and ionized helium lines. Of course this ratio is very sensitive to changes in temperature, since with decreasing temperatures, the number of neutral hydrogen atoms which produce dark lines increases, and the intensity of the Balmer lines too increases, while at the same time the number of ionized helium atoms decreases. The values obtained for the temperature were between 32,000° and 35,000° K. It is of great interest to compare the temperature of the existing stars, obtained directly from the study of their spectra, with the temperature obtained by an indirect method from the study of the spectrum of the gas excited by the same stars (Table 4).

TABLE 4

Temperatures in °K. of the exciting stars, obtained by various methods

Object	Value from spectral class	Zanstra's method	Stoy's method
IC 418	33,200	25,000	18,000
IC 2149	32,500	40,000	26,000
NGC 2392	34,500	35,000	56,000
IC 4593	33,400	25,000	31,000
NGC 6210	32,900	30,000	45,000
NGC 6543	33,000	35,000	33,000
NGC 6826	34,600	30,000	40,000
NGC 6891	32,900	30,000	42,000

The agreement between the various methods can be considered fairly satisfactory as can be seen from Table 4. In this table, however, there is no data for the exciting stars which have only a continuous spectrum and for which the determination of temperature from the type of spectrum is impossible, nor is there any data for those nebulae which have invisible nuclei, as for example NGC 7027. For the latter Wurm has estimated a temperature between 110,000° and 200,000° K.

The electron density can be evaluated either from the intensity or from the number of the Balmer lines which can be observed. The higher the density the more intense and broad is the line, and the number of visible lines decreases since near the limit of the series they become so close as to give a continuous spectrum. The relationship between the lines and the electron density is explained by the fact that the free electrons produce an electric field which acts upon the emitting or absorbing atom, thereby producing a broadening of the line by Stark effect. The greater the electron density, the greater is the electric field and hence the observable effect. This electron density is a little lower than that of ordinary stars of class O of population I. On average it is 10^{13} electrons per cubic centimetre.

From the spectroscopic data we can determine the value of gravity which is found to be of the same order as that for the ordinary stars of class O of population I. The mass and the semi-diameter can also be evaluated. The semi-diameters are about the same as that of the Sun and the masses are slightly greater than that of the Sun. This last result is of particular interest, since from their brightness, estimated to be about one thousand times greater than that of the Sun, we would be led to expect masses from 5 to 10 times as large as the solar mass.

Aller obtains also an extremely important result for the chemical composition of the nuclei of nebulae. The ratio between the number of atoms of hydrogen and that of the atoms of helium present in the atmosphere of the nebular nuclei is between 1·5 and 2, while in the stars of class O of population I the same ratio is about 10. Does this mean then that the nuclei of planetaries are much richer in helium? Results so far obtained lead us to believe that this is so. Moreover the percentage of carbon, nitrogen and oxygen varies from one object to another and there is no indication of the clear division into the carbon and nitrogen sequence as is the case with the Wolf-Rayet stars of population I. In these two sequences two classes can be distinguished, one of stars with carbon lines in their spectra and total absence of nitrogen lines, and the other class with stars which have spectra where the reverse occurs. In the spectra of nuclei of planetaries the lines of both elements are present. We must here observe that all these anomalies in the chemical composition apply to the light elements, H, He, C, N, O, which are involved in the nuclear reactions which are the source of stellar energy. The difference in the abundance of these elements between stars of population I and nuclei of the planetaries of population II must have a profound physical meaning connected with the stellar evolution.

III.11 Relation between stellar temperature and electron temperature of nebulae.

The electron temperature of 30 nebulae studied by Aller, show that these temperatures are between 6,000° and 15,000° K. and it seems that they are independent of the temperature of the nucleus.

In theory it is possible to establish what the relation should be between the temperature T_N of the nucleus and the electron temperature T_e. Let us assume that the nebula is formed exclusively of hydrogen and let us take into account the two conditions necessary for the radiation field to be in equilibrium. These two conditions are: (1) that to each photo-ionization at the ground level of the hydrogen atom should correspond a recombination at any level; (2) that all the radiation absorbed by a given volume of gas is re-emitted. On this assumption it is possible to calculate T_e as a function of T_N. It is found that T_e increases with increasing T_N but at a much slower rate. For $T_N = 20,000°$ K., T_e has almost the same value $T_e = 18,000°$ K. When T_N is 80,000° K., T_e is only 57,000° K., and finally when T_N reaches 320,000° K., then T_e is 132,000° K.

As we have already mentioned, the observation does not confirm these calculations; T_e is almost constant and is independent of the temperature of the nucleus. Even if the nebula really contained only hydrogen, we must remember that apart from photo-ionization, the free electrons in collision with the hydrogen atoms excite them and the atom returning to its normal level emits a line at the expense of the kinetic energy of the electron. Therefore the mean velocity of the free electrons and hence the electron temperature, will be lower than would be the case if the phenomenon was regulated by the mechanism of photo-ionization. In actual fact nebulae contain, apart from hydrogen and helium, a certain amount of carbon, oxygen, nitrogen and neon as well as other metallic atoms. A great part of the kinetic energy of the electrons is dissipated in the excitation of these atoms to their metastable levels. It follows that the more intense are the forbidden lines, the greater is the amount of kinetic energy of the free electrons which is transformed into radiation. T_e therefore depends not on T_N but rather on the number of atoms having metastable levels of low excitation potential which are easily excited by electron collisions.

III.12 Structure and internal motions of planetaries.

We have been discussing the distribution of planetaries in our Galaxy and this has given us some indication to which population they belong. We have also studied the spectrum and the methods used for interpreting it and finally we have discussed the nature of the central stars. All these data are very important for the information they give about the physical nature and about the chemical composition of nebular matter.

Another subject of great importance to us is the actual distribution and motion of the gases. This subject presents many problems, the solution of which would throw a light on questions such as the past history of planetaries, their development and their decay. So far we have considered a planetary only as an extended envelope of gases very rarefied and of a shape approximately spherical. A glance, however, at any photograph of nebulae will reveal that their real structure is much more complicated. Filaments appear to cross them in all directions and their shape is generally far from spherical. The study of the distribution of the intensity of radiation in the various parts of a nebula, possibly photographed in monochromatic light by means of interference filters, can give some indication of the disposition of the radiating gases.

There are still several questions that require an answer. Questions such as whether the gases are motionless, expanding or contracting, whether the nebula is in rotation and whether it is agitated by turbulent motions. Once again an answer to the question of the motion of the gases is to be sought in the study of the nebular spectrum. The Doppler effect, as is well known, enables us to determine whether a radiating gas is approaching or receding from us. We shall have to consider, therefore, both the structure of the nebula, that is the distribution of nebular matter, and its motion. Only then, having collected all the information obtained from various sources, shall we be able to attempt an understanding of the birth, the development and the decay of planetaries.

THE STRUCTURE OF PLANETARIES. Planetaries present a spherical symmetry or at least a symmetry of revolution around an axis, which leads us to think of it as a process of ejection of gases from the central star. A careful examination will show irregularities in the appearance of planetaries. On the other hand, diffuse nebulae have strange and irregular shapes which are reminiscent of clouds in our own atmosphere and therefore have asymmetrical forms.

Observations of planetaries show that they have sharp and well-defined edges. Their hydrogen is completely ionized by the ultra-violet radiation of the central star and produces a recombination spectrum. At a given distance from the star, where the whole of the ultra-violet radiation has been absorbed by the process of photo-ionization, we shall also find neutral hydrogen, the electrons of which are at rest at the ground level and will not be emitting any radiation. The zone of transition between the region of the ionized hydrogen, which is emitting radiation by recombination, and the region of neutral hydrogen, which is not emitting, is very narrow according to Strömgren's calculations, and therefore the edges of the visible part of the planetary appear very sharp. Moreover it is possible that if the gas has been ejected from the star with a given initial velocity and it continues to expand, its density, at a certain point, will become so low that it feels the effect of the resistance of the interstellar matter, which will brake the expansion, condense the external parts of the nebula and cause the formation of well-defined edges.

Photographs obtained in monochromatic light with interference filters, confirm the theoretical predictions of Bowen on the stratification of the emitting atoms. This stratification produces a greater density of the atoms of high ionization potential in the internal regions and of the other atoms in the more external regions.

The ring shape, which is common to many planetaries, is due to the fact that the envelope surrounding the central star is not a gaseous sphere of decreasing density from the interior to the exterior. Often this envelope is a real shell, an envelope of gas ideally limited between two spherical surfaces; this, to a terrestrial observer, appears as a ring, since the line of sight will go through a greater amount of gas at the edge than at the centre of the nebula (fig. 11). In the

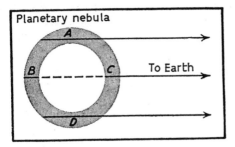

Fig. 11. Ring planetary nebula

interior, near the central star, the quantity of gas is very small and its condition is not favourable to the production of a spectrum of recombination. In fact in the immediate neighbourhood of the star, the velocity of the free electrons of thermal origin will be very strong, and there will be very little probability, if any, that hydrogen and helium ions will recapture an electron and hence emit their typical spectrum.

It is to be noted that each nebula has its own characteristics, according to whether the gases are distributed in one sphere only enveloping the star or in a shell which appears to us as a ring or double envelope. Because of the stratification of the elements, the shape will appear different according to the radiation we use for the observation. All these characteristics will be described in greater detail later, when we discuss some of the most interesting objects.

INTERNAL MOTIONS OF PLANETARIES. The existence of motion in the nebular gases is revealed by the Doppler effect. The first astronomers who made accurate studies of this subject were Campbell and Moore. Out of the 43 planetaries they studied, they found that 23 showed definite evidence of the existence of internal motions, 17 showed no such evidence, and 3 gave doubtful results. Campbell and Moore thought that these motions were due to a rotation of the nebula. However, several objections existed to the acceptance of this interpretation. The lines of the spectrum often appeared very broad and in some cases even double, but if the envelope were in rotation these lines should appear only curved. In fact if the slit of the spectrograph is placed in a direction at right angles to the axis of rotation

71

of the nebula (fig. 12) the limb A, which is approaching the observer, will give a line which is shifted towards the violet, while the limb B, which is receding, will give a line which is displaced towards the red, and the total effect will be that of a distorted line. If, on the other hand, the slit is placed parallel to the rotation axis (fig. 13)

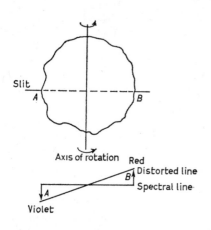

FIG. 12. Distortion of a spectral line produced by rotation; slit of spectrograph at right angles to the axis of rotation

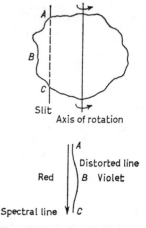

FIG. 13. Distortion of a spectral line produced by rotation; slit of spectrograph parallel but not coincident with the axis of rotation

then the line will still appear distorted, since the points A and C have a velocity of rotation which is smaller than that of point B. Velocity of rotation alone, however, does not explain the doubling and the broadening observed. Campbell and Moore did not consider the possibility that the nebular gas might be expanding, as did Perrine. If the nebula is expanding, the gas nearer to us will move in the direction of the line of sight and will, therefore, produce a line displaced towards the violet, while the parts of the gas further away, which are moving in the opposite direction, will produce a line shifted towards the red. The fact that several lines are not only double but broadened or distorted, can also be explained easily enough by the hypothesis of expansion rather than by that of rotation. Moreover it is apparent that the expansion of the envelope is not uniform since turbulent motion of large masses of gases must exist.

It is interesting to note that when a nebula appears on a photograph to have a simple and regular structure, the spectral lines too are sharp, in other words they do not show the presence of different gaseous masses which have various velocities. When, on the other hand, nebulae present a structure which is rather complex and irregular, with many filaments and many regions where the intensity changes rapidly from one point to another, then they also have spectra with broad lines, which are an indication of turbulent motion occurring in the gaseous mass.

Wilson recently made a study of the internal motions of nebulae and obtained an interesting and new result. In the high dispersion spectra obtained at Mt. Wilson, the structure of the nebular lines is very clear. These lines appear broad at the centre of the nebula and become narrower as the edge of the nebula is approached. Often they are clearly divided into two components, which we will call 'red' and 'violet' according to whether they are shifted towards the red or violet from their normal position. The ratio between the intensity of these two components shows that there are as many nebulae with the violet component which is more intense than the red, as there are nebulae with the red component more intense than the violet. The doubling of the line at the centre is an indication that the gas is expanding, with the part nearer to us approaching and the part further away receding from us. As we move from the centre of the nebulae, where the expansion occurs in the direction of the observer and therefore the velocity is purely radial, to the edge, the expansion occurs in planes which are increasingly inclined to the direction of observation, hence the radial component of the velocity decreases. When we reach the limb, the velocity is purely tangential as the expansion occurs in a direction at right angles to the line of sight, and the Doppler effect will be reduced to zero (fig. 14). The fact that there are nebulae with the violet component more intense, and nebulae with the same component less intense than the red, proves that the nebular gas is completely transparent. Were it not so, the red component originating in the part of the nebula remote from us would always be weaker than the violet component. The observed difference in intensity of the two components can then be interpreted as being produced by an irregular distribution of the gas.

It may appear surprising that such an extended mass of gas as that which constitutes a planetary should be so completely transparent. When we described how the emission spectrum of a nebula is

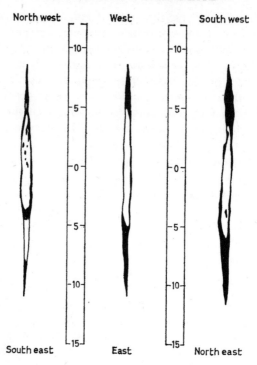

FIG. 14. N₁ line in the spectrum of NGC 7662. Position of slit: North west to South east on the left; West to East in the centre; South west to North east on the right

produced, we said that the nebular gas absorbs completely the ultra-violet radiation of the exciting star and becomes ionized; in the re-emission the observed spectrum is formed. The complete absorption, however, occurs for radiations of wavelengths shorter than λ 1000 Å.; in fact only these photons have sufficient energy to ionize the atoms of the nebula. Radiations of longer wavelength, whether emitted by the star or re-emitted by the nebula, cannot be absorbed by atoms which are in the ground state, namely in the orbit nearer to the nucleus, since the radiation has no sufficient energy for ionizing them, but the quanta could be absorbed by atoms which are in other states. For example, a hydrogen atom which is in the second excited state, that is with the electron raised to the second orbit, by collision or by absorption of a photon, could be ionized by absorbing a photon of wavelength λ 3647 Å. Even if the star is very hot and is, therefore, emitting a great number of photons, it is very unlikely that either a photon or a collision could raise a large number of atoms to excited states, since the radiation must be distributed in all the great volume occupied by the nebula which has very low density. Hence all the hydrogen is practically at the normal level and therefore is in condition of absorbing only radiations of wavelength shorter than λ 1000 Å., while the others will pass undisturbed.

Let us now return to Wilson's investigation. He measured the separation between the red and violet component. This separation corresponds to the difference $\triangle v$ between the velocity of expansion of the two parts of the nebula, that is, that which approaches us and that which recedes from us. The investigation shows that the separation is not the same for all ions, but depends on the ionization potential. Ions which have a greater ionization potential also have a smaller separation which increases regularly with decreasing potentials. Hydrogen is an exception; although it has an ionization potential of 13·5 eV., that is to say, lower than that for the OII and the NII ions, it behaves like OIII and NIII. This fact seems to indicate the existence of a clear stratification of elements. It is, therefore, very important to investigate whether a correlation exists between the dimensions of nebular images in various radiations and the separation $\triangle v$ of the same lines. We have already remarked that the dimensions of the various monochromatic images are an index of the stratification of various ions, those of greater excitation being nearer to the nucleus, while the others are further away. Wilson finds, however, that the correlation is only qualitative and not quantitative. Some nebulae which have similar monochromatic images have strong $\triangle v$ differences and vice versa.

The behaviour of hydrogen is not really strange. Since this element has only one electron, it will be ionized in all the regions of the nebula as far as those reached by radiation of wavelength less than λ 911 Å. Recombination will produce an emission spectrum in all these regions and therefore also in those in which NIII and OIII lines are produced.

In conclusion, Wilson's results show that the innermost regions of nebulae, regions that is where very highly ionized atoms are to be found, expand much more slowly than the outer regions. The expansion velocity ranges between 10 and 50 km./s.

III.13 Evolution of planetaries.

The problem of interpreting the kinematic phenomena which take place in a nebula is extremely complex on account of the several factors which have to be considered. Among these are: the complicated internal structure of a planetary; the differences in velocity between parts of a nebula; the presence of irregular filaments and the various forces (pressure of radiation, gravitational pull of the nucleus, friction with interstellar matter) which act upon the gas. All theoretical discussion involves simplifications and models which generally are far removed from reality.

Gurzadian has attempted to explain the above phenomena and at the same time has tried to study the origin of a planetary and trace its evolution in time. According to Gurzadian the envelope around the central star, which appears to us as a ring, was emitted by the nucleus in a limited period of time of the order of a few thousand years. As the envelope expands its density diminishes. At a given moment the density of the interstellar medium is no longer negligible when compared with that of the envelope and the braking action produces a condensation of the nebular gas at the edge of the envelope which would explain the well-defined limb of planetaries.

If we assume that at the beginning of the explosion the envelope formed is not quite spherical but has prominences and hollows, it is interesting to consider what would happen when these meet the interstellar gas. The parts which are protruding will be the first to meet the resistance of the interstellar gas, while the hollows, which are lower, will meet it later, when the expansion which is taking place has already reduced the density. It can be foreseen, therefore, that inequalities will be more accentuated until the planetary will become unstable and will divide into separate clouds. According to Gurzadian's calculations, this separation should take place when the radius is approximately 200,000 A.U., since instability is reached when the radius is equal to the cube root of the ratio between the mass of the planetary and the density of the interstellar medium. This value actually represents the upper limit of the observed values, confirming the suggestion that beyond this limit the planetary cannot be stable any longer. If we assume that the average velocity of expansion of a planetary is of the order of 50 km./s. and if we divide the maximum permissible radius (200,000 A.U.) by the velocity, we find that the time necessary for the planetary to reach the maximum dimension is given by

$$3 \times 10^{18} \text{ cm.}/(5 \times 10^6 \text{ cm./s.}) = 6 \times 10^{11} \text{s.}$$

namely, approximately 20,000 years. This period is extremely short compared with the life of a star and would explain why these objects are so rare. Only one planetary has been discovered in one of the hundred or more globular clusters belonging to the Galaxy. The fact that only one object of this type exists among the 10 million stars is a proof of its scarcity.

Novae and supernovae have some affinities with the planetaries; indeed it was even thought that planetaries were the final product of a nova explosion. Again according to Gurzadian, the envelope of a nova, which has a mass only 10^{-5} of the Sun's mass, becomes unstable when the radius is only 10,000 A.U., and its life can last about 30 years. Neither novae nor supernovae can therefore be the ancestors of a planetary.

It is probable that the velocity of expansion of planetaries is slowing down. Several causes intervene to brake the motion of the gas. First we have the gravitational pull of the central star, secondly the braking action of the interstellar gas, and finally we have the pressure of radiation of the emissions which take place in the interior of the planetary and which correspond to the most intense line of hydrogen in the ultra-violet series.

Gurzadian has also attempted to predict what will be the development of a planetary with time, basing his work on the observations of the structure of several planetaries and on the hypotheses on the way in which the ejection of matter from the central star takes place. It could well be that these theories, with the progress of observations, may prove untenable in the future, but at the present state of our knowledge they appear to explain most of the facts. The first stage would be represented by a spherical gaseous envelope, relatively dense, surrounding the star which ejected it. The gas would then expand in space, becoming less dense and taking the shape of a sphere which is observed by us in the form of a ring. The pressure of radiation that this sphere exerts towards the exterior would produce a second layer more tenuous and less bright, which is observed by us as a second ring. This latter would tend to become less dense and soon will be invisible. In the end we shall be left with a planetary consisting of a central nucleus surrounded by one spherical envelope only, while between the star and the spherical envelope there will be very little gas.

Although Gurzadian's theories are new and interesting they are not totally satisfactory. They are based on old observations while new investigations by Minkowski at Mt. Palomar introduce new facts which can partly contradict Gurzadian's arguments. Moreover nowadays there is a tendency to believe that the existence of magnetic fields in the gaseous mass may be of great importance.

From all we have said it appears that while the knowledge of the spectroscopic mechanism which produces the nebular spectrum is very satisfactory and the interpretation of the observations is almost complete, the structure and the motions of planetaries appear to be more difficult to explain. In fact it would be safer to say that their evolution is far from clear. Perhaps a certain amount of help will be given by the recent work of Iosif Šklovskij. His investigations lead us to review some of the theories already discussed.

At the beginning of this chapter we mentioned the very difficult problem still unsolved of the determination of the distance of planetaries. To give an indication of the uncertainty involved we shall give some of the values obtained by different methods for NGC 7293. This is the only planetary for which a direct measurement of its distance by means of its trigonometrical parallax has some meaning. For this planetary the value of the parallax measured is substantially greater than the mean error. Van Maanen found that the distance of NGC 7293 is of the order of 30 parsecs, while for other 21 planetaries he estimated their mean distance to be of the order of 1,400 parsecs; therefore it is not possible to measure directly each distance by non-statistical methods.

Zanstra, with completely different methods based on physics, obtains for the same planetary NGC 7293 the distance of 350 parsecs, while Berman, whose results we have previously mentioned, obtains a distance of 1,050 parsecs.

The new approach suggested by Šklovskij derives from a formula that he gave for the determination of the distance R of the planetaries. According to this, the distance R is proportional to the fifth root of the square of the mass of the planetary and inversely proportional to the angular diameter and to the fifth root of its surface brightness. Šklovskij obtains this relation from the fact that the quantity of light produced by one cubic centimetre of nebula must be proportional to the number of protons and free electrons which, recombining, give the spectrum of the nebula. From this it follows that the surface brightness I, which can be measured directly, is:

$$I = Cm^2/r^5$$

where C is a constant. Since $r = \phi R$, where ϕ is the angular diameter and R the distance, it follows that:

$$I = Cm^2/\phi^5 R^5 \quad \text{and} \quad R = cm^{2/5}/\phi I^{1/5}$$

where c is another constant equal to $C^{1/5}$.

The masses are not known and for them it is necessary to adopt a probable value, assuming that they are all the same. An error in the mass will produce only a small error in the distance since mass, in the above formula, has only an exponent 0·4. Therefore if the mass varies from 1 to 5, the distance will vary only from 1 to 2.

Because of the constant in the formula it will be necessary to calibrate the scale of distances by applying the relation to several objects the distances of which have been obtained by other means. Šklovskij's calibration is obtained by means of the distances determined by proper motion and by the radial velocities of the nuclei. The method has been already mentioned earlier in this chapter. The results obtained from this new method are very different from the earlier results. For instance, in the case of NGC 7293 a distance of 50 parsecs is found, which agrees better with the value obtained by van Maanen. We should note that for a distance greater than 250 parsecs the mass of NGC 7293 would be equal to or greater than ten times the solar mass, while for a distance of 50 parsecs it would be of the order of 0·2 times the solar mass, and this is a more probable value. It is easy to understand how the calculation of the mass is related to the distance. From the angular semi-diameter, once the distance is assumed, it is possible to obtain the linear semi-diameter and hence the volume of the planetary nebula. This can be assumed to be wholly composed of hydrogen. As the electron density is known from spectroscopic observations, it is easy to calculate the mass by multiplying the volume by the mass of the protons contained in one cubic centimetre.

As a consequence of Šklovskij's new distances, which appear more probable than previous ones, we shall also have new values for the absolute magnitude of the nuclei. The apparent magnitude of the nuclei can be obtained by direct measurement, and if we assume that the nuclei are nearer to us this implies that their absolute brightness must be smaller. Again let us refer to NGC 7293 which has an apparent magnitude of 13·5 and would therefore have an absolute magnitude of 10, if its distance is of the order of 50 parsecs. If, on the other hand, we accept the greater distance given by Berman, 1,050 parsecs, then its absolute magnitude would be 3. The result of using the new method for the determination of the distance of planetaries is that the absolute magnitude of the nuclei will range from —1 to 10 and will not tend to concentrate around zero or one as was the case when the previous methods for estimating distances were used. These results are of a revolutionary character and affect considerably the conclusions that we can draw about the past and future history of planetaries.

The new absolute magnitudes of the nuclei, taken together with their surface temperatures, lead us to attribute to these stars characteristics which are very similar to those appertaining to the white dwarfs, that is those stars which have an exceptionally high density. The development of a planetary as suggested by Šklovskij, is as follows. At the very beginning of its life as a nebula it is of very small dimensions, very similar to a star; as the gas expands it produces a nebula of greater dimensions and of less density. At this point Šklovskij follows Gurzadian hypothesis. At the same time the nucleus also evolves from a star of type O, Wolf-Rayet, towards a type of star which is exceptionally hot and dense. It is worth remembering that several white dwarfs have continuous spectra in which absorption lines are almost non-existent, like the spectra of several nuclei of planetaries. A confirmation that a planetary evolves towards a phase of white dwarf is given by the fact that, according to Šklovskij's calculations, every year three new planetaries are formed in our Galaxy and three others dissolve in interstellar space, leaving behind the nucleus stripped of its envelope. Therefore 3×10^9 white dwarfs must have been produced in 10^9 years, and this figure is very near to the total number of white dwarfs which is thought to exist in the Galaxy.

What would be the stage before that of a planetary? Possibly the ancestors of planetaries are the red supergiants, which are stars with a very extended and cold atmosphere, and which, according to most recent views, have also a hot, small central nucleus. Among all the red supergiants, the variables RV Tauri stars have a spatial distribution very similar to that of the planetaries, and their dimensions and absolute magnitudes are very similar to those of the smaller, bright

3727 Å

4340 Å

5007 Å

1. Slitless spectrogram
of planetary NGC 6720.
Lick Observatory

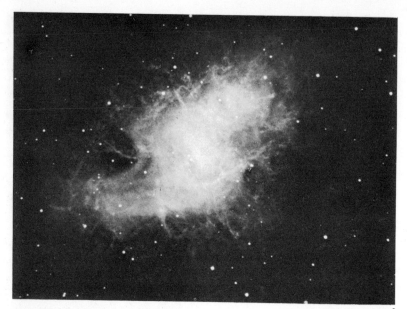

Blue, λ3100–λ5000 Å

Red, λ6300–λ6750 Å

2. The Crab Nebula NGC 1952. Photographs in blue, yellow, red and infra-red. 100-inch Mt. Wilson

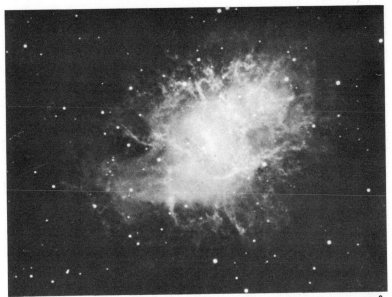

Yellow, λ5200 -λ6600 Å

Infra-red, λ7200–λ8400 Å

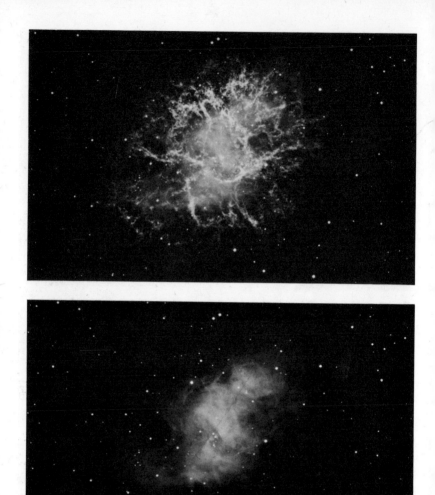

3. The Crab Nebula NGC 1952. Two views: above $H\alpha$; below green light ($\lambda 5200$–$\lambda 6200$). Note filamentary structure above, and amorphous and diffuse structure below

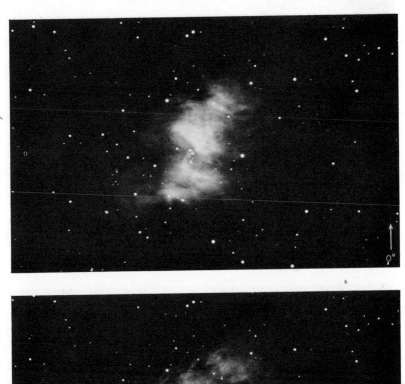

4. The Crab Nebula NGC 1952. Two views in polarized light; electric vector 0° and 45°. Taken in green light. 200-inch Mt. Palomar

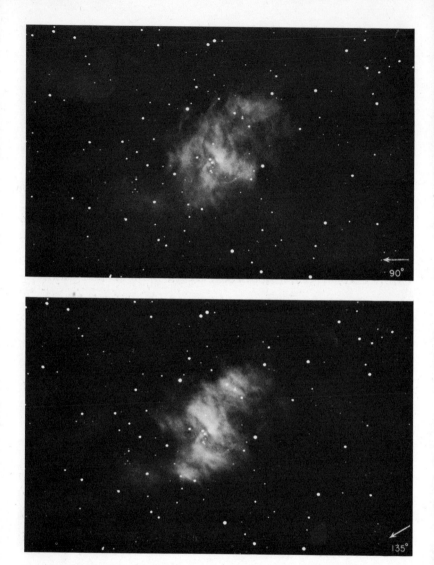

4a. The Crab Nebula NGC 1952. Two views in polarized light. Electric vector 90° and 135°. Taken in green light. 200-inch Mt. Palomar

5. The Owl Nebula in Ursa Major M.97—NGC 3587. 60-inch Mt. Wilson

6. The Ring Nebula in Lyra M.57—NGC 6720. 200-inch Mt. Palomar

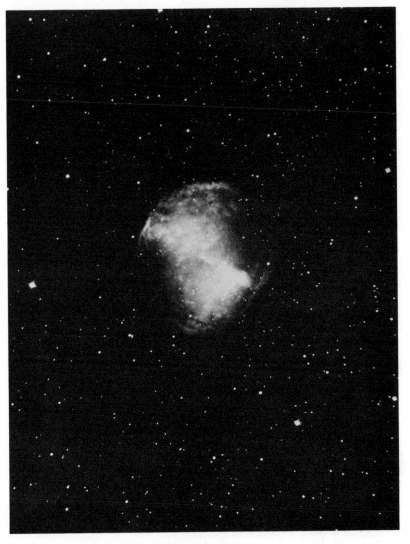

7. Dumb-bell Nebula in Vulpecula M.27—NGC 6853. 100-inch
Mt. Wilson

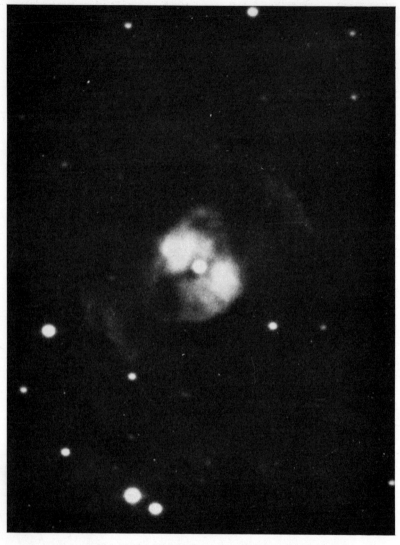

8. Planetary nebula NGC 2371–2. Lick Observatory

9. Planetary nebula in Aquarius NGC 7293. Photographed in red light.
200-inch Mt. Palomar

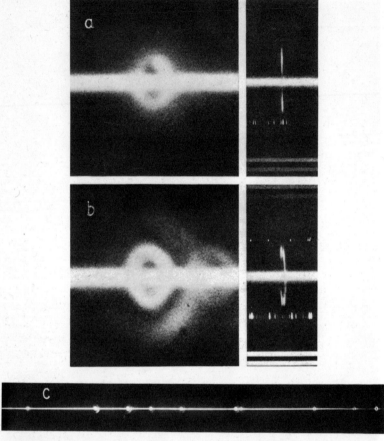

10. Slitless spectrogram of NGC 2392. (a) left: enlargement of the monochromatic image λ3426 Å. [NeV] of (c). (a) right: λ3426 Å. obtained with a slit spectrograph. (b) left: enlargement of monochromatic image λ3868 Å [NeIII] of (c). (b) right: λ 3868Å. obtained with a slit spectrograph.

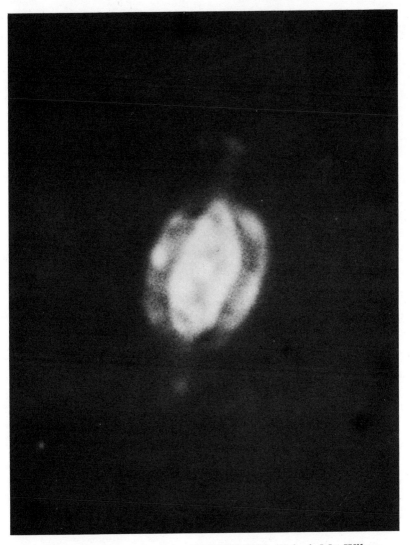

11. Planetary nebula in Aquarius NGC 7009. 60-inch Mt. Wilson.

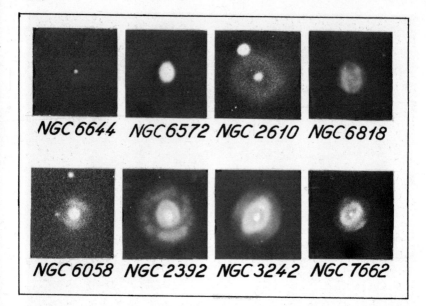

12. Probable evolution of planetary nebulae from star-like appearance to ring envelope and to double ring.

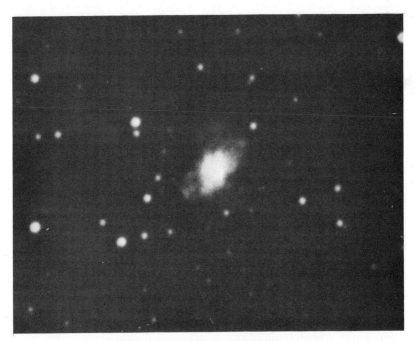

13. Nebula NGC 2440. Lick Observatory

14. Nebula NGC 6210. Lick Observatory

15. Nebula NGC 4361. Lick Observatory

16. Nebula NGC 7026. Lick Observatory

planetaries, which probably are younger. The RV Tauri are those stars which probably would best represent the stage preceding the planetary phase.

III.14 Description of the most important planetaries.

The general information on planetaries given in the previous pages is the result of a study of individual planetaries and of an attempt to generalize all the information collected in the study of as many planetaries as possible.

Let us now turn our attention to some of the planetary nebulae which are distinctive on account of their dimension, spectrum or shape. We will analyse all their details which being peculiar to each one of them cannot be included in a general description of planetaries as a whole. The best known, because of their dimensions and their characteristic appearance, are the Ring Nebula in Lyra, the Owl Nebula in Ursa Major, the Dumb-bell in Vulpecula and the giant of all planetaries, the one in Aquarius. The Crab Nebula is an exceptional object, indeed for a very long time it was even doubtful whether it could be considered as a planetary at all. It is almost certain now that the origin of this object is very different from that of the other planetaries, as it is the remnant of an ancient supernova. Nevertheless we will include a description of it here since it is really more like a planetary than a diffuse nebula. The Crab Nebula is so exceptional among the celestial objects that its characteristics deserve a very detailed description.

In addition to the five objects mentioned which are conspicuous for their dimensions and appearance, we shall describe also some other planetaries which are worth mentioning either because of their shape or because of some other special characteristic. These characteristics may be found in their spectra or in the spectra of the nuclei, and may indicate exceptional physical conditions of the gas or of the central star. Finally we will also describe some planetaries chosen because of the type of their internal motions.

THE CRAB NEBULA. M.1–NGC 1952. R.A. 5h 29m; Decl. +22° [1]

The Crab Nebula has a very complicated structure and its apparent dimensions are 6′ × 4′. It was discovered by Messier in 1758. Lord

[1] All the co-ordinates given in the following pages refer to the Epoch 1960.

81

Rosse called it 'Crab' because of its shape. It was first photographed in 1892 by Roberts. About thirty years ago it was discovered that the cloud of gas of which it is composed had a considerable angular motion, as if it was expanding with a constant velocity. The beginning of the expansion appears to go back eight or nine centuries ago, and therefore it has been assumed that this nebula represents the remnants of the supernova which appeared in A.D. 1054. Old Chinese records, which give the position of this 'star' and which state that it was comparable in brightness to Venus and was visible in daylight, confirm this assumption. From the spectrum of this nebula we know that its velocity of expansion is about 1,100 km./s. Combining this value with the expansion in a plane perpendicular to the line of sight, we obtain the distance of this object. Its distance is 1,100 parsecs and therefore we can calculate that at its maximum this supernova reached a brightness 300 million times that of our Sun. At the centre of the nebula, two faint stars can be detected. One does not belong to the nebula as is shown by its proper motion, while the other is a blue star of apparent magnitude 16 and with spectral characteristics similar to those of white dwarfs. Probably this is the supernova, now 400 million times fainter than at the time of its explosion.

A peculiarity of this nebula is the intense continuous spectrum, which is associated with the line spectrum typical of gaseous nebulae. This peculiarity led Hubble to affirm that in the spectrum of this nebula, the background produced by the overlapping of the emission lines was so intense that it could almost be classified as a continuum. Investigations carried out on photographs taken with filters and on spectra, have given a better knowledge of this object. Baade, at Mt. Wilson, obtained photographs with various filters which isolate the blue and red regions of the spectrum ($\lambda\lambda$ 4300; 5900; 6500; 7800 Å.). (Plates 2 and 3.) The first and last of these photographs show only diffuse light, while the second and third show intense filaments which form a network with very little central nebulosity. From this it is deduced that the nebula must consist of two parts; an external system of filaments and an inner amorphous mass. The line spectrum is produced in the envelope of filaments, while the continuum originates in the interior of the amorphous mass. The latter is responsible for more than 80% of the light of the nebula.

According to Baade it is not yet possible to identify the star which is responsible for the excitation of the nebula. A decisive proof will be available only when its proper motion is better known.

PLANETARY NEBULAE

Minkowski, with the help of the 100-inch reflector of Mt. Wilson, has studied the emission spectrum of the filaments and has observed the lines of H, HeI, HeII, NII, OI, OII, OIII, and SII. The hydrogen lines are rather weak and the spectrum of the diffuse nebulosity is continuous with the exception of a faint discontinuity at the limit of the Balmer series. This continuous spectrum contains almost the whole energy radiated by the nebula, and its intensity distribution is not the same as that of a black body. The colour temperature at λ 4500 Å. is about 8400° K. and at λ 6000 Å. is about 6700° K. Because of the absence of absorption in the nebula, the continuous spectrum cannot be due to diffusion, but it must be a real emission spectrum. The nature of this continuum has for a long time been very difficult to interpret. Baade and Minkowski had attempted to explain it by suggesting that it was due to a continuous emission of ionized hydrogen; that is to say that it was due to the variations of kinetic energy of free electrons, passing near hydrogen nuclei. They met with many difficulties. In order to explain the intensity of the spectra, they had to assume that the kinetic temperature of the nebula was of the order of 100,000° K. and that the electron density was about 1,000 atoms per cubic centimetre. As a result the total mass of the nebula would be twenty times the Sun's mass. If the nebula is actually the remnant of the supernova of A.D. 1054, it is very unlikely that it would have such a large mass, since the star which exploded could not have a mass much greater than a few times that of the Sun. Moreover it is estimated that the mass ejected in the explosion of a supernova is only of the order of the mass of the Sun or even less. In addition, in order to be able to explain the continuous spectrum of the nebula, the exciting star should have a surface temperature greater than 500,000° K. and a radius two hundredths of that of the Sun. These values are very improbable. Finally it is difficult to explain how filaments which have a temperature and a density of 15,000° K. and 1,500 atoms per cubic centimetre respectively, could co-exist with the amorphous mass which has a similar density but which has a temperature ten times as high.

All these difficulties were eliminated in the hypothesis put forward by Šklovskij, according to which the radiation of the nebula is due to a non-thermal emission by relativistic electrons which are in motion in the magnetic field of the nebula itself. This mechanism of emission, known as synchrotron mechanism, because it was discovered in the laboratory in the synchrotrons, produces a radiation polarized in a direction perpendicular to that of the magnetic field. The hypothesis was confirmed by the observations of the astronomers in the Crimea and at Leyden. They measured the polarization of the light emitted by the various parts of the nebula and found that the polarization can be as much as 100% for some of its condensations (Plate 4). Observations show that the 'continuous' light of the nebula is predominantly polarized in one particular direction, and this gives some idea of the structure and intensity of its magnetic field. The energy of the luminous electrons must be comparable to that of cosmic rays. Oort considers that the blue central star is the residual of the explosion, because in a period of about three months a tenuous light-wave travels through the nebula and towards the exterior and then disappears a few months later in a region intensely luminous. These waves travel with a velocity which is one-tenth of that of light and are polarized like the synchrotron radiation, and therefore we must be dealing with electrons which have a great energy. Perhaps every three months an eruption of the residual nucleus takes place, with emission of swarms of particles which give to the nebula that strange halo of light.

The synchrotron mechanism explains also the emission of radio waves both by the Crab Nebula and other galactic and extra-galactic radio sources. The Crab Nebula is a unique object whether it is considered among the galactic nebulae or among radio sources— among the former because the majority of them have an optical spectrum which can be explained by thermal emission by free electrons, and among the latter because it is the only galactic radio source which emits a non-thermal spectrum in the optical as well as in the radio domain. So far, in the whole of the universe, only one galaxy is known, M.87, which emits an optical synchrotron spectrum. In order to have a synchrotron emission in the optical domain, there must exist relativistic electrons which have energy much greater than that necessary to explain the emission in the radio domain. Therefore both in M.87 and in the Crab Nebula there must exist suitable conditions for the production of relativistic electrons which have very high energy.

THE OWL NEBULA. M.97–NGC 3587. R.A. 11h 11m ; Decl. +55° 15′

Plate 5 is a direct photograph of the Owl Nebula taken at Mt. Wilson with the 60-inch reflector. The two circular dark patches visible against the fairly uniform, lighter background, are reminiscent of the round eyes of an owl, and hence the name given to this object.

This nebula is the third largest of the planetaries.

The diameter joining the two brighter ovals is 199″ and the diameter at right angles to it is 203″. It is a rather faint object and its central star has a visual magnitude of 14. It was observed about a century ago (1858) by Herschel who gave a very descriptive account of it. He noted that the light from this object was very uniform and bright and came to the conclusion that it could not be a spherical conglomeration of stars because otherwise there would be an increase of brightness at the centre. He concluded that this object was either a hollow spherical shell or a flat disc, at right angles to our line of sight, though this latter suggestion he considered highly improbable.

Recent studies carried out by Minkowski and Aller at Mt. Palomar show that the structure of the Owl Nebula is uniform, without filaments or condensations which are so frequently found in large planetaries. Photographs taken in different radiations, by means of interference filters, reveal that all the images are very similar both in dimension and in general appearance. This would suggest the lack of stratification of the various elements. It is rather hard to understand why this nebula does not present the filamentary structure which is characteristic of the majority of planetaries and is an indication of turbulence. Another peculiarity of this nebula is that its electron density, which is less than 100 electrons per cubic centimetre, is exceptionally low for a planetary. On average the electron density of a planetary is between 1,000 and 10,000 electrons per cubic centimetre. The density of the Owl Nebula is comparable to that of diffuse nebulae. Probably this planetary is in an advanced stage of evolution, in which the matter ejected by the central star is already scattered in a very tenuous envelope of low brightness.

From the study of the distribution of the intensity of light in the various parts of the nebula, Minkowski and Aller reached the conclusion that this nebula is probably a hollow shell (as Herschel had suggested) with two large and diffuse condensations of luminous matter, symmetrically placed.

An object which presents considerable similarities to the Owl Nebula is a nebula discovered by Jones and Emberson in 1939 and which has been photographed in $H\alpha$ light at Mt. Palomar. This nebula has the following co-ordinates: R.A. 7h 50m; Decl. $+53°$ 41′ and has the appearance of a hollow sphere with two symmetrical condensations. As in the case of the Owl Nebula this too shows no effects of stratification. Its brightness is very low and this probably explains why it was discovered only in 1939, but its dimensions are greater than those of the Owl Nebula, being 348″ × 435″.

Yet another planetary of similar appearance to the Owl Nebula is NGC 6058, with co-ordinates: R.A. 16h 5m; Decl. +40° 47′.

THE RING NEBULA IN LYRA. M.57–NGC 6720. R.A. 18h 52m; Decl. +32° 58′

This nebula is the fourth largest among the best-known planetaries. Its shape is noticeably elliptical; its major axis is 83″ and its minor axis is 59″. It is well known for its beautiful ring which has sharp internal and external boundaries. The central star has a visual magnitude of 15·4 and a photographic magnitude of 13. Spectroscopically it presents a continuum without any lines, either in absorption or in emission. This fact, coupled with the blue colour of the nebula which is indicated by the difference between its visual and photographic magnitude, points to a strong similarity between the spectrum of the nucleus and the spectra of some characteristic white dwarfs which have been studied by Greenstein. These white dwarfs, like many of the planetary nuclei, have a deep blue colour indicating a high surface temperature, and the hydrogen absorption lines are so broad and shallow as to be hardly visible. This may confirm Šklovskij's theory which reduces the distances of planetaries and hence the brightness of their nuclei, to values similar to those of white dwarfs.

The characteristic ring-like shape is purely an optical effect, as we have previously explained. The gaseous shell envelopes the central star and as, at the edges, our line of sight travels through more matter than at the centre, the envelope appears to us as a ring.

To consider planetary envelopes as spheres or homogeneous spherical shells is a very rough approximation. The Owl Nebula is very near to this approximation, but not the Lyra Nebula which shows a ring with a very obvious filamentary structure clearly visible in Plate 6. The study of the intensity distribution in its various parts and for various radiations, leads to very important results. The maximum surface brightness is at the ends of the minor axis of the ring. The distribution of intensity along the major axis, measured in the monochromatic radiations corresponding to the forbidden emission lines of [OII] and [NeIII] and of the permitted lines of HeII

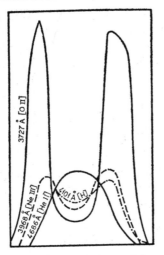

FIG. 15. Intensity distribution across monochromatic images of the Ring Nebula NGC 6720

and of H, is given in fig. 15. The ring shape is represented by the two peaks of maximum intensity separated by a deep central minimum and can be seen for all radiations with the exception of λ 4686 Å. HeII which has a distribution of maximum intensity at the centre, decreasing towards the edges of the sphere limited by the ring. This behaviour can be understood if we bear in mind the high temperature of the central star. The HeII lines are formed by the recombination of an ion of HeIII with an electron, namely by means of a primary mechanism. The ultra-violet radiation of the star will have completely ionized the He atoms in the interior of the envelope, but every time an ion recaptures an electron, a bright line of the HeII spectrum is produced. The same happens for the hydrogen atoms. Since their ionization potential is only 13·6eV. against 54·4eV. required by HeII, the majority of the electrons will be torn away from the atom by energies which are greater than the minimum required for the ionization, and as a result the electrons will have high velocities. Recapture will be difficult and will happen only rarely until greater distances from the star are reached.

The forbidden lines of [NeIII] and of [OII] are formed by a secondary mechanism of excitation by collision of free electrons which will bring the atoms of NeIII and of OII to an excited metastable state. It follows that the lines of NeIII are formed mainly in regions where the ultra-violet radiation, capable of ionizing neon three times, has been already completely absorbed. The OII lines, on the other hand, are produced in regions which are further still and where the oxygen atoms are only once ionized.

Because of the density of the star's ultra-violet radiation which is present at various distances, the monochromatic image in HeII light is considerably smaller than the images in H and NeIII light, and these are smaller than that in OII light.

The presence of filaments complicates both the problem and the study of these objects, compelling us to consider a simple model of a homogeneous gaseous mass in order to simplify the question. Their presence is not difficult to understand, indeed the difficulty consists in explaining the absence of filamentary structure in objects like the Owl Nebula. According to hydrodynamics, gases which are in conditions similar to those existing in planetaries, must have turbulent motions resulting in the presence of filaments and condensations of gases.

OTHER RING NEBULAE. In addition to the Lyra Ring Nebula, there are several other planetaries which have a similar structure. NGC II 418 has a very bright, perfectly oval ring with the two axes measuring 14″ and 11″ respectively. The central star belongs to class Of and has a magnitude of 9. As in the case of the Ring Nebula, here too there is a high concentration of light at the ends of the minor axis. The stratification effect is clearly visible. The monochromatic image in the radiation of the forbidden line λ 3868 Å. [NeIII] is clearly smaller than the images in the radiation of $H\beta$, [OIII], [SII], and they, in their turn, are smaller than those in [OI] and [NII] light.

Another good example of a ring nebula is NGC 2022. Here the elliptical ring has dimensions 22″ × 17″ and a very faint and extended envelope (28″ × 27″) surrounds the ring. In this case the brighter parts are concentrated at the ends of the major axis.

NGC 2610 is another ring nebula (Plate 12). This planetary, the dimensions of which are 38″ × 31″, does not present details of fine structure. NGC 6369 is a beautiful ring almost perfectly circular and regular, but very faint. Its diameter is 28″.

NGC 6894 is yet another planetary which has an almost circular but faint ring with a diameter of 44″.

PLANETARY NEBULAE

DUMB-BELL NEBULA. M.27–NGC 6853. R.A. 19h 58m;
Decl. +22° 36'

This object is the second in size among the large planetaries. The two bright condensations, almost spherical in shape, are reminiscent of a dumb-bell and hence the name given to this object. The central star (mag. 12) has a spectrum consisting only of continuum without any bright or dark lines. The filamentary structure varies from one ion to another. In the [NII] and $H\alpha$ photographs the planetary presents a granular appearance and has a shape almost like a sandglass. In [OIII] photographs thin filaments are very clearly seen. (Plate 7.)

This behaviour would suggest a very complex form of stratification. Voroncov-Velyaminov and Kramer studied this planetary in 1937 and came to the conclusion that its structure is so complicated that it could not be interpreted by a unique theoretical model.

NEBULA M.76–NGC 650. R.A. 1h 40m; Decl. +51° 23'

This planetary is similar to the Dumb-bell in its irregular and complicated shape. Its dimensions are similar to those of the Ring Nebula in Lyra and can therefore be considered as one of the largest in the planetary family. The dimensions of its central part, which is elongated and bright, are $87'' \times 42''$. If we take into account the external part composed of irregular and faint filaments, similar in shape to parts of a ring, then the diameter is $157''$. The visible part of this planetary appears devoid of any symmetry of revolution. Strömgren has suggested a model for this planetary according to which the whole nebula has a symmetry of revolution, but we can see only a part of it. The part we see is that reached by the ultra-violet radiation of the star, capable of ionizing the atoms and enabling them to produce a recombination spectrum. In the part of the planetary not reached by the ultra-violet radiation because it has already been absorbed, the gas will consist of neutral atoms in the normal state, hence not radiating. Strömgren's model suggests the existence of a gaseous shell with an internal surface which is elliptical and with an external surface which is almost spherical and less dense, the whole enclosed in a much larger spherical shell. The elliptical shell has parts which are denser than others. The thinner parts will be transparent enough to the ultra-violet radiation, so that the layer of the external shell nearest to it can be reached and ionized. The denser parts of the internal shell, on the other hand, will not allow the ultra-violet radiation from the star to reach the exterior and not even reach the more remote parts of the spherical shell.

NGC 2371–2 (Plate 8) is very similar in shape to NGC 650–1, and Strömgren's model can be also applied to it. In this planetary the two broken branches of the external shell are more clearly visible than in the previous planetary. The same model can probably also be used for NGC 6778, which has the appearance of a sand-glass, provided that we study it along the axis in which we have the greatest concentration of light. The other two arms, which are at right angles to the other axis, represent perhaps the two branches of the external envelope.

NEBULA IN AQUARIUS. NGC 7293. R.A. 22h 28m; Decl. −21° 3′

The nebula in Aquarius is the largest planetary so far known. Its apparent dimensions are $15' \times 12'$, that is to say its greatest diameter is about half the apparent diameter of the Moon or Sun (32′). This planetary is a beautiful object having the shape of a ring (Plate 9). On the remarkable photograph taken with the Mt. Wilson telescope, several details of its structure are visible, such as the thin and sharp filaments, the very well defined internal boundary of its ring and the more diffuse external boundary. A very tenuous ring, just visible, surrounds the star, and its dimensions are $6' \times 4'\cdot6$.

This planetary, which has the largest apparent diameter, is probably the nearest to us. It is the only object of this family for which it has been possible to make a determination of the trigonometrical parallax which is greater than the observational error. The presence of the faint internal ring and of the brighter external ring, suggests that stellar matter has been ejected at different times through the ages.

The photographic apparent magnitude of its nucleus is 11. Since its trigonometrical parallax determined by van Maanen is $0''\cdot038$, corresponding to a distance of 38 parsecs, its absolute magnitude is 8·9. ($M = m + 5 + 5 \log p$.) Its high temperature would suggest that we are dealing here with a white dwarf. Berman, from statistical evidence, obtained for this object a distance 25 times greater, that is 1,050 parsecs, and hence an absolute magnitude for its nucleus of 0·9. The central star in this case would not be a white dwarf but would be a star placed in the branch of blue stars in the diagram of population II. It could however be considered as being of type O or a Wolf-Rayet of population II. From this example it is clear what the consequences are of not knowing with certainty the distances of planetaries. Indeed this uncertainty affects not only the evaluation of their dimensions (hence volume and mass) but also the knowledge of the physical conditions of the nucleus. Moreover it makes it extremely difficult to try to put forward theories about the evolution, origin and development of such planetaries. As we have already mentioned, the value of the parallax obtained by van Maanen is probably the most reliable.

NEBULAE WITH DOUBLE RING. The great nebula in Aquarius suggests that its ring is really formed of two rings, which are well separated in some parts, and joined together into a single mass in others. It may be useful here to mention some examples of planetaries which have a double ring, such as NGC 2392 in Gemini, NGC 7009 in Aquarius and NGC 7662 in Andromeda.

NGC 2392 (R.A. 7h 27m; Decl. $+21°$ 0′) has a very conspicuous central part which consists of a ring barely separated from the central nucleus, and of a region slightly less bright (Plate 12). The external ring, on the other hand, is very well defined and presents a fine structure with well-marked filaments and irregularities. The central star is fairly bright and has an apparent magnitude of 9. Its spectrum has many dark lines of HeII, HeI and H as well as a few bright lines. The dimensions of the internal ring are $19'' \times 15''$, while those of the external ring are $47'' \times 43''$. Between the two rings there is a separation of 7″ to 8″. Plate 10 shows two parts of the spectrum of NGC 2392, taken with a slitless spectrograph. The one marked 'a' corresponds to λ 3426 Å. [NeV], and that marked 'b' to λ 3868 Å. [NeIII]. These photographs show a very clear example of stratification. In 'a' only the first ring is visible, while in 'b' both rings can be seen. As in other cases already mentioned, the ultra-violet radiation of the star capable of ionizing neon four times, does not reach the regions of the external ring, as it is already all absorbed, but enough ultra-violet radiation arrives to ionize neon twice. The structure of NGC 2392 is very complex as it appears from the spectrograms obtained with slitless spectrographs in radiation λ 5007 Å. [OIII], $H\beta$, and λ 4686 Å. HeII. The image produced by the nebular line has dimensions which are greater than the other two and $H\beta$ also produces an image which is slightly larger than that of λ 4686 Å. The phenomenon already observed for the lines NeIII and NeV is here repeated. The external ring is very clearly visible in radiation [OIII] and $H\beta$, but can just be seen in radiation HeII. The internal motions are very complicated. Wilson has found considerable differences in the separation of individual lines of various elements due to the velocity of expansion of the nebula.

NGC 7009 (R.A. 21h 2m; Decl. $-11°$ 32′) has a character of its own. The internal ring is very elliptical and much brighter than the external ring. The latter is almost circular and has two luminous concentrations at the ends of the projection of the minor axis of the first ring. The structure of this nebula is very complicated and the images obtained in various radiations are different. As usual the image in radiation HeII is the smallest and the presence of the external ring is very difficult to detect (Plate 11).

NGC 7662 (R.A. 23h. 24m; Decl. $+42°$ 19′) has two rings. The internal ring is almost elliptical, while the external, which is much fainter, is almost circular (Plate 12). Photographs in various radiations show strong variations in the dimensions of the images. The smaller images are those obtained in radiations λ 3425 Å. [NeV] and λ 4686 Å. HeII; while those obtained in radiations λ 3868 Å. [NeIII] and λ 5007 Å. [OIII] are the larger. The central star of this planetary is a variable with a period of 27 days and magnitude 12 to 16.

III.15 Classification of planetaries according to their shape and their probable evolution.

Apart from the planetaries already described, there exist several other objects characterized by their shape which can be exceptionally regular or irregular, or by some unusual feature. If we assume that planetaries had their origin in the ejection of matter from the central star, as is suggested by their shape which always presents a symmetry of revolution, we can classify these objects according to their shape and attempt to see in their various forms successive stages of the evolution of planetaries.

In its original stage a planetary is very similar to a star. The gaseous mass ejected by the central star has still dimensions which are so small as to be undistinguishable from the nucleus. NGC 6644 is an example of this stage in the life of a planetary. Its apparent diameter is $2'' \times 3''$, which is very similar to that of star images affected by seeing (about $2''$ or more).

The next stage is probably represented by planetaries of the type of NGC II 4776 or NGC 6572. In these the gaseous mass ejected by the nucleus occupies a greater volume and is therefore easily distinguished from a star (Plate 12).

In the third stage, the ejection of stellar matter has ceased. The gas has taken the shape of a spherical shell which we observe as a ring. This shape is produced either by the braking effect of the interstellar matter or by the definite boundary between the region of ionized atoms (capable of producing the recombination spectrum) and the region of atoms of neutral hydrogen.

The ring nebulae, which we have already described, can be subdivided into classes. The ring may have a uniform thickness (NGC II 418 or NGC 2610) or may be thinner at the ends of one of its axes Ring Nebula in Lyra or NGC 6772, NGC 6781, NGC 6818). Finally there is the type of ring which is completely open at the ends so that two arcs are left (NGC 6058 or NGC 6563).

In class IV are grouped nebulae with double ring, which perhaps show that two successive explosions of the central star have taken place. Examples of this stage are to be found in NGC 1535 or NGC 2022, in which the further ring is so tenuous and diffuse in the interstellar space as to be hardly visible. NGC 2392, with its internal ring barely separated from the central nucleus, represents an intermediate stage between class II and class III corresponding to an era very close to the stellar explosion, while the external ring, which is in process of disruption, would point to a previous explosion which took place in a more remote past. Another beautiful example of this class is NGC 3242, which has an elliptical internal ring and an external ring which is much fainter and which has a complex structure. Two objects very similar to this last planetary are NGC 7009 and NGC 7354. NGC 6804 has two well-defined rings which are almost circular and the internal ring is much brighter than the external. NGC 7139 and NGC 7662 are very similar to the previous one, with two circular rings.

The internal ring was produced by an explosion nearer in time, and the weaker external ring is the residual of an older explosion. The appearance of the two rings points to two separate phases of the life of a nebula and the way in which the gaseous envelope evolves. At first dense and bright, with hardly any fine structure, it becomes a weak and tenuous envelope full of filaments, ramifications, and lacking in homogeneity.

A nebula which has probably reached the last stages of its life is NGC 246. Its central star (9·5 magnitude) is at the centre of a very faint nebulosity, circular in shape and of large dimensions, $4' \times 3'\cdot5$. The greatest part of the matter forming the nebula has escaped into interstellar space and soon the nucleus, stripped of its envelope, will become a white dwarf.

III.16 Nebulae of exceptional shape.

Several planetaries cannot be classified in any of the above classes because they are very different from the objects typical of each class. Some of them have very unusual shapes.

NGC 2440 and NGC 7027 are both very irregular in shape and no trace of symmetry is apparent. NGC 2440 (Plate 13) consists of an elongated mass of dense gases through which it is impossible to detect the central star. An irregular and fainter shell envelops the central mass. It is also impossible to see the central star in NGC 7027. This nebula is composed of two masses of gas which are separated by a darker region. The two masses themselves present some dark markings which suggest that they too are divided.

J 320 is a nebula with some peculiar features. The bright gaseous mass, oval in shape, is surrounded by a faint ring seen edgeways. This shows that we are dealing here with a real ring and not simply with the projection of a spherical shell. J 320 has a shape reminiscent of that of Saturn.

NGC 6210 (Plate 14) is very similar in appearance to J 320. It has a thin ring almost at right angles to the major axis of the central mass. The central mass is subdivided into a bright central part which surrounds the nucleus, and a faint mass.

Another object which probably is a ring nebula, is NGC 4361 (Plate 15). This planetary has two arms which start from the internal nebulosity surrounding the star and they wind around it like a spiral, forming the external ring.

NGC 6543 is similar to NGC 4361 and could probably be considered as a ring nebula although its ring has more the appearance of a helix. A second arc of a ring, which is further away, gives the appearance of a coiled spring.

NGC 6309 has two parts. One consists of the central star and of half a ring round it, the other part appears like the other half of the ring ejected and still attached to the first half by two very slender arms.

Although NGC 7008 is very irregular in shape, it could probably be considered as a ring nebula. The central star is of 12th magnitude.

There are also three more stars which appear to be embedded in the nebula and around each one of them a darker circle is visible. It is also probable that these stars are not physically linked with the nebula, but just happen to be near it.

NGC 7026 has a very peculiar shape. It looks like an *H* (Plate 16). Perhaps this too could be classified as a ring nebula. The very elongated ring has two long arcs which are very bright, while the two short ones are hardly visible. A bridge of nebulosity joins the two longer arms enveloping the central star, and in this way they form, as it were, the horizontal line of the *H*. Slender filaments lengthen, on both sides, the arcs of the internal ring.

III.17   Planetaries with an invisible central star.

In some planetaries the central star is enveloped by such a dense nebulosity that it becomes invisible. Its presence is inferred from the spectrum which is very similar to that of planetaries with a visible nucleus. Indeed, since the radiation from the nucleus produces the nebular spectrum, it is possible to deduce not only the presence but also the physical characteristics of the nucleus itself.

The following are some of the planetaries with an invisible nucleus: NGC 2440, NGC II 4634, NGC 6537, NGC 6884, NGC 6886, NGC 7027, NGC II 5217. They all have a similar shape, with the exception of NGC 2440 and NGC 7027 which, as already mentioned, are very irregular. The main characteristic, common to all of them, is that they consist of a dense mass of luminous matter of an irregular shape, sometimes circular, sometimes elliptical, surrounded at times by diffuse and tenuous matter. We are probably witnessing here one of the early stages of the life of a planetary. From the nucleus a great deal of matter has been ejected and the star is still enveloped as if in a cocoon. After several thousands of years the cloud will become thinner and take the shape of a shell which will last until a further ejection of matter produces a second shell.

In the case of NGC II 2165, NGC 6565, NGC 6741, the fact that the central nucleus is not visible is not easily explained. These three objects are very much alike. They all have an oval ring which is uniformly bright at the edge and much fainter at the centre. The faint central nebulosity ought to allow us to see the nucleus. The fact that we do not see it may mean that the luminosity of the nucleus is exceptionally faint.

CHAPTER IV

Irregular bright nebulae

IV.1 Introduction.

THE prototype of irregular bright nebulae is the well-known nebula, visible to the naked eye, in Orion's sword, near ι Orionis. These irregular bright nebulae are regions of the sky where bright clouds of irregular shape are found. Generally speaking, these regions have hardly varied in the few decades during which they have been observed visually or photographically. Their dimensions may be as small as a few minutes of arc or as large as a few square degrees, and with long, very slender filaments. In the region, for instance, around γ Cygni, there is a very great nebulosity in the shape of large irregular and bright masses which cover two or three square degrees of the sky.

A very beautiful object, which was named by Max Wolf 'North America' because of its shape, shows a mixture of stars and of bright nebulosity. This nebulosity is particularly noticeable because of the contrast it makes with the very dark neighbouring regions.

Generally speaking, near these bright nebulosities there can be seen large regions where stars do not seem to exist. This is due to the dark absorbing matter which prevents the light of the stars, within or behind it, from reaching us. The dark masses, which are occasionally very large, have an irregular shape. Sometimes they appear as long narrow lanes or channels crossing swarms of stars. As an example we can mention the constellation Cepheus, where a large region is covered by dark masses and dark channels scattered around a bright nebula of irregular shape, at the centre of which a few very bright stars are visible. These appear to be connected with the bright matter which in its turn is surrounded by the dark matter. Often the dark masses appear as if they were projected against the bright nebulosity, presenting a strong contrast in a few irregularly shaped regions, while sometimes the dark matter appears as small globules which are very dark.

The general appearance of these configurations is of great interest. Although they are rather too faint to be observed visually, they appear very clearly in photographs, particularly in those obtained with emulsions which are sensitive to blue or red light. The difference of shape, size and brightness of these nebulae can be very great in photographs taken in blue or red light. This confirms what we know from the spectral analysis, namely that the emission of the gases of the bright nebulae is concentrated only in some wavelengths. Hence photographs obtained in different regions of the spectrum are very different. This difference is even stronger in monochromatic photographs obtained with narrow band-pass filters.

An examination of the distribution of the bright and dark nebulae show that they are located in the Milky Way, that luminous belt which encircles the heavens. The Milky Way is almost a great circle passing through the main constellations (Cassiopeia, Perseus, Auriga, Monoceros, Argo, Crux, Centaurus, Scorpius, Sagittarius, Aquila, Cygnus), and astronomers have adopted it as the galactic equator in a system of co-ordinates which is independent of the solar system. The galactic co-ordinates (longitude and latitude) have as a plane of reference, the galactic equator. This is the plane of the great circle passing as nearly as possible through the centre of the belt of stars which we call the Milky Way, and makes an angle of about 63° with the celestial equator. The axis, perpendicular to the galactic plane, defines the two galactic poles. The north pole (R.A. 12h 40m; Decl. +28°) is in Coma Berenices, and the south pole (R.A. 0h 40m; Decl. −28°) is in Sculptor. The position of celestial objects can be found by using the galactic co-ordinates instead of the equatorial co-ordinates given in most stellar catalogues. The galactic longitude is measured along the galactic equator. The point of zero longitude on the galactic equator is the point where the galactic equator crosses the celestial equator. Galactic latitude is measured from the galactic equator.

It is not possible to assert that the distribution of dark and bright irregular nebulae is a simple concentration along the galactic plane. Generally the nebulae are associated with stars of population I of the early types of Draper classification, namely O, B, A, which are supergiants of a very high temperature and which are found in the spiral arms of the Galaxy. The gaseous masses and the solid particles which form the nebulae, appear to us either bright or dark according to their position and distance from these stars. The distribution of nebulae, therefore, depends on the concentration of stars O, B, A, and on the quantity of interstellar matter which exists in the spiral arms of the Galaxy. Nowadays these spiral arms can be detected by investigating in various ways, the rotation of the Galaxy around its centre. We know that our solar system is placed at about 1° north of the galactic equator and in a position which is off centre. In fact we can see the centre of the Galaxy at a great distance away, in the direction of Ophiucus and Sagittarius, at 330° of galactic longitude. The distribution of nebulae naturally depends on our position, and while we see them concentrated in a region around the centre we see very few in the opposite direction. Near the centre of the Galaxy, groups of stars of classes O, B, A, which are at a distance of approximately 1,500 parsecs, include some of the most important of these nebulae which outline one of the spiral arms situated between the centre of our Galaxy and the Sun.

Confirmation that aggregates of supergiants of population I are associated with nebular matter in the spiral arms is obtained by the observation that a similar effect exists in the Andromeda Nebula.

IV.2   Spectra of bright irregular nebulae.

Spectra of nebulae can be divided into two classes, the first containing bright line spectra with or without a continuum, and the second containing spectra with continuums with superimposed dark lines. To the first class belong planetaries and some of the irregular nebulae, while to the second belong only irregular nebulae. Hubble, in 1922, in a general study of these nebulae, noticed that there was a close relation between their spectral type and that of the stars enveloped by them. Stars which are associated with irregular nebulae are generally cooler than the central stars of planetaries. When the stars are of type O to B, the spectrum of the nebula is a bright line spectrum. If, however, the star belongs to a more advanced type than B, and therefore has a temperature which is lower than approximately 20,000° K., then the nebulae have a spectrum which consists of a continuum on which we find superimposed the same dark lines as those present in the spectrum of the associated stars. Hubble put forward the suggestion that the source of luminosity of these nebulae was the radiation emitted by the stars themselves. As a result, nebulae, therefore, would have no luminosity of their own, but the luminosity would be the result of excitation produced by the radiation of stars of very high temperature, or by reflection of the light of cooler stars. Hubble came to the conclusion that these nebulae were made up of clouds of particles (atoms, molecules, or corpuscles of greater dimensions) which are illuminated by the stars which are within them.

The structure of nebulae and the distribution of the internal stars, seem to suggest that the association between them is only temporary. This may be the fundamental distinction between planetaries and irregular nebulae. In the planetaries the internal stars maintain their central position in the enveloping nebulosity. Important information on this particular point can be obtained from comparing measurements of radial velocity of the stars and of the nebulae.

We have already mentioned that Huggins had discovered some bright lines in the spectra of nebulae, which for a very long time could not be identified with the lines of any terrestrial element. In 1914, Fabry, Buisson and Bourget, with the help of the interferometer, were able to determine the wavelength of two bright lines in the violet (λ 3726 Å. and λ 3728 Å.) which did not correspond to any known lines produced by terrestrial elements. The mystery was solved by Bowen with his identification of the forbidden lines. Bowen has suggested that the emission spectra of these nebulae are produced, following various processes, by the excitation of the atoms of which they are constituted. Radiation from stars of very high temperature ionizes the atoms of nebular matter. The recombination of ions and electrons produces the emission of permitted lines in the visible region of the spectrum and of some lines in the ultra-violet. In this manner we can explain the presence of the lines of hydrogen, of helium and of other elements. Moreover, the electrons which leave the atom as a result of the ultra-violet radiation of the exciting star, can transmit their energy to ions which are then raised to metastable levels. Since collisions are rare, they will cascade down and produce the forbidden lines. The same process is therefore at work here as in the case of planetaries.

In nebulae where the exciting stars are at a temperature lower than 20,000° K., the amount of ultra-violet radiation is not enough to ionize hydrogen and the luminosity of the nebulae is due only to reflection of light by the solid particles, but fluorescence phenomena may still take place. In this case the spectrum consists of a continuum with dark lines superimposed. Observations show that the colour of the nebula itself is very similar to that of the illuminating star and a little more blue.

All nebulae have practically the same chemical composition. Wyse has studied the spectrum of the Orion Nebula and of planetaries with the 36-inch telescope at Lick Observatory and a three-prisms spectrograph. He finds that the difference of intensity in the lines of the spectra of the various nebulae studied can be attributed to differences in their physical conditions rather than to their chemical composition. The lines of the Balmer series and λ 3727 Å. of OII are generally very intense. A continuous spectrum is also present, and when the distribution of its energy is compared with that of neighbouring stars of known energy, it corresponds to the temperature of the hotter stars, such as those belonging to class O. It is in the continuum that the main spectral difference is found between spectra of planetaries and spectra of irregular nebulae (Plates 17, 18).

Extended nebular regions, with linear dimensions of the order of 100 parsecs, such as those belonging to Orion and Cygnus, present hydrogen lines as well as the lines of oxygen and of ionized nitrogen. The OIII lines are generally found at the centre of these regions and then they disappear gradually towards the periphery.

These nebulae consist mainly of hydrogen with a small quantity of helium and other gases. Some solid particles of H_2O, CH_4, CO_2 and other common compounds, are also present and this explains the property that nebulae have of reflecting the light of the stars.

Measurements of polarization of the light emitted by these reflecting nebulae are scarce. These measurements are of great interest since they give an indication of the size of the particles responsible for the diffusion of the light. It is certain that polarization does exist in these nebulae and it is of the order of 10% as, for instance, in the nebulosity surrounding the Pleiades and in NGC 7023.

Besides polarization, the 'blueing' effect observed in the light diffused by nebulae has given information about the diffusing solid particles. In fact hypotheses on the way in which nebulae can diffuse stellar light have enabled astronomers to determine the dimensions of the particles. Let us try to discover what are the particles which can produce diffusion. Free electrons which are present in nebulae diffuse, equally, radiations of all wavelengths and therefore they cannot be the cause of nebulae being bluer than the exciting stars. Atoms and molecules cannot be responsible for the diffusion since their presence would give rise to dark lines and bands superimposed on the continuous spectrum of the stars embedded in the nebula. Instead, the dark lines observed are those of the stars themselves and have also the intensity we would expect. Moreover the diffusion law for atoms is such that it would make the nebula appear much bluer than the colour observed. Solid particles with a diameter of the order of a tenth of a millimetre or more could not cause the observed phenomenon, since they would absorb equally all radiations, and the mass of the nebula would be such as to produce perturbations in the motion of neighbouring stars and this effect is not observed. The only particles, therefore, capable of producing a selective diffusion, which could explain the observed 'blueing' effect, without producing dynamic effects on the neighbouring stars, are those with diameters between 1,000 and 10,000 Å.

The nature of these particles is not very clear. Probably they are particles produced by the joining together of molecules of the most common elements in the universe, and in the same proportions as are to be found in stars and in the Sun. Investigations by Struve, Greenstein and Henyey, have shown that nebulae are highly reflective, much more reflective than if the solid particles were mainly metallic, as was at first thought. The reflecting power of nebulae is similar to that of ice. Since the most abundant elements in the universe, apart from H and He, are the light elements C, O, and N, it is thought that the solid particles are probably molecular compounds of these light elements and hydrogen. Possibly a small percentage of metals may also be present.

IV.3 Radio emission from irregular nebulae.

As we have already stated, nebulae are mainly composed of ionized hydrogen in the neighbourhood of the hotter stars, and of neutral hydrogen in the other regions. The ionized hydrogen emits a continuous spectrum due to the variations of the kinetic energy of the free electrons. This spectrum is particularly intense, because of the absorbing properties of the gas in the centimetre-wave region. In this region of the radio spectrum, radio emissions are observed from all the regions where clouds of HII exist.

Neutral hydrogen, in the normal state, does not emit any radiation in the visible domain, and in the radio domain emits only one spectral line of a wavelength of 21 cm. This line is emitted every time the only electron of the hydrogen atom reverses its spin, that is to say when the electron, which is rotating in the same direction as the nucleus, performs a somersault and changes its own direction of rotation in relation to that of the nucleus. Both the bright reflecting nebulae and the dark nebulae, which are mostly composed of neutral hydrogen, produce this emission on a wavelength of 21 cm. Since we are dealing with a spectral line, its Doppler displacements in the various parts of the nebula, enable us to obtain a knowledge of the internal motions of the gas (*see also* Nebulae in Orion, p. 107).

In addition to the nebulae, the radio emission of which is explained by the presence of HI or HII, there exists a group of strange luminous nebulosities which are often characterized by expansion of the gas from a common centre and which emit a non-thermal radio spectrum, which can be interpreted by means of the synchrotron mechanism. It is almost certain that we are dealing here with objects similar to the Crab Nebula, namely with remnants of ancient super-novae. As an example of this class we can quote the Veil Nebula in Cygnus.

If we imagine the expansion of the gas to be reversed, assuming that the velocity of expansion has remained more or less constant, we find that the gas must have been in a common centre about 10,000 years ago. In other words the explosion of the supernova must have taken place 10,000 years ago.

It is probable that these peculiar nebulae differ from the Crab Nebula or from that identified with the radio source Cassiopeia A, only by the longer interval of time which has elapsed from the time of explosion.

IV.4   Description of the most important bright irregular nebulae.

Nebulosity in the Pleiades. R.A. 3h 41m; Decl. +23° 9′.

The strange nebulosity which exists in the Pleiades is limited to the five principal stars, the magnitude of which varies between 3 and 4·5. Tempel, in 1859, was one of the first to discover, with the aid of a small telescope, the nebulosity surrounding Merope. Nebulosity around the other four stars was discovered later and was confirmed by photographs.

The stars, which belong to class B5, are enveloped by a bright and irregular nebulosity which is limited in extension. That surround-ing Maia is the largest, while the smallest is that around Taigeta. Modern photographs show that the whole region contains nebular matter, with long filaments which extend from star to star. In his *Atlas of the Milky Way*, Barnard wrote: 'One startling fact brought out by the study of these photographs is that the Pleiades, and their involved nebulosities, are but the central condensation of an enormous nebula, intricate in details and covering at least 100 square degrees of the sky.'

The denser parts of the nebulosity are seen in the region of the brighter stars, and the long parallel filaments are particularly conspicuous over Merope.

Since the spectrum of the nebulosity is identical with that of the stars enveloped by it, we reach the conclusion that this is a case of light reflected by very small solid particles which reflect and diffuse the light from these stars.

Using the nebular spectrograph of the McDonald observatory, Greenstein and Henyey measured the colour index of the stars. These measurements show that in the case of Merope (class B7n), the photo-electric colour excess is negligible. This means that the star is not reddened by the nebular matter and therefore the star Merope must be in front of the nebular matter. On the other hand, since the mean colour index of the nebulosity is approximately -0.2, we reach the conclusion that the nebular matter is bluer than the exciting stars.

NEBULAE IN ORION. M.42–NGC 1976. R.A. 5h 30m; Decl. $-5°$ 4′. M.43–NGC 1982. R.A. 5h 30m; Decl. $-5°$ 3′. NGC 1977. R.A. 5h 30m; Decl. $-4°$ 9′.

M.42 (Plate 19) is the great nebula in Orion, of which Huygens in 1656 made a sketch. This nebula is accompanied by two nebulae: M.43 and NGC 1977. It has been widely observed and photographed with various filters. Strictly speaking, a very large nebulosity covers the whole of the constellation of Orion. A nebular ring surrounds the stars of the belt and of the sword in Orion and covers an area of approximately 450 square degrees. M.42 has ramifications which extend in all directions together with dark and bright patches of nebular matter. Its distance, according to Trumpler, is 550 parsecs. Its estimated angular diameter is 50′.

There are four main exciting stars in the 'Trapezium' which is situated in the bright south-eastern part of the nebula. The brightest star belongs to class O7 while the others belong to classes B1 and B6. A little further away, three more bright stars can be seen; the brightest is of class O9. To the north, in the centre of M.43, there is a star of class B1. The density is very low indeed and the high ionization must correspond to a temperature of 12,000° K. From the monochromatic images obtained in the various radiations, it is possible to determine the distribution of atoms of a given type.

Ultra-violet photographs obtained by Rosino show that the radiations in this region are mainly due to the oxygen doublet λ 3727 Å. When long-exposure photographs are taken, M.42 and M.43 appear to be joined together and are parts of one whole. Monochromatic photographs show that OIII is concentrated around the exciting stars. From the isophotic contours it can be seen that the principal nebula is composed of a plane layer of gas of almost constant thickness, which makes an angle of 42° with the plane perpendicular to the line of sight. Infra-red photographs show that the 'Trapezium' is really a cluster of thousands of faint stars embedded in the nebulosity. Only the brightest of these stars can be observed.

In some respects, Orion reminds one of the cluster and nebulosity of the Pleiades. Inside the cluster there are several stars of class B, and many of them are irregular variables, with sudden variations which are sometimes fast, sometimes slow. This may be explained either by the interaction of stars and nebular gases, or by absorption due to the passing of nebular matter in front of the stars. There is reason to believe that the turbulent filaments which are visible in nebulae, are the places where stars are born, which then appear as if they were distributed in regular chains. Fesenkov does not detect these chains in the Orion Nebula, probably because of the perturbation produced by the considerable absorption of the nebular matter. Filaments, or chains, are very common in several parts of the universe, as for instance in the galaxies.

In 1951 Haro at Tonanzitla (Mexico) obtained photographs of the Orion Nebula with blue and red filters. In these plates, condensations of cloud-like form are visible and filaments often present a well-developed structure of parallel lines. This uniformity, however, is limited to areas of only about one square degree or possibly less. In the southern part of the nebula, there is a number of superimposed arcs; some of them are very bright, while very slender filaments are visible in the photographs obtained with both blue and red filters. Trumpler, in the year 1931, discovered the existence of a cluster containing many red stars, in the Orion Nebula. These red stars could be photographed only with infra-red emulsions and were found

104

to be associated with the bright blue stars of the 'Trapezium'. Baade and Minkowski suggested that the 'Trapezium' stars and the infrared components in the neighbourhood of the cluster are in a region relatively empty or, at least, in a region where the clouds of absorbing matter are much more transparent than in other parts of the nebula. Haro discovered, in this nebula, over 200 stars with emission lines of hydrogen. These stars are of a type not to be found outside the nebula. Some of them are variables and appear to form a group which has special spectral characteristics and are variable because of the presence of nebular matter. Struve has put forward the hypothesis that these stars are in the process of formation, inside the nebula itself.

Wurm and Rosino, at Asiago, have recently obtained photographs of the Orion Nebula with several liquid filters which transmitted various radiations. Two filters transmitted red light, another one the forbidden line of ionized sulphur λ 6730 Å., another the $H\alpha$ and the neighbouring forbidden line of ionized nitrogen, and finally, of the two remaining, one transmitted the intense green line λ 5007 Å. of OIII and the other the continuum in a region around λ 5200 Å. From these photographs it was found that the brightest star of the 'Trapezium' belongs to class O. The ultra-violet light emitted by this star is responsible for the greatest part of the fluorescent radiation of the nebula. All the photographs taken in these several radiations show a general similarity, although there are some remarkable exceptions. For instance there are two small globules; one which is round in shape and could have a star at its centre, is south of θ^2 Orionis, while the other, west of θ^2 Orionis, is of an elongated shape. Both these globules are clearly visible in the photographs taken with filters which let through the lines of sulphur and hydrogen but are not visible at all in photographs taken with filters which let through oxygen lines or the continuum.

The photograph of the nebula taken in the region of the continuum resembles that taken in the OIII light, more than that taken in the hydrogen light. Photometric measurements, made in the various radiations, lead us to conclude that the light emitted by the nebula cannot be considered to be produced mainly by hydrogen atoms.

Tcheng Mao-lin and Dufay, at the observatory of Haute Provence, have studied the spectrum of the nebula in Orion, between λ 3700 Å. and λ 5000 Å. with the 48-inch telescope. They have succeeded in identifying several lines and in measuring their wavelengths. These lines were all those of the Balmer series up to H_{16} (λ 3703·9 Å., Plate 18) and those of HeI, CII, CIII, OII, NII, NIII, FeII and Fe III. From these observations and from those of spectra of gaseous nebulae, it is possible to reach the conclusion that iron is as common in nebulae as it is in stars.

According to Greenstein's investigations in the green region of the spectrum of the nebula in Orion, the lines of doubly ionized oxygen and the $H\beta$ are very conspicuous, and the lines of the Balmer series in the violet are also clearly visible. At the limit of the series there is a wide emission band in the ultra-violet region, which is produced by the capture of free electrons by protons. From this it appears that the Orion Nebula must contain many protons and also many free electrons. In the infra-red region the lines of the Paschen series can be seen, and they become closer to each other at the limit λ 8206 Å. The Paschen continuum extends towards the visible part of the spectrum. The study of the continuum in the spectrum of the Orion Nebula suggests that it is produced also by diffusion of the star light, by solid particles such as dust or interstellar particles.

Both in the Orion Nebula and in the Pleiades, it has been found that the nebular matter is bluer than the exciting stars. Greenstein found that the colour temperature of the continuum at either side of the Balmer series is 12,000° K., and that the energy distribution, beyond the limit of the Balmer series, proves the large optical thickness of the nebula. This is also confirmed by the appearance of the absorption lines of helium.

The four stars of the 'Trapezium' are spectroscopic binaries. The faintest of the group, HD 37021, belonging to θ^1 Orionis, is known as the variable BM Orionis. Struve and Titus, by means of the HeI lines of the spectrum of these stars, have determined the radial velocities with the quartz spectrograph of the McDonald observatory, in order to find out whether or not these velocities were in agreement with the mean radial velocity of the nebula. The radial velocity of the four stars is found to be much greater than that of the nebula itself, which is +17·5 km./s. The difference between the mean radial velocity of the four stars and that of the nebula is +15·0 km./s. Two hypotheses can be put forward to explain this difference. Either we are dealing here with a gravitational displacement towards the red (Einstein effect) or there exists a systematic motion of the stars through the nebula. In favour of the first hypothesis we can recall that displacements towards the red of the same order, have been found in stars of great masses discovered by Trumpler in the clusters, and the fact that the two greatest displacements are those of the two brightest stars. In favour of the second hypothesis there is the fact that the masses of the four stars are not of a size to justify the displacement towards the red, according to the mass-luminosity relation for spectroscopic binaries of the type of these four stars. In this case, it might be thought that the associations of stars of class O, such as those of the 'Trapezium', namely very young stars, are in a stage of expansion. Blaauw and Morgan, when discussing the spatial motion of AE Aurigae and μ Columbae, show that their motion is away from the Orion Nebula and with a velocity of 127 km./s. These two stars are of class O9 and B0 respectively, and they move in exactly opposite directions, starting from the neighbourhood of the Orion Nebula. Blaauw and Morgan formulate the hypothesis that the two stars had the same origin in the great nebular mass, 2·6 million years ago. The question whether the velocity excess of the four stars is due to gravitational displacement towards the red or is due to a systematic motion of the stars through the nebula remains unanswered.

In the normal state of hydrogen, the energy difference between two hyperfine states gives rise to a radiation of wavelength of 21 cm., and the corresponding line is emitted only in the region where hydrogen is present in a neutral state. Measurements of the line's profile and displacements give information on the motion, density and temperature of the clouds of neutral hydrogen along the line of sight. Some of the measurements taken at Harvard observatory show that this gas does not appear to be concentrated where the density of the particles is high. Moreover the profile of the 21-cm. line could be interpreted as an expanding envelope of neutral gas, the centre of which corresponds to the supposed origin of the two above-mentioned stars, namely AE Aurigae and μ Columbae.

In 1954, measurements of radio emission from the Orion Nebula on a wavelength of 9·4 cm. were made at the *Naval Research Laboratory* in Washington. If the source of radio emission is taken to be of spherical shape and at a distance of 500 parsecs, the mean electron density at $7'·5$ from the centre of the source is estimated to be 400 cm.$^{-3}$. These results seem to agree well with the hypothesis of a thermal emission from a very dense region of HII in the Orion Nebula (Plate 20).

Recently (1959) very interesting colour photographs of this nebula were obtained at Mt. Palomar. They show the distribution of a blue fluorescent light at the external edges and of a reddish light in its more internal parts.

ROSETTE NEBULA IN MONOCEROS, NGC 2237, 2238, 2239, 2246. R.A. 6h 28m; Decl. +5° 0'.

The large diffuse nebulosity NGC 2237 (Plate 21) surrounds the open cluster NGC 2244 and includes also the other NGC objects. The 48-inch Schmidt of Mt. Palomar has enabled Minkowski to photograph this remarkable nebula and the region near it, as a whole. The main star of the open cluster, S Monocerotis, is surrounded by bright and diffuse nebular matter. The light of the nebula in the red region of the spectrum is due to the emission of $H\alpha$. Apart from the hydrogen lines there are also other emission lines of OII, OIII, and NeIII in the spectrum. The nebula, which is surrounded and enveloped by absorbing matter, is particularly interesting for its symmetrical shape and for the great number of small, well-defined, dark clouds which appear projected against the nebula. Its shape suggests that the bright part of the nebula is an ionized region formed around the exciting stars and surrounded by dark clouds of reasonably high density. The exciting stars are of classes O6 to O8, of apparent magnitude 7 and absolute magnitude —4. The distance of the nebula is estimated to be about 760 parsecs, with an apparent diameter of 80', corresponding to a linear diameter of 17 parsecs.

Kron, at Lick observatory, has determined the brightness of the nebula in light of $H\alpha$, finding it to be $2 \cdot 5 \times 10^{-3}$ erg. $cm^{-2}s^{-1}$. Assuming that the nebula is an interstellar homogeneous medium, and that the electron temperature is 10,000° K., then the electron density is 32 cm^3.

Spectroscopic investigations are required in order to establish whether the ring-like appearance of the nebula is due to high ionization at the centre or in fact represents the real distribution of matter. The smaller dark clouds, scattered among the bright matter, appear as spots with dimensions similar to those of faint stellar images. Their real shape and size will have to be studied with more powerful instruments before it is possible to establish whether they really are 'globules' (Plate 22). The apparent diameter of the smallest formations seems to be less than 5", and if they are at the same distance as the nebula itself, then their diameter is smaller than 4,000 A.U. The mass of the bright nebula is estimated to be 10,000 times that of the Sun.

This nebula, called Rosette because of its shape, is situated together with the Orion Nebula and the North America Nebula, in the spiral arm of the Galaxy, which extends from 40° to 190° of galactic longitude, and is approximately 3,000 parsecs long and 600 parsecs wide.

TRIFID NEBULA IN SAGITTARIUS. M. 20–NGC 6514. R.A. 18h 0m; Decl. −23° 2′.

This is one of the most beautiful of the irregular nebulae (Plate 23). It was first observed by Messier in 1764 as a cluster, and identified as a nebula by William Herschel. It was observed by John Herschel at the Cape, who gave it the name of Trifid (meaning, divided into three). The apparent divisions are due to absorbing matter closely connected with the nebula itself; only about half of the nebula is divided into three. Its distance is of 1,400 parsecs and its diameter is approximately 10 parsecs. The Trifid is an object of symmetrical shape, with density which decreases rapidly from the centre outwards. It can be said that this is very near to the 'classical' sphere illuminated by a central star of luminosity $2 \cdot 9 \times 10^{36}$ erg/s. studied by Strömgren. Incandescent gas, much of which probably was freed in the evaporation of solid particles, produces the emission lines of H, OII, OIII, and NeIII.

Duncan, who has photographed this nebula with the 100-inch at Mt. Wilson, has called attention to the typical bright edge around a dark cloud in the south-eastern part of the nebula. Photographs with short exposures, taken by Thackeray with the 74-inch Radcliffe reflector at Pretoria, reveal interesting features which can be of great importance in interpreting the nature of the interaction of dark and bright matter where they come into contact. Thackeray finds that the nebular lines N_1, N_2, $H\beta$ and $H\gamma$, have maximum intensity on the brighter, central edge of the nebula, and the ratio between the intensity of the hydrogen lines and the intensity of N_1 and N_2 is a maximum at the same edge. The spectrum shows also the existence of a faint continuum in the same region which surrounds the central star.

This nebula, like the Orion Nebula and M.8, emits radio waves of high frequency. The absence of perceptible radiation at longer wavelengths shows that the source of radiation is purely thermal, that is to say that the radio emission is produced by collisions between electrons and protons. A temperature of the order of 10,000° K.

explains in most cases the intensity of the radio waves observed in this and other similar nebulae.

NEBULA IN SAGITTARIUS. M.8–NGC 6523. R.A. 18h 1m; Decl. −24° 23′.

This nebula consists of an open cluster (NGC 6530) combined with a bright, diffuse nebula (NGC 6523) which has an extremely complicated and confused structure (Plate 24). It is crossed by a very dark region in a direction from north-west to south-east. Dark patches of absorbing matter, which are small and of irregular shape, are scattered all over the nebula. Some of these small dark patches can be seen in the brightest parts of the nebula, and it appears as if the absorbing matter is not completely opaque, but allows through some of the light of the brightest parts. M.8 is at a distance of approximately 1,600 parsecs and its longest diameter is 90′, hence its linear diameter is 34 parsecs.

Messier, in 1764, was the first to observe this object which he considered to be a star cluster. It was Lacaille who, later, described it as a nebulosity enveloping a great number of stars. John Herschel, observing the same object at the Cape, thought that it was related to the nearby Trifid Nebula.

Like the spectrum of M.16 and M.20, that of M.8 shows bright lines. The continuous spectrum is partly due to diffuse light and partly to fluorescence produced by the high-frequency radiation of the exciting stars. M.8 together with M.16, outline one of the spiral arms of our Galaxy, situated between the Sun and the centre of the Galaxy.

Photographs of M.8, taken by Thackeray with the Radcliffe reflector and a red filter, isolate the central region of the nebula in radiations $H\alpha$ + NII, and in the OIII radiation, when a green filter was used. This central area, to the east of the star Herschel 36, has the shape of a sand-glass, with the dark division in its narrowest point (approximately 2″). Both the parts of the sand-glass present a very complex structure with several dark divisions. Moreover these parts show at least three concentrations thought to be of stellar character, with diameters of the order of 1″, namely of the size of the smallest stellar images.

Spectra of the brightest parts of the nebula have a very intense continuum in addition to a mixture of the typical emission lines (HeI, H, OIII, OII, NIII). The main difference between this spectrum and that of the Orion Nebula is that the line λ 3869 Å. of NIII is very faint, while the λ 4069 Å. (SII and CIII) is very bright, moreover all the hydrogen lines appear intense compared with the OIII lines. The general character of the spectrum seems to suggest that the brightest part of M.8 is much less ionized than the Orion Nebula, and that the permitted lines are stronger than the forbidden lines.

A characteristic of the type of nebula just described is that the dark regions show bright edges, generally in the direction of a central bright star or group of stars, and that the edge is brighter in the part nearest to the star. The fact that these bright edges have a bright line spectrum leads us to formulate the hypothesis that they are regions of excitation at the limit of interaction of dark and bright matter, as happens, for instance, in the shell surrounding Nova Persei. If we assume a direct interaction, it is very important to have a knowledge of the motion of the dark matter in relation to the central stars. It is very difficult to measure the radial velocities and the proper motions required to obtain this knowledge. According to Thackeray, the appearance of the phenomenon shows that the motion of the dark matter must take place in a direction towards the central region, and this is confirmed also by the configurations of M.16 and of the Trifid Nebula.

Observations of the nucleus of M.8, which has a spectrum with bright lines as well as a very intense continuum, show that the brightest regions of a nebula can be closely linked with relatively faint stars, an association perhaps of the type of T Tauri.

An abundance of Bok and Reilly's globuli characterizes M.8. Dufay remarks that nine globules appear perfectly spherical and ten slightly oval. Their diameters range between 5″ and 10″ and their linear dimensions between 7,000 and 12,500 A.U.

The excitation of luminescence is attributed by Hubble to stars of class O5 and B0; the first is 9 Sagittarii and the second HD 164816, but Strömgren considers that this second star is of little importance compared with the first. The radius of the sphere, around 9 Sagittarii, where the hydrogen is ionized, is about 10 parsecs, and therefore there are approximately 60 atoms of hydrogen per cubic centimetre. The total mass of the gas contained in the nebula is several thousand times that of the Sun.

NEBULA M.16–NGC 6611. R.A. 18h 16m; Decl. —13° 49'.

This nebula is in Scutum. It was first discovered by Messier in 1764 and he considered it to be a star cluster, the stars of which were 'mixed with a faint light'. It was Barnard, in 1815, who discovered the real nebula (Plate 25).

The most striking part of this nebula is the central dark region. This is divided into three almost parallel parts which lie in a direction south-east to north-west, pointing to the cluster. The most northerly dark part appears partly blurred by the bright nebulosity which is in front of it and which is near to the star that is situated in the hollow between this part of the dark region and the next. Thackeray has studied the spectrum of this 'hollow' which is the brightest part of the nebula, and the adjacent regions. He finds that all the nebular lines (N_1, N_2, $H\beta$, $H\gamma$ and OII) increase in intensity on the bright edges. The intensity of both the nebular lines and of the total blue light is almost 2·5 times that of the surrounding nebulosity. Near the edges there is a sudden change in the intensity ratio $H\beta$/N, in the sense that $H\beta$ is relatively more intense near the edge.

The bright edges are visible in the ultra-violet photographs as well as in those taken with blue and red filters, but the continuum, at the limit of the Balmer series, probably contributes to the ultra-violet as much as the λ 3727 Å. [OII]. There are only a few noticeable differences between the photographs taken in blue and red light. There exists a great number of dim red stars in the cluster which can be either intrinsically red stars, or stars reddened by interstellar matter. In the blue and ultra-violet photographs, a prevalence of the nebulosity surrounding the cluster can be seen, and this shows a striated structure similar in some ways to that surrounding the Pleiades.

NEBULA M.17–NGC 6618. R.A. 18h 18m; Decl. —16° 12'.

Nebula M.17 is in Scutum. Because of its shape it has been given various names, such as Omega, Horseshoe and Swan. According to Duncan the last name is perhaps the most suitable when the nebula is observed with a medium-sized telescope.

M.17 was discovered by Messier in 1764 and there are many drawings and photographs of it. John Herschel, in 1833, described it thus: 'Its form is very remarkable, consisting of two loops like a capital Greek "Omega"; the one bright and the other exceedingly faint.'

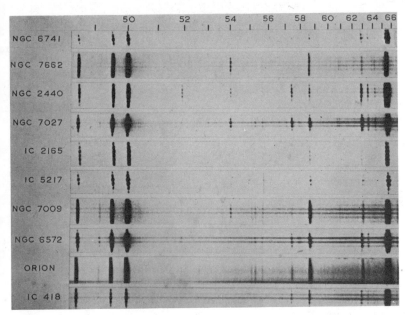

17. Spectra of some planetary nebulae and of the irregular nebula in Orion. The bright line spectra have great similarity. The continuum in the spectrum of the nebula in Orion is a little more intense

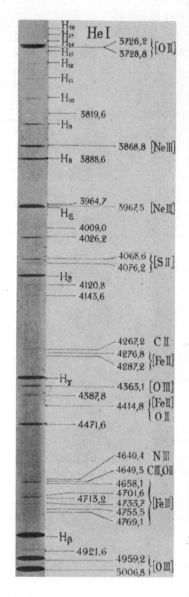

H₁₆	
H₁₅	He I
H₁₄	3726,2
H₁₃	3728,8 }[O II]
H₁₂	
H₁₁	
H₁₀	
	3819,6
H₉	
	3868,8 [Ne III]
H₈ 3888,6	
	3964,7
Hε	3967,5 [Ne III]
	4009,0
	4026,2
	4068,6
	4076,2 }[S II]
Hδ	
	4120,8
	4143,6
	4267,2 C II
	4276,8
	4287,2 }[Fe II]
Hγ	4363,1 [O III]
	4387,8
	4414,8 {[Fe II] / O II
	4471,6
	4640,4 N III
	4649,5 C III,O II
	4658,1
	4701,6
	4713,2 / 4733,7 }[Fe III]
	4755,5
	4769,1
Hβ	
	4921,6
	4959,2 }[O III]
	5006,8

18. Spectrum of nebula in Orion with wavelengths and identification of the bright lines

19. The Great Nebula in Orion M.42—NGC 1976. 100-inch Mt. Wilson

20. Nebula in Orion following ζ Orionis NGC 2024. 100-inch Mt. Wilson

21. Rosette Nebula in Monoceros NGC 2237. Photographed in red
light. 48-inch Schmidt, Mt. Palomar

22. Rosette Nebula in Monoceros NGC 2237. Enlarged section. Photographed in red light. Note the 'globules'. 48-inch Schmidt, Mt. Palomar.

23. Trifid Nebula in Sagittarius M.20—NGC 6514. Photographed in red light. 200-inch Mt. Palomar

24. The 'Lagoon' Nebula in Sagittarius M.8—NGC 6523. Photographed
in red light. 200-inch Mt. Palomar

25. Nebula in Scutum M.16—NGC 6611. Photographed in red light. 200-inch Mt. Palomar

26. Filamentary Nebula in Cygnus NGC 6960. 100-inch Mt. Wilson

27. Star clouds in the Milky Way, Sagittarius region. Photographed with
a Tessar lens of 10-inch focus

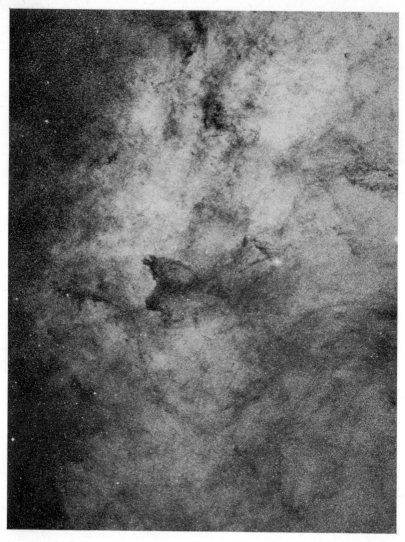

28. Star cloud in the region of Sagittarius, photographed in red light.
48-inch Schmidt, Mt. Palomar

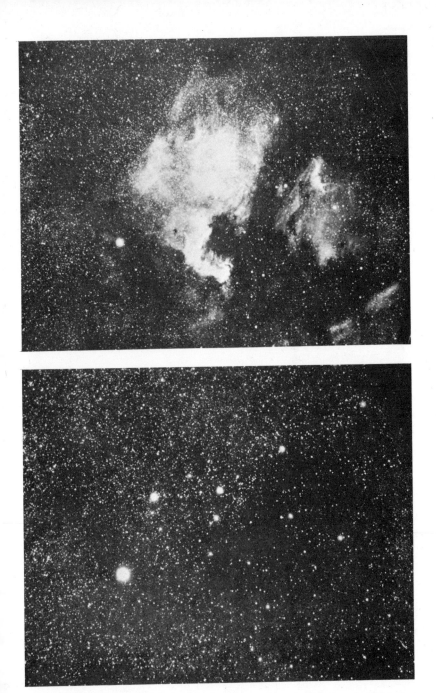

29. North America Nebula photographed in red light (above) and infra-red (below)

30. Dark nebula in Orion, 'The Horsehead'. 100-inch Mt. Wilson

31. Dark nebula near ρ Ophiuchi

32. Dark nebula near θ Ophiuchi

33. Dark nebula Barnard 86 in Sagittarius. 100-inch Mt. Wilson

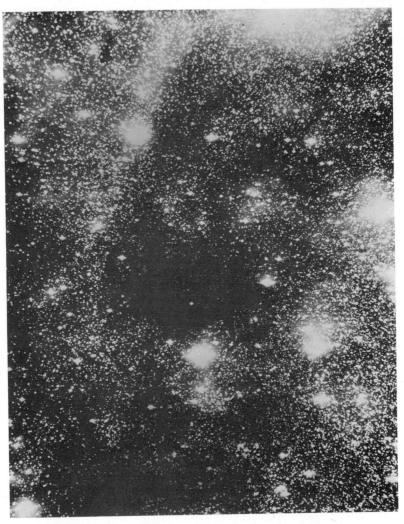

34. Dark nebula Barnard 92 in Sagittarius. 100-inch Mt. Wilson

35. Irregular nebula in Cygnus NGC II 5146

IRREGULAR BRIGHT NEBULAE

M.17 appears to be composed of filaments and has many dark regions. The most noteworthy is a rectangular region situated near the western edge of the nebula. Its distance is approximately 2,000 parsecs and its dimensions are $26' \times 20'$. The mass of the bright region is much greater than that of the Orion Nebula and it is about 800 times that of the Sun.

According to Duncan, the absorption regions of M.17 seem to be of a different kind from those of M.8 and M.16. The dark region, of the western edge, is terminated on the west by a faint bright nebulosity. Of great interest are the dark filaments which cross the bright matter, particularly near the head and neck of the 'swan'. Some of these appear to radiate from a point near the base of the neck of the 'swan'.

NEBULA NGC 6960. R.A. 20h 45m; Decl. $+30° 35'$.

One of the main characteristics of this object is the existence of bright filaments associated with the star 52 Cygni (Plate 26), which extend for more than one degree in a direction north–south. To the west, towards the middle of the long filaments, is situated 52 Cygni, a star of fourth magnitude.

John Herschel made a drawing of this object and has given us the following description: '. . . it passes through the double star 52 Cygni, as a long, crooked, narrow streak, forking out in two or three places.'

This nebula, which has also been described by Lord Rosse, has been much studied and photographed. In this region there are many irregular nebulosities, seen particularly in red light photographs as is shown in wide field photographs obtained at Lick Observatory (1913) and later by Šajn and Hase (1952). These photographs also include NGC 6979, 6992 and 6995. Everywhere are found faint nebular masses which link with others which are brighter. Duncan points out the existence of faint filaments which extend to the west of 52 Cygni from both sides of the main nebula, near its southern end. This nebula is the frontier between the region in the east, containing many faint stars, and that in the west with very few stars. Obviously this must be a case where absorbing matter exists.

The spectrum of the filaments is that of a hot gas without any evidence of solid particles. Photographs taken at Mt. Wilson with an interval of 40 years give some information on the motion of the filaments in the direction at right angles to the line of sight, without showing any appreciable variation in their delicate and fine structure.

113

Šajn and Hase have studied the preferential orientation of the filaments and other details of the structure of this nebula with relation to the existence of local magnetic fields.

Photometric measurements, made by Fesenkov and Rozhkovskij, of some of the stars in four stellar chains which are joined to the filaments of this nebula and of NGC 6992, show that as far as type and colour are concerned, they belong to the central part of the main sequence and therefore to the class of dwarfs. The radial velocities of the filaments vary between 10 and 100 km./s. There is enough proof to show that the star chains are mingled with gas and cosmic dust.

NEBULA NGC 6992. R.A. 20h 55m; Decl. $+31°$ 32'.

This nebula, known as the 'Network Nebula', is in Cygnus. It has an extremely interesting and complicated structure, with several filaments which extend almost 1° 3' in declination.

John Herschel made a drawing of this object in 1833 and described it thus: 'The nebula is of great extent, passing obliquely through and rather under a small constellation, being densest where under it; but it is extremely faint and only to be seen with an eye well prepared and in a very clear night. The whole neighbourhood seems affected with wisps or cirrostratus-like masses of nebula.'

Lord Rosse noticed that NGC 6992 was similar to NGC 6960 but on a larger scale. The dark spaces have a roundish appearance similar to sacks, particularly along the main fold where the nebula is brighter. No star which might be a source of excitation appears to be enclosed in the nebula.

The form of the nebulosity is such as to suggest that it is the remnants of the explosion of a nova or supernova. This view is not confirmed by the measurements of radial velocities which do not indicate a definite expansion. Spectroscopic observations and photographs, obtained with filters, show that practically the whole of the radiation is concentrated in the emission lines and that there is no reflection from particles. Spectrograms of the brightest parts of the nebula show that λ 3727 Å. of OII is the most intense line, followed in intensity by the $N_1 + N_2$ (OIII), while the lines $H\gamma$, OIII (λ 4363 Å.) and NeIII are much fainter. The relative intensities show significant fluctuations from one filament to another. The long nebular filaments appear to be parallel to the direction of the galactic plane and suggest the presence of a galactic magnetic field.

Oort has suggested that the faintly luminous edges of the dark clouds of this nebula, as well as other similar large objects, can be excited by collisions between interstellar clouds of gas and cosmic dust. Photographs in red light (between $\lambda\lambda$ 6400 Å. and 6600 Å.) of the region enclosing this nebula, as well as the neighbouring NGC 6960 and NGC 6995, obtained with the 48-inch Schmidt at Mt. Palomar by Minkowski, lead us to believe that all this network of bright nebulae is the remnant of the explosion of a supernova.

According to the measurements made by Humason, some of the luminous filaments have a velocity of approach of 45 km./s. Combining this value with that of the expansion of nebulae, which according to Hubble is of 6″ per century, we obtain a distance of 310 parsecs, and the diameter of the whole system is 15 parsecs. From this, Struve and Oort suggest that the explosion of the supernova, which is supposed to have given origin to this nebula, may have occurred 30,000 years ago.

NEBULA NGC 7000. R.A. 20h 56m; Decl. +45° 4′.

The appearance of this nebula led Wolf to call it North America. It consists of a mixture of stars and nebulosity situated in Cygnus approximately 3° east of α Cygni. To the east and west dark regions exist which join together at the southern point of the bright nebula (Plate 29). To the west and south of this there are vast, faint, luminous patches.

In the photographs obtained by Duncan in 1923 with the 100-inch reflector, a great number of dark and bright details can be seen in the region corresponding to the 'Gulf of Mexico'. The brightest part of the nebula is the irregular edge which limits the 'Gulf of Mexico' from the north-east to the south-west. The central part of the 'Gulf' appears to be almost devoid of bright nebulosity for a diameter of approximately 15′, while in it the star density is certainly less than a tenth of that existing in the bright nebulosity to the east of this edge. The main nebulosity in the south-east of the 'Gulf' appears to have almost parallel bands which are crossed by dark regions. The luminous region to the north of the nebula is of a brightness almost uniform and much fainter than the region at the southern end, and is intersected by two dark areas. Of these the most northerly has a width of approximately 8′ and is well defined by an irregular edge at its south-eastern end. The southerly dark area is 13′ long and 5′

wide and has a direction north–south. It is not completely dark and shows some faint bands which are curved.

Pikelner, at the Simeis Observatory (Crimea), has carried out spectrophotometric research on this nebula and has determined the relative intensity of the hydrogen lines and of N_1, N_2, λ 3727 Å. and λ 5577 Å. From these he was able to deduce the absolute intensities, the exciting star being HD 199579 of class O7. From the absolute luminosity and from the region of ionization, Pikelner obtains a density of 10 atoms of hydrogen per cubic centimetre. The total mass of the nebula is several hundred times the solar mass.

CHAPTER V

Irregular dark nebulae and interstellar matter

V.1 Introduction.

WE HAVE already mentioned the discovery of dark masses which cover regions of the sky. In photographs and visual observations, these regions reveal themselves by the almost total lack of stars and by contrast with regions filled with a great number of stars, like clouds of stars which appear brighter than other parts of the sky (Plates 27 and 28).

The nature of these dark masses, which according to reliable hypotheses was not expected to be very different from the nature of irregular bright nebulae, can be determined from the study of the absorption of the light from the stars either embedded in these masses or perhaps existing behind them. The absorption can be either total or selective, and it is possible to find in the spectra of these stars dark lines due to the presence of atoms in the dark nebulae.

When discussing bright nebulae we have already explained that a cloud of gas and cosmic dust, existing in interstellar space, will appear to us as a diffuse bright nebula only if there exists a star inside it or in its neighbourhood, which could produce the excitation of the gas of the cloud. When these stars are not present then the cosmic clouds will absorb and diffuse the light of the stars which are behind them and the result is a dark nebula. These have an irregular shape and vary in size. Sometimes they appear simply as bands of dark matter, like long and narrow lanes, across areas crowded with stars, at other times they appear as spots or globules, some darker than others, which are seen projected against the background of bright matter.

117

A typical example of the association of dark and bright matter is to be found in the dark nebula known as the 'Horsehead' on account of its shape. This looks almost like a black storm-cloud with its edge illuminated by the Sun. The dark cloud absorbs the light of the stars which are hidden behind it, outside the cloud there are numerous stars, almost ten times as many as inside it.

Another typical region is found in the southern hemisphere, and is known as the 'Coal Sack'. This appears very dark, due to contrast, in fact through the 'Sack' one can detect stars which appear very dim because of its absorption. Another example is the giant dark nebula in Ophiucus which covers an area of 1,000 square degrees of the sky.

We shall see, later on, that one of the characteristics common to nearly all galaxies is a band of absorbing matter in their equatorial plane. In our Galaxy, too, we find a similar characteristic, in fact near its equator no galaxies can be seen. This dark matter is distributed very unevenly in the sky. Trumpler found that the average absorption, in the neighbourhood of the galactic plane, was of the order of one magnitude at a distance of 1,500 parsecs from the Sun, but in some regions could be even larger.

Stars further away from us and which are near the galactic plane have been observed to be generally redder than they should be according to their spectral type. This reddening effect has been attributed to interstellar matter, which has a selective coefficient of absorption, and lets through a greater percentage of red than blue radiation.

The colour of the fainter stars of known spectral type makes it possible to determine how much they have been reddened by the passage of their light through the dark gaseous mass. The degree of reddening depends upon the average dimensions of the particles of the cosmic dust which constitutes these dark nebulae. Schalen, observing this reddening effect, suggested that it was produced by small cosmic particles with a diameter of about $2 \times 10^{-2} \mu$. It is not possible to determine the nature of these particles, that is to say whether they are constituted of ice or metals. Later it was found that these dark nebulae are rich in oxygen and in light elements, such as carbon, nitrogen and hydrogen. The existence of neutral hydrogen was confirmed by the reception from space of radio waves of a wavelength of 21 cm.

The 'colour excess' gives the measure of the reddening of a given star produced by the obscuring matter. If we measure the colour index with a photo-electric photometer and we compare it with the real colour index which the star should have according to its spectral class, we obtain, by difference, the colour excess expressed in stellar magnitudes. Assuming that the colour excess is due to the presence of absorbing matter, it will give a measure of the reddening of the light of the star when passing through cosmic clouds. These cosmic clouds have various sizes. The 'Coal Sack' probably appears to us so conspicuous because it is relatively near to us, within 150 parsecs. This object covers a very wide angular field, but had it been at a greater distance it might never have been discovered. In fact at ten times the distance it would cover only 1% of the area at present covered, moreover the contrast of the stars which are in front of it would be completely lacking. It might be supposed that the absorbing interstellar medium is scattered everywhere and that the dark nebulae are masses of gas and dust mainly responsible for the absorption and diffusion of light.

Very little is still known about the size and distribution of these dark clouds. The distance of a dark nebula can be estimated in the following way. Two equal areas are chosen, one inside and the other outside the nebula, and stars, up to a given apparent magnitude and of the same spectral type, included in these areas, are counted. As long as we limit ourselves to count fairly bright stars, we find that the number in both areas is approximately the same, which means that the stars in question are all placed in front of the nebula. Starting from a given magnitude the number of stars inside the nebula begins to be smaller than that of the stars in the area outside the nebula. As we progress to fainter stars, the area inside the nebula is found to have even fewer stars than the other area. From a given magnitude onwards, the difference in the number contained in both areas remains constant, which means that we have reached the end of the nebula and that we are counting stars which are beyond it.

We can assume that, on average, stars of the same spectral type and of a given apparent magnitude, are at the same distance or, in other words, that they also have the same absolute magnitude. In this case the magnitude at which a difference in number between the two areas begins to appear will give the distance of the part of the nebula nearer to us, and the magnitude, where the difference in number remains constant, will give the distance of the part of the nebula further away from us. The two curves, which give the number

119

of stars as a function of the apparent magnitude contained in the two areas, will become parallel after a given magnitude, and the difference in stellar magnitude of the displacement of one curve with respect to the other, will give the total absorption of the nebula (fig. 16). In repeating the same star count for the infra-red, visual or photographic apparent magnitudes, it is possible to obtain a measure of the selective absorption of the nebula.

When the distances of the nebulae are known, it is easy to obtain their real dimensions from their angular diameter. There is a great variety of objects, from small round and dense globules with diameters of the order of between 0·1 and 0·01 of a light-year, to very large clouds with diameters of hundreds of light-years.

Hartmann, in 1904, discovered in the spectrum of some very remote stars, the dark lines of interstellar calcium, which were called 'stationary lines' as opposed to the lines of the stars which were displaced in varying degree by effect of their radial velocities. While Hartmann's discovery shows the existence of atoms in the interstellar matter, Trumpler's research shows the existence of granular matter. Later in the spectra of stars which are very distant from us, besides the lines of ionized calcium were discovered lines of sodium, potassium, titanium, iron and the radicals CH and CN, and it has been possible to prove the existence of cosmic clouds which are in relative motion.

Adams, in the year 1948, observed that in many stars the K line of CaII appeared divided in several components. This is due to a Doppler effect, produced by the motion of the absorbing atoms. On average the velocity, measured from the displacement of the lines, follows the galactic rotation. The individual clouds of gas produce components with velocities of the order of 5 km./s. and in some cases even multiple lines with velocities of about 50 km./s. A cloud in Sagittarius has the velocity of 96 km./s. The approximate limits of some such clouds in motion can be detected in the spectra of several stars near the masses of gas.

Stars which are deeply embedded in large clouds of solid absorbing particles do not produce intense K lines. Greenstein and Struve have discovered that the K line appears very weak in the spectrum of a star which is at a distance of 100 parsecs and which is subject to a 4 magnitude absorption by the dense and dark cloud near ρ Ophiuchi. This shows that although the density of the solid matter is low, the density of CaII must be even lower. From this we conclude that the

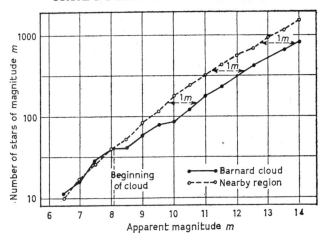

Fig. 16. Determination of the distance of a dark cloud. The full line gives the star counts in an area within the cloud and the dashed line gives the counts relating to a nearby area. Starting from the apparent magnitude 8, the two curves separate. If the stars chosen for the counts are of the same spectral type, and therefore have approximately the same absolute magnitude M, from the difference M–m it is possible to obtain the distance at which the cloud begins. At a distance corresponding to the apparent magnitude 9 of the stars of the region near the cloud, the two lines become nearly parallel and are displaced by one magnitude; this means that we have reached the end of the cloud which produces an absorption of one magnitude

reddening has no close correlation with the intensity of the interstellar lines.

On the whole the composition of the interstellar matter must be very similar to that of the stars. It must mainly consist of electrons, protons, atoms of neutral hydrogen and helium and, in smaller quantity, of atoms and radicals of the above-mentioned type as well as of very minute solid particles. The absorption produced by this mixture of atoms and cosmic dust can be divided into two parts. One with a general or neutral coefficient of absorption which is independent of the wavelength, and the other a selective one since it increases with decreasing wavelengths. From the diffusion and from the absorption produced in the interstellar matter, it would appear that the diameter of the particles which produce the observed selective absorption, must be of the order of $10^{-1} \mu$, and therefore much larger than the diameter estimated by Schalen. It is very improbable, however, that the interstellar matter should consist only of atoms and of particles with a diameter of $10^{-1}\,\mu$. It is possible that particles with larger diameters exist, but we can state that those with diameters of $10^{-1}\,\mu$ are those which, with a smaller mass, produce the maximum effect in the absorption.

We have already stated that the interstellar matter, both the more concentrated type existing in dark nebulae and the thin and wispy type which is to be found in all our Galaxy, have the property of absorbing the light of a star selectively. That is to say, the blue radiation is more weakened than the red and the red radiation more than the infra-red, and as a result of this the observed spectrum appears to us 'reddened'. Recent research by Miss Divan has shown that the law governing the absorption of the light of the stars by interstellar matter, that is to say the law according to which the percentage of reddening varies with wavelength, is the same in the whole of the galactic system. These results prove that the particles which compose the cosmic dust are of the same dimensions and of the same nature throughout the whole of the Galaxy.

The ratio of gas and solid particles in a dark nebula is not well known, and it is possible that the ratio varies from object to object. Until recently it was not known whether hydrogen existed in dark nebulae; however in recent years radio astronomy helped in the solution of this particular problem. It has been possible to discover the presence of neutral hydrogen which emits the 21-cm. line but no line in the visible region of the spectrum. The problem concerning the possible existence of molecular hydrogen is however still unsolved.

According to our present knowledge it is thought that dust represents only one or two per cent of all interstellar matter. The rest consists of hydrogen and other elements, possibly in the same percentage as is found in the stars.

The density of the interstellar gas in the neighbourhood of the Sun is of one hydrogen atom per cubic centimetre. Since a hydrogen atom has a mass of 10^{-24} g/cm.^{3}, the density of interstellar matter (neglecting the very small contribution of other elements) is 10^{-24} g/cm.^{3}. The average density of our Galaxy in the neighbourhood of the Sun is three times greater, which proves that the interstellar hydrogen, in the neighbourhood of the Sun, represents about 30% of the mass. In the clouds the density can be ten times greater or even more.

Clouds of interstellar matter, on average, have a velocity of 5 to 10 km./s., but motion with velocities up to 100 km./s. has been observed. On the other hand, collisions between clouds are, in a cosmic time scale, very frequent, amounting to one in every ten million years. These inelastic collisions would have a braking effect on the motion of the gases. The cause which maintains this motion is the difference of temperature between the various parts of the gas; in fact the hydrogen surrounding the hot stars is all ionized, and its thermal agitation corresponds to a temperature of about 10,000° K. According to Strömgren, a very hot star of spectral class O, ionizes the hydrogen contained in a sphere of 400 light-years radius: the Sun, on the other hand, would produce only a negligible effect. Beyond the limits of this sphere of HII there is the neutral hydrogen, the thermal agitation of which corresponds to a temperature which is only between 50 and 100° K. The hot gas tends to expand, thereby producing a very great pressure on the colder gas. As a result, an expansion of the nebular gas is produced, and the density of the HII regions is about 200 times less than that of HI regions.

Strong accelerations of the gas occur when a small cloud happens to be near a hot star. The part of the cloud which is nearest to the star becomes heated and expands; in so doing it pushes further away the gas on the far side from the star. Spitzer has called this mechanism 'interstellar rocket'.

According to theory, the expansion of a hot rarefied gas in a denser and cooler medium gives rise to instability. We can predict the formation of tongues of cold gas which will intermingle with the hot gas. Observations in fact show the presence of dark tongues of gas which appear over the bright part of several irregular nebulae. The use of filters and of photographic emulsions sensitive to limited regions of the spectrum, have shown the considerable differences existing between photographs of the same region of the sky taken in blue, red or infra-red light. The form and the intensity of the various celestial objects, stars, clusters and nebulae both bright and dark, can appear completely different in the various wavelengths. For example, the Cloud B, east of 45 Ophiuchi, photographed in the region of λ 8300 Å., shows a grouping of star clouds with small dark gaps. When the same region of the sky is photographed in blue light, the star clouds do not appear, instead we have only a great number of individual stars accompanied by a very faint nebulosity. A large field in Aquila, when photographed in blue light, shows a faint bright nebulosity divided by an elongated dark cloud. The same region, in an infra-red photograph, shows an intenser and more extended bright nebulosity divided by a well-defined dark stripe. The nebulae 'North

America' and 'Pelican' (Plate 29), photographed in a very narrow region of the spectrum around $H\alpha$, appear very bright with interspersed dark regions. When, however, they are photographed in the infra-red the nebulosity disappears and instead we are left with a great number of well-defined stars and a dark region devoid of stars in the area corresponding to the 'Gulf of Mexico' in the North America Nebula. In Barnard's photographic atlas of selected regions of the Milky Way (published in 1927 by the Carnegie Institution, Washington) there are listed 349 dark objects which are designated by the letter B followed by a number. For each one of them Barnard has given a description. In the following years many more similar objects have been photographed, not only in blue light as was done by Barnard, but also in other regions of the spectrum by means of combinations of suitable filters and emulsions.

V.2 Polarization of the light of the stars.

In 1949, Hall and Hiltner, independently, discovered that the light from the stars is polarized. Let us explain briefly what we mean by polarized and unpolarized light.

According to the classical model, we can represent the emission of light by an atom, as produced by the vibrations of an electron which is attracted by the nucleus, by a force similar to an elastic force. If the electrons of the emitting atoms vibrate all in the same direction, we say that the light is polarized. The intensity will be zero in the direction of vibration and maximum in a direction at right angles to it. If the vibrations, on the other hand, occur in all directions, then we say that the light is unpolarized. Light is said to be partially polarized when the vibrations occur in all directions at right angles to the direction of propagation of the ray, but there are two preferred directions, at right angles to each other, in one of which a maximum and in the other a minimum number of electrons vibrate.

If the light passes through an analyser, it is possible to detect whether the light is unpolarized or partially polarized, and in the latter case it is possible to determine the percentage of polarization. When the intensity of the light reaches a maximum intensity, in a particular direction which is, for example, 10% greater than the minimum in the direction at right angles to it, we then say that the light is 10% polarized. If the source is in a magnetic field, then this will compel the electrons to vibrate in some directions which depend on the lines of force of the magnetic field, and this will produce polarization of the light.

The Sun, the great majority of stars, the domestic electric bulb, emit unpolarized light. Hall and Hiltner's observations of a great number of stars show that some of them emit light which is 10% polarized, while for others polarization is much smaller or may be even non-existent. Polarization of the light is determined by means of photo-electric polarimeters. With these instruments, measurements of the brightness of the stars in various planes of vibration can be compared. The polarization effect does not depend either on the luminosity or the spectral type of the star, but it is dependent on the quantity of interstellar matter through which the light of the star has to travel. Thus stars which are more affected by the 'reddening effect' are those which have the greater polarization. From this it naturally follows that polarization is not an intrinsic quality of certain types of stars, but rather that it is related to the presence of clouds of interstellar matter.

We know that the elongated solid particles which constitute cosmic dust, have the property of absorbing more radiation, when the vibrations happen to be in the direction of the longer axis. Therefore if all the particles were elongated and all had the same direction, the light from the stars, which must travel through these clouds, would become polarized. But why should all these particles be orientated in the same way? The existence of a galactic magnetic field may be the explanation. Spitzer and Tukey, as well as Davis and Greenstein, have put forward the theory of the galactic magnetic field in order to explain the observed polarization.

Spitzer and Tukey, investigating this problem, found that the observed polarization of the light of the stars may be due to elongated metal particles, and that in order to have all these particles in the same direction, a magnetic field of at least 10^{-4} gauss would be required. It appears that the magnetic field of the Sun is variable with time between 5 and 50 gauss; the terrestrial magnetic field is of a few tenths of a gauss.

Davis and Greenstein think that it is more likely that the elongated particles consist of ice crystals with about 10% of metals. A magnetic field of only 10^{-5} gauss would be sufficient to produce the alignment of these particles. In order to explain the planes of polarization observed in the light from the stars, the lines of force of the magnetic field should be directed along the arms of the galactic spirals.

Very recently the magnetic field has been observed directly by means of the Zeeman splitting of the 21 cm line of neutral hydrogen, which appears in absorption in the spectra of strong radio sources. A field from 10^{-5} to 10^{-6} gauss has been found. The direct measurement was possible because the Zeeman splitting is proportional to the field and to the square of the wave-length; therefore a field too weak to give a measurable splitting in the optical region gives a splitting large enough to be measured in the radio spectrum. The presence of this field would explain the arrangements of clouds in spiral form and could also explain the origin of the great energy which is revealed by cosmic rays. The filamentary aspect of the dark nebulae perhaps shows the direction of the magnetic field. Relativistic electrons moving in the magnetic field of the Galaxy could explain the radio emission of the Galaxy as due to synchrotron mechanism (see also p. 83, radiation from the Crab nebula).

V.3   Description of some outstanding irregular dark nebulae.

DARK NEBULAE IN TAURUS. R.A. 4h 21m; Decl. $+28°$ 10′.

In this region evidence is very strong of the existence of dark matter in space. The dark matter appears in irregular channels crossing, from west to east, regions which are very crowded with stars. One of these lanes stretches to the south-east for about 3° and reaches another dark nebula to which it is partially joined. To the south another similar lane is found which stretches for 3° to 4° and ends at a point of right ascension 4h 21m and declination $+24°$ 46′. These lanes are well defined, without any stars and with some patches which are denser. McCuskey has found that the total absorption in various points of the dark masses varies between 0·5 and 4 magnitudes. The colour excess in the stars of early classes distributed in the dark regions, which is obtained from the blue-yellow colour index, shows an absorption of 2 magnitudes. The distance of the clouds is between 100 and 250 parsecs and total absorption appears to occur near 200 parsecs.

DARK NEBULA IN ORION, 'THE HORSEHEAD'. R.A. 5h 39m;
Decl. $-2°$ 30′.

This well-known dark nebula (IC 434) south of ζ Orionis (Plate 30) was discovered in 1887 by astronomers at Harvard Observatory. A luminous fringe stretches from north to south and has a prominence in the shape of a horse's head. This prominence is very dark and projects towards the western region which contains a great number of stars, while the eastern part of the region is filled by a large dark mass devoid of stars. The bright fringe is very irregular and appears like the edge of a rather thin layer, slightly gibbous, and is seen edgeways by the observer. On the north-east corner of the dark mass, superimposed on it, is the bright nebula NGC 2023 which surrounds a star of magnitude 8·5. The 'Horsehead' is the dark nebula B.33. The bright fringe, according to Duncan, is the dividing line between the dense dark mass in the east and the thin, bright nebula in the west. If the two masses have a relative motion towards each other, a concentration of bright nebulosity is produced along the line of contact which is the fringe-like structure observed. The faint luminosity to the west must be transparent enough to transmit the light of the stars in the background, while the dark matter in the east covers completely all the stars which are behind it. IC 434 is only part of a very wide region which stretches for several degrees to the north-east and to the south and which envelops M.78.

The luminous fringe consists of ionized hydrogen. It was evidently formed at the edge of the expanding large mass of neutral gas, possibly by shock waves. This could have taken place when the great expanding mass, moving at a velocity of about 10 km./s., collided with the surrounding interstellar matter.

The distance of the dark nebula is approximately 460 parsecs. Very strong radio signals on a wavelength of 21 cm. (hydrogen line) are received from this region of the sky.

THE GREAT DARK NEBULA AROUND ρ OPHIUCHI. R.A. 16h 23m; Decl. −23° 40′.

This is one of the most extraordinary parts of the sky. The bright nebula which is to the north of ρ Ophiuchi and surrounds it, has for background a dark area from which dark lanes branch off towards the east (Plate 31). The background of the sky is uniformly covered by many faint stars, and the dark nebula occults those which are furthest away. The dark lanes to the east of the bright nebulosity are very long and well defined. The main lane, 40′ wide, stretches for more than 6° and then continues with some interruptions until it reaches the θ Ophiuchi region, a total length of more than 10°.

At the southern edge of the dark nebula we find, enveloped in bright nebulosity, the stars 22 Scorpii, σ Scorpii, Antares and the globular cluster M.4.

The distance of the nebula is 215 parsecs.

DARK NEBULA IN THE REGION θ OPHIUCHI. R.A. 17h 23m; Decl. —24° 15'.

This region, which should be considered connected with that of ρ Ophiuchi, has parts which have a very great number of stars, while other parts are completely devoid of stars (Plate 32).

The dark nebula B.78 is to the east and to the south of θ Ophiuchi, with a lane which stretches for 4° towards the west where there are star clouds. θ Ophiuchi is in a region which is studded with stars and which, to the east, comes to an abrupt end at the limit of B.78. To the north of these stars is found B.72, which is a smaller and darker nebula than B.78 and is in the shape of an S. Many large dark masses are scattered over the whole region. As Barnard remarked, this is one of the most surprising regions of the sky.

DARK GLOBULES IN THE REGION OF θ OPHIUCHI. R.A. 17h 27m; Decl. — 26° 5'.

The regions in Sagittarius and Ophiucus are populated not only by star clouds and dark patches but also by 'dark globules' as, for instance, in M.8. A great number of dark patches appear on the bright background which is covered by stars. If we suppose that they are at the same distance as the dark nebulae, the diameter is of the order of 30,000 A.U. for the better-defined objects.

According to Bok and Reilly, these patches are found at the rate of one per square degree, in the regions where the density of stars is sufficient for them to be seen in contrast against the background. Other very small and well-defined globules are seen projected on the star clouds in Scutum.

A few spots very like globules are to be seen also on the North America Nebula, but generally speaking these are less well defined than those in M.8.

The photographic absorption produced by the globules has been measured. A minimum of absorption can be estimated by comparing the surface brightness of the globule with that of the nearby regions, where there is no absorption. For globules with diameters between 10,000 and 35,000 A.U. the absorption is between 2 and 5 magnitudes, and for larger globules the absorption is of the order of one magnitude. Further investigations, with instruments of the type of Schmidt cameras, are necessary in order to clarify the nature of these objects. For this, star counts in blue, red and infra-red light are required as well as measurements of surface brightness and a comparison with neighbouring regions of the same area where there is no absorption.

DARK NEBULAE IN THE GREAT STAR CLOUD IN SAGITTARIUS.
R.A. 17h 54m; Decl. −32° 8′.

To the west of the great star cloud in Sagittarius and along the galactic equator, there is a very dense ramification of dark matter associated with the dark nebulae in Ophiuchi (Plates 33 and 34). The few class B stars which are visible in it are very reddened. The photographic absorption for some of them is as much as 5 magnitudes at a distance of a few hundred parsecs from the Sun. With ordinary photographs or by visual observations, it is found that the remotest regions of the Galaxy are occulted by the dense absorbing clouds which are in a region between 320° and 330° of galactic longitude and −3° and +3° of galactic latitude. On the other hand, if infra-red plates with suitable filters or photo-electric instruments are used, it is possible to obtain images of regions of the Galaxy which are beyond the dark clouds.

DARK NEBULAE IN AQUILA AND IN SAGITTARIUS. R.A. 18h 28m; Decl. −14° 9′.

In the region in Sagittarius which has for centre the point given by the above co-ordinates, there is a star BD (−10° 4713) of magnitude 5·5 which is surrounded by a bright nebulosity of approximately 15′ in diameter. The star is in a region 2° 5′ in diameter from which several lanes and patches of dark matter branch off. A wide and curved dark lane stretches to the south-east and forms the eastern edge of a great star cloud which has the shape of a wedge which reaches almost to the star BD (−10° 4713). At the base of the wedge there is another dark nebula, elliptical in shape and studded with faint stars. In the same region are found M.16, which is a mixture of stars and nebulosity, and M.17, the 'Omega' Nebula.

CHAPTER VI

Our Galaxy

VI.1 Introduction.

SINCE the early dawn of civilization, man has created myths about the appearance of the starry vault of the sky.

Galaxy, meaning 'Milky Way', was the name the Greeks gave to that whitish band which crosses almost the whole of the sky, and which is so clearly visible in a clear moonless night.

In an autumn evening at our latitude, the W of Cassiopeia is to be found in a north-easterly direction, between the zenith and Polaris. The whitish band of the Milky Way can be seen through Cassiopeia in a direction south-west and towards the cross of Cygnus separating itself into two branches, the most westerly towards Hercules and Ophiucus and the easterly one towards Aquila and Sagittarius and then loses itself in the haze of the horizon. Starting from Cassiopeia again, this time moving to the east, we can follow the whitish lane of the sky across Perseus and Auriga, and, later in the night, we can see it a little to the east of the V of Taurus and the Pleiades. Further south it passes east of Orion, crosses Gemini, Monoceros and Argo. An observer in the southern hemisphere would see the Milky Way cross the whole of the sky, passing from Monoceros and through Carina and Crux to reach Scorpio and Sagittarius. When looking at the projection of the Milky Way on a celestial globe, we can see that it appears as a broad band encircling it, almost as a great circle, passing through the above-mentioned constellations. The two poles of this circle are 90° north and south of the galactic plane. The north pole is in Coma and the south pole in Sculptor.

VI.2 The Milky Way.

The Milky Way was observed through a telescope for the first time by Galileo in 1610. Only then was it possible to realize that its milky appearance was due to an enormous number of stars. Later astronomers realized that the stars might not be placed as they appeared, namely as a band encircling the celestial sphere as a true two-dimensional surface, but that the stars could well be distributed in space also in a third dimension. Thus the idea grew that the Milky Way was a gigantic system of which the Sun was part.

The fact that we belong to this system, and that therefore we see it from the inside, makes it extremely difficult to understand its structure. The discovery of great families of stars, or island universes, has given us a better idea of the appearance of our own system when seen from the outside. This would appear as a very flattened ellipsoid (the possible existence of spiral arms will be discussed later), with a great concentration of stars and a great quantity of dark matter (dust and gases) in its equatorial plane. This image of the external appearance of our Galaxy helps us to interpret what we can see from the interior. The Milky Way, which encircles the whole of the celestial sphere as a great circle, is simply the intersection of the equatorial galactic plane with the celestial sphere. When an observer looks in the direction of one point of the Milky Way, his line of sight is in the equatorial galactic plane, that is in the plane where there is a great conglomeration of stars. When, on the other hand, he looks in any direction away from the Milky Way, his line of sight is not any longer in the equatorial galactic plane.

According to present usage, by Milky Way we mean the profile of our stellar system projected on the celestial sphere, while by Galaxy we mean the whole of the stellar system of which we are a part. Systems similar to our Galaxy are called 'external galaxies' or, more simply, 'galaxies'. In this way it is possible to eliminate the ambiguity of the term nebula which originally was applied both to galactic nebulae (consisting of masses of gases and dust as we have already described) and to stellar systems which used to be called 'external nebulae'.

Once it is established that the Galaxy is a gigantic system consisting of stars, gas and dust, we have to study several aspects of it; geometrical, dynamical and physical, in order to understand it properly.

1. Geometrically: we shall have to determine its shape, its dimension, and determine in which part of it the Sun is situated.

131

2. Dynamically: we shall have to find the laws which regulate the motion of its bodies.

3. Physically: we shall have to discover what is the nature of the bodies which form the system and how these bodies are distributed in the various parts of the Galaxy.

In order to determine the position of a star in the Galaxy, it is useful to adopt a system of co-ordinates called 'galactic co-ordinates'. This system takes as a reference plane the galactic equator. As in terrestrial co-ordinates, the 'galactic latitude' will be the arc measuring the distance of an object from the galactic equator, and the 'galactic longitude' will be the arc which measures the distance of a galactic meridian from a point taken as zero. This point, which in terrestrial co-ordinates is that where the Greenwich meridian cuts the equator, in galactic co-ordinates is one of the two points where the celestial equator cuts the galactic equator. Of the two points the one with right ascension 280° has been chosen as the zero point. Both galactic latitude and longitude are measured in degrees.

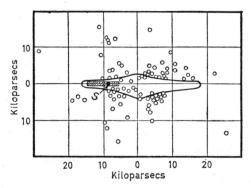

FIG. 17. Galaxy surrounded by globular clusters marked by circles. S is the Sun; the shaded area is the zone accessible to optical radiation. 1 kiloparsec= 3,260 light years

VI.3   Geometrical structure of the Galaxy.

WILLIAM HERSCHEL'S INVESTIGATIONS. If we knew the exact position in space of all stars visible to our telescopes, we would also know both the form and the dimensions of the Galaxy, or at least of its part nearest to us. Unfortunately we can only determine with ease the direction in which we see a star, or, more simply, its spherical co-ordinates, galactic or equatorial, but its distance is known with far less accuracy, even in the few cases of objects near to the Sun.

William Herschel was the first to attempt a census of the Galaxy. His method was based on statistics. Herschel chose some regions distributed at random in the sky as sample areas, and counted all stars visible with his telescope and divided them according to their magnitude. His son John carried on this work and extended it to the southern sky. They succeeded in showing that the majority of stars are concentrated in the neighbourhood of the galactic plane. Their method consisted mainly in comparing the number of stars of a given magnitude contained in one square degree of the sky at a high galactic latitude, that is far from the Milky Way, with one square degree at a low latitude. The smaller the magnitude of the stars studied, the greater is the galactic concentration. Table 5 shows the results of similar recent investigations.

TABLE 5

Apparent Magnitude	Number N of stars per square degree at latitude l			
	$l<20°$	$20°<l<40°$	$l>40°$	$N(l<20°)/N(l>40°)$
≤8	8	5	3	2·7
12	430	230	138	3·1
16	15,000	6,000	2,700	5·5
20	280,000	64,000	21,000	13·3

How can we interpret these results? First of all let us say that as a first approximation the magnitude of a star is a measure of its distance. If all stars had the same intrinsic brightness the different intensity of their appearance would depend only on their actual distances. We know, however, that matters are not as simple as that. The intrinsic brightness of stars can vary between very large limits, from 10,000 times less bright to 200,000 times brighter than the Sun. Stars of the same spectral type have, however, also similar intrinsic brightness, and therefore an estimate of their apparent brightness gives us already some measure of their relative distance. Moreover, even without dividing the stars into spectral classes, exceptionally bright stars are very few and stars which are very faint appear scarce because our telescopes can detect only those which are nearer to us. The stars of medium brightness, which are more numerous, will

133

have a greater weight in a statistical analysis and therefore it will be justifiable to assume that faint stars are, on average, also the furthest stars. We know that the Sun is within the Galaxy from the fact that the latter is seen projected as a circle on the celestial sphere and therefore it follows that if the galactic system is very flat, that is mainly concentrated on the equatorial plane, the very remote stars can be found only when we look in the direction of the galactic plane, while stars which are nearer to us can be found when we look in any direction.

We ought to point out that the results obtained by the Herschels, father and son, were purely qualitative. They had no measure of stellar distances and their main hypothesis was that the fainter stars were also, on average, the furthest. With this hypothesis William Herschel was able to calculate that the thickness of the galactic system was about one-fifth of the diameter in the galactic plane.

The census carried out by the Herschels gave, therefore, the following results:

(a) the existence of a galactic concentration, which means that the star density increases with decreasing latitude;

(b) a complete absence of concentration in longitude.

All this led to the belief that the Sun was almost at the centre of the Galaxy, so that an observer looking in any direction along the equator would find that the star density remained almost constant; moreover, whether the latitude corresponding to the direction of observation was positive or negative, the star density depended only upon the absolute value of latitude.

KAPTEYN'S INVESTIGATIONS. In Herschel's time the absolute magnitudes of the stars were completely unknown. One could only assume that the fainter a star appeared, the further its distance would be. With the first determinations of trigonometrical parallaxes and later with the discovery that the absolute magnitude of a star is closely related to its spectral type, it became possible to determine with greater accuracy stellar distances and hence obtain a better knowledge of the dimensions of our stellar system. Since intrinsically faint stars are seen with difficulty at great distances, it is convenient to use for sounding, stars of classes O, B, A, which are among the brightest and therefore are visible at great distances.

The statistical investigations of the twentieth century, mainly directed and co-ordinated by Kapteyn at Groningen in Holland, while giving important results in the field of kinematics, gave the same conclusions as the investigations carried out by Herschel. The star density decreases regularly in all directions as we go further from the Sun, which therefore ought to be at the centre of the Galaxy, in a region of maximum concentration of stars. Today we know that this interpretation is not correct, because the Sun actually occupies a position somewhere nearer to the edge of the Galaxy.

RECENT VIEWS ON THE GALAXY. We shall now describe a model of our Galaxy (fig. 17) according to recent investigations and further on discuss how the conclusions were reached.

The Galaxy has the shape of a very flattened ellipsoid. Its dimension, in the galactic plane, is about 80,000 light-years. In a direction perpendicular to this plane the thickness of the system varies from approximately 16,000 light-years where the central nucleus is, to no more than 4,000 light-years at the edges, where the Sun is. The distance of the Sun from the galactic centre is about 27,000 light-years.

How is it that the statistical investigations of Herschel, and those more recent of Kapteyn, had led to the belief that the Sun was at the centre of the Galaxy? This can be explained by the fact that the interstellar gas which is particularly abundant in the direction of the galactic centre, absorbs the light of the stars and makes them appear fainter. The result of this is that we have a decrease of the apparent number of stars almost equally in all directions; in fact the actual increase in the number of stars in the direction of the galactic centre is masked by the increase of interstellar absorbing matter.

INVESTIGATIONS BY SHAPLEY. Shapley, during the years 1916–19, undertook an investigation of the globular clusters. These are agglomerations of tens of thousands of stars which become denser as we approach the centre of the cluster. If we study the spatial distribution of these globular structures, we find that the same number is to be found to the north as to the south of the galactic plane. In other words, the galactic equator is a plane of symmetry for the system of globular clusters. We do not see these clusters, however, in all directions. The majority of them are visible in the direction of Sagittarius. Almost one-third of all the known globular clusters is concentrated in this area, which covers only 2% of the whole sky.

Since the globular clusters form a system which has for plane of symmetry the galactic plane and since they contain at most a million stars, against about a hundred thousand millions contained in the Galaxy, they must be subject to the gravitational attraction of the Galaxy and must rotate around its centre. If the globular clusters are mainly concentrated in the direction of Sagittarius, this indicates that the galactic centre must be in Sagittarius. This is the conclusion reached by Shapley.

After this discovery, several facts became obvious which up to then could not be explained. The Milky Way is denser in Sagittarius than in the opposite direction towards Taurus and Auriga; moreover, not only the globular clusters, but also several other remote objects congregate particularly in the direction of Sagittarius. Among these objects there are the planetaries, novae, diffuse bright and dark nebulae and variables of type RR Lyrae.

RR LYRAE STARS. These variable stars have become one of the most satisfactory means of determining stellar distances. They are named after RR Lyrae, the first of this family to be discovered. They are blue stars with a brightness which varies periodically by one magnitude, generally in a period of time between 10 and 24 hours. Their absolute brightness is about 100 times greater than that of the Sun, but their apparent magnitudes are all very small, which indicates that generally, they are all at a great distance away from us. These stars are very common in globular clusters and since their absolute magnitude is known, they have been of great help to Shapley in determining the distance of the globular clusters.

The RR Lyrae stars which are not in globular clusters, are found mostly in the direction of Sagittarius, and their apparent magnitude gives the measure of the distance of the galactic centre.

The RR Lyrae stars have made it possible to determine the fact that globular clusters form a system which is almost spherical, centred in the galactic centre and having a diameter of approximately 150,000 light-years. In other words, the globular clusters are distributed within a sphere having the same centre as the Galaxy and a diameter of 150,000 light-years. The RR Lyrae stars which are visible in the direction of Sagittarius have, moreover, made it possible to estimate the distance of the galactic centre from the Sun, as being from 25,000 to 30,000 light-years.

When determining the distance of the galactic centre, we must bear in mind one of the difficulties which up to 1918 had led astronomers to believe that the Sun was at the centre of the Galaxy. Interstellar dust and gases which constitute the dark interstellar matter are visible in parts of the sky where they are highly concentrated and completely opaque such as the 'Coal Sack', but where they are less dense they produce an absorption. This not only produces a diminution of the brightness of stars embedded in them or which happen to be behind them, but also causes the effect known as 'interstellar reddening'. The violet radiations are absorbed more than the red ones. As a result of this a star of class B, for instance, with a surface temperature between 15,000° and 20,000° K., will present spectral lines typical of its class, but the continuum, and hence the colour of the star, will be that typical of a star of temperature between 5,000° and 6,000° K.

As we have already shown in an earlier chapter when discussing interstellar matter, the study of the reddening effect allows us to estimate the decrease in apparent magnitude due to absorption. Baade, in 1950, while studying photographs of Sagittarius taken in red light in order to reduce the absorption effect, found a great number of RR Lyrae stars the apparent magnitudes of which were mostly between 17 and 18. Since the interstellar absorption in the direction of Sagittarius is estimated to be of 3 magnitudes, the apparent magnitude of the stars visible in this region is 14·5. Their absolute magnitude is zero and therefore their distance from us is 28,000 light-years. This must also be the distance of the galactic centre. The number of RR Lyrae stars reaches a maximum at the apparent magnitude 17·5 (fig. 18). It is reasonable to assume that the greatest number of these stars is to be found at the centre, where the star density must be at a maximum, and that their number decreases together with the general decrease of star density, as we move away from the centre.

Our modern telescopes show that the number of visible stars increases with increasing apparent magnitude until a maximum is reached, after which it begins to decrease. If we extrapolate the curve we find that the number of stars of magnitude 26 (which are not visible even with the powerful telescope of Mt. Palomar) is very near zero. This means that our system is an isolated system in space and that our means of observation can reach its limit. If, on the other hand, instead of observing in the direction of the galactic plane, we observe regions near the galactic poles, where the interstellar matter

137

is very scarce and therefore the absorption negligible, we see more galaxies than galactic stars.

A very different result is obtained when we divide galaxies according to their apparent magnitude as we do for stars. There is no evidence of diminution in their number per unit volume with increasing distance. In other words, this indicates that our observational means are not yet capable of reaching the limit (assuming that it exists) of the universe containing the galaxies.

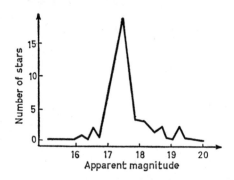

Fig. 18. Distribution according to apparent magnitude of RR Lyrae stars visible in the direction of Sagittarius

We have divided the discussion of the subject into three parts: (1) geometrical, (2) kinematical, (3) physical. We shall see that these three parts are often very closely linked. The knowledge of the physical and kinematical conditions is necessary to extend our knowledge of the geometrical aspect. The geometrical and kinematical aspects help to complete our knowledge of the physical aspect and vice versa. After this first examination of the geometry of the Galaxy we shall deal with the kinematical and physical field. When we have studied the three fields, we shall once again return to the general subject of the complete structure of the Galaxy.

VI.4 Galactic motions.

The shape of the galaxies, particularly of the spiral galaxies which have an appearance not unlike that of a Catherine-wheel, suggested that they were rotating around an axis perpendicular to their equatorial plane. Spectrographic observations and the presence of the

Doppler effect confirmed these suppositions. Even before this confirmation was obtained for the galaxies, it was thought that our own
Galaxy was rotating. We know that in the case of the solar system,
the planets can revolve around the Sun without falling on it, because
the gravitational force is balanced by the centrifugal force. The
Galaxy is also a system where the majority of its mass is concentrated in the nucleus where there is a very great number of stars
and a great amount of interstellar matter. If its components were
stationary, they would fall to the centre of the system. The force
which prevents their fall and keeps the system in a state of equilibrium is the centrifugal force. Poincaré, in 1923, calculated that a
period of rotation of 500,000,000 years would be sufficient to prevent
the fall of the components to the centre of the Galaxy. In the same
year Charlier pointed out that the plane containing the orbits of the
planets around the Sun appeared to move with a period of 370,000,000
years with reference to the whole Galaxy. Strictly speaking we ought
to consider the planes of the orbits of the planets, but since the inclinations of these planes to the ecliptic are very small, we can consider them to be in one plane. Now, according to dynamics, this
plane should be constant in space, and Eddington, in order to explain
the observations obtained, formulated the hypothesis that the whole
Galaxy was rotating.

The observations now available give us considerable information
on how the Galaxy is rotating. Normally it cannot be expected that
the Galaxy should rotate like a solid body, for instance, like a wheel
in which all the points have the same angular velocity while the linear
velocity increases in proportion to the distance from the centre. It is
more probable that the rotation of the Galaxy is similar to that of
our solar system, where the planets nearer to the Sun have greater
linear and angular velocity than those further away. In the solar
system the greatest part of the mass is concentrated in the Sun, all
the planets contributing less than one-tenth, but in the Galaxy there
is no such concentration of very large mass in one central body. The
law of motion of its components will therefore be more complex than
that of the components of the solar system.

We shall now discuss the observations and their interpretation
which led astronomers to a good knowledge of the motion of the
Galaxy. If the law governing the rotation of the Galaxy is similar to
that governing the rotation of the planets in the solar system, then
we can expect that stars in the neighbourhood of the Sun, describing

very similar orbits, would not move at random, but will all have approximately the same direction and the same velocity.

SOLAR MOTION. The first investigations were directed to ascertain whether the Sun moved in the Galaxy and, if so, how it moved. These investigations showed that if we take as a system of reference the group of stars near to us, and we assume that their motion has a random distribution and that the system is therefore on average at rest, the Sun appears to move with a velocity of 20 km./s. in a direction called the 'apex'. This point is near Vega in Lyra. The velocity of motion of the Sun is completely different, however, if as a system of reference we take the globular clusters. In this case the velocity is 200 km./s. while the direction is not very different, the motion being towards Deneb in Cygnus. This discrepancy confirms the fact that the two systems of reference, namely the stars near to us and the globular clusters, do not constitute a system at rest but have proper motions which are different from each other. It follows, therefore, that what we measure is not the velocity of the Sun with reference to the centre of the Galaxy, but only the velocity of the Sun with reference to the centre of gravity of the system used.

PREFERENTIAL DIRECTIONS OF MOTION. The direction of the galactic centre as seen from the Earth and from the Sun is in Sagittarius. It is possible to establish on the galactic plane the direction of the galactic centre as well as the directions at 90° and at 180° from it and locate them in the constellations. Thus we have Sagittarius in the direction of the galactic centre (327° galactic longitude), Auriga in an opposite direction (anti-centre) at 180° from the centre (147° galactic longitude), and Cygnus and Carina at 90° from the centre. Of these last two the former has a galactic longitude of 57° and the latter of 237° (fig. 19).[1]

Kapteyn, in 1904, observed that stars near to us, that is those with distances less than 1,000 light-years, do not move at random in space, but rather in some preferred directions. If the Sun were stationary and the stars near to us had random velocities in all directions, then a diagram of the velocity vectors would give as locus of the extremes of the velocity vectors a curve which is almost a circle. The presence of a motion of the Sun towards the 'apex' would

[1] Galactic longitude is measured anti-clockwise for an observer looking at the galactic centre from the north galactic pole.

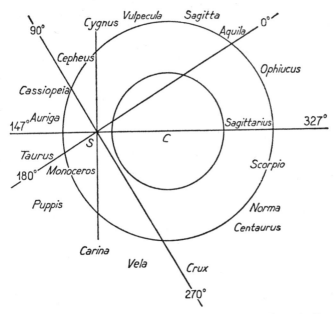

Fig. 19. Constellations crossed by the Milky Way as seen from the Sun

distort the circle into an ellipse, the major axis of which would be directed to the 'antapex'. The random velocities of the stars would combine with the solar velocity towards the 'apex' (fig. 20a), resulting in a general motion in an opposite direction.

Kapteyn's observations show that we have neither a circle nor an ellipse, but rather a curve with two lobes which indicate the preferential directions (fig. 20b). When these two directions are corrected for the effect of the solar motion, we find that the stars form two main streams through space. These are flowing towards opposite regions of the sky, towards Scutum and Orion: the first is a constellation near Sagittarius and the second a constellation near Auriga, namely in the two directions which we now know to coincide with the galactic centre and the galactic anti-centre.

Attempts made to understand the observations in Kapteyn's time were not very successful, but following observations enabled astronomers to understand clearly the galactic motions.

ASYMMETRY. As long as we examine stars in our neighbourhood

141

OUR GALAXY

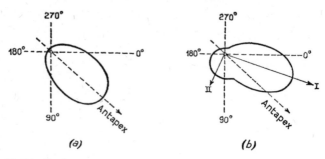

Fig. 20. Distribution of stellar motions with reference to the Sun. (a) assuming that the nearest stars have motions at random in all directions. (b) assuming there are two preferred directions of motion I and II

with velocities not greater than 60 km./s. the only outstanding phenomenon we find is the existence of two preferential directions. Let us now consider stars with velocities greater than 60 km./s. There are not many of these, but they do present us with a remarkable phenomenon. All these stars move only towards one part of the sky, which is at 90° from the galactic centre and is in the direction of Carina. This means that stars in our neighbourhood with velocities not greater than 60 km./s. have velocities which are directed in all directions in the sky although with a greater preference towards Scutum and Orion. On the other hand, stars with velocities greater than 60 km./s. are to be found only within an angle of approximately 120°, the bisecting line of which is directed towards Carina, that is in a direction at right angles to that of the galactic centre.

High-velocity stars show very clearly the phenomenon of asymmetry. This is a phenomenon common to all stars though perhaps in a less marked way. Strömberg has shown that even the stars near to us with velocities not greater than 60 km./s. have a slight preference towards a motion in the direction of Carina, rather than Cygnus. This tendency is shown also by the fact that the directions of the preferential motions are not diametrically opposite to each other, nor are they in the direction of the centre and anti-centre, but the axis of the preferential motion is a broken axis and forms an obtuse angle the bisecting line of which passes through Carina.

The globular clusters show this phenomenon of asymmetry in a more accentuated way. Their velocity with reference to the Sun is of the order of 200 km./s. and they all move in the direction of Carina. Besides the globular clusters, which as satellites are part of our own

142

galactic system, the galaxies show in a very marked way the pheno-menon of asymmetry, and this is a very important fact. Since the galaxies have no link with our Sun why should they all move in the same direction with reference to it? It is much more probable that the centre of gravity of their system is at rest with reference to the Galaxy and what we observe is only the reflection of the galactic motion of the Sun.

With this in mind we shall see later how easily we can explain both asymmetry and preferential motion.

INTERPRETATION OF ASYMMETRY. Observations show that the globu-lar clusters, as seen from our Sun when it is assumed to be stationary, appear all to move in the direction of Carina with a velocity of the order of 200 km./s. But this is purely a question of relative motion. We could assume the globular clusters to be at rest and the Sun to move at a velocity of 200 km./s. in the direction of Cygnus, opposite to Carina. The latter interpretation is much more satisfactory as it explains many other observed facts. The galaxies being independent of the Galaxy should have motions which are distributed at random with reference to the galactic centre and therefore should form a system with a centre of gravity which is at rest. They appear to move in the direction of Carina with a velocity of about 250 km./s., only because our point of observation in the solar system is itself moving at 250 km./s. in the opposite direction. This direction, Cygnus, is at right angles to the direction of the galactic centre, so the Sun, with reference to the galactic centre, must have a velocity of 250 km./s. in a direction perpendicular to the line joining the Sun to the galactic centre.

As we have already mentioned, the globular clusters are a family of satellites of the Galaxy. Their distribution in space is such that, unlike the Galaxy, they form a system almost spherical and slightly flattened, centred in the galactic centre and having a radius equal to or a little greater than 150,000 light-years. The degree of flattening of a system is an index of its velocity of rotation. The greater the velocity of rotation, the greater is the flattening of a system, indeed it was this that suggested to the early investigators that the galactic system might be endowed with a great speed of rotation. It is there-fore probable that the system of globular clusters has only a small velocity of rotation around the galactic centre. Observations actually confirm this. The globular clusters appear to move in the direction of Carina with an average velocity of 200 km./s. We cannot exclude the possibility that it is the Sun which is moving with this velocity towards Cygnus. Since the velocity of the Sun when referred to the galaxies is of 250 km./s. (assuming the centre of gravity of the galaxies to be really at rest with reference to the galactic centre) it follows that the globular clusters are also moving in the direction of Cygnus with a velocity of 50 km./s. Then both the Sun and the globular clusters are moving with velocities of 250 and 50 km./s. respectively, in the direction of Cygnus, that is in a direction which is at 90° from the galactic centre. This direction is that which would be followed by a body moving on a circular orbit centred in the galactic centre.

In a similar way we could explain also the asymmetry of motion observed for the stars known as high-velocity stars. These have velocities greater than 60 km./s. with reference to the Sun and appear to move all in a direction opposite to Cygnus. Actually they too move in the direction of Cygnus, but have velocities which are smaller than that of the Sun and of neighbouring stars. Their velocity is between 100 and 150 km./s. instead of 250 km./s. (fig. 21) and therefore they are not really stars endowed with high velocity. We shall see later, when dealing with the physical aspect of the Galaxy, that the high-velocity stars belong to given stellar classes and have therefore similar physical characteristics. It suffices to say at present that their spatial distribution is such as to indicate that they form a sub-system less flattened and with slower rotation than that which is much flatter and formed by stars in the neighbourhood of the Sun.

We owe the idea of these sub-systems to Lindblad. He has suggested that the Galaxy is composed of a number of sub-systems having for a centre the galactic centre and having the galactic plane as plane of symmetry. These systems are composed of objects having common physical characteristics. Each one of these sub-systems has its own degree of flattening according to its own rotational velocity. One sub-system consists of the Sun and of those stars which have a velocity less than 20 to 30 km./s. with reference to the Sun. Its rotational velocity around the galactic centre is of the order of 220 to 250 km./s. Very bright and massive stars of classes O and B which are to be found near the galactic plane, form a very flattened sub-system rotating rapidly, probably with a velocity of rotation a little higher than that of the Sun and its neighbouring stars. On the other hand the RR Lyrae stars form a system which is less flattened. A great number of these stars are to be found at a rather high galactic latitude and the sub-system as a whole has a velocity of rotation which is less than the velocity of rotation of stars of classes O and B and also of the stars in the neighbourhood of our Sun. Among RR Lyrae stars there are many high-velocity stars. The sub-system of the globular clusters is the least flattened of all and is also the one which has the lowest velocity of rotation.

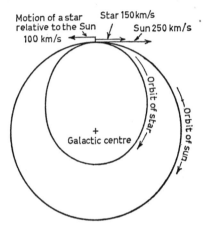

FIG. 21. Asymmetry of motion of the high-velocity stars

Further on, when dealing with the physical structure of the Galaxy, we shall deal with the physical significance of these sub-systems. The question that presents itself at this stage is why the velocity of stars moving in the direction of Cygnus is never greater than 60 km./s. These stars would have velocities greater than 300 km./s. with reference to the galactic centre (250 km./s. velocity of the Sun plus 60 km./s. velocity of the star with reference to the Sun), and this is approaching the actual velocity of escape from the Galaxy. Therefore stars with velocities greater than 60 km./s. have already escaped from the gravitational pull of the Galaxy.

EXPLANATION OF THE PREFERENTIAL MOTION. The Sun moves with a velocity of 250 km./s. in a direction at right angles to the line joining it to the galactic centre. This means that its orbit is almost circular and the stars which are nearest to us also move in similar orbits.

The velocity of the Sun with reference to the stars near to us is about 20 km./s., while the velocities of the stars, when they are corrected for the solar motion towards the 'apex', will be in all directions and will have values between 20 and 30 km./s., that is, they will be equal to the difference between the Sun's velocity and that of the stars themselves.

Let us consider stars in the neighbourhood of the Sun, which have orbits passing through the same point A (fig. 22). Their velocities

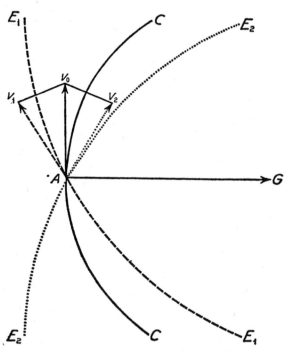

Fig. 22. Preferential motions

will differ according to the eccentricity of their orbits. On average, however, the component of the velocity according to AG will be zero and the average of their velocities will coincide with the velocity v_0 of the circular orbit CC passing through A. The difference between the average velocities v_0 and the individual velocities v will be represented by vectors in directions very near to that of the centre and anti-centre. This would explain the preferential motions observed by

Kapteyn for the velocity of the individual stars with reference to that of the centre of gravity of the whole system. The velocity of the latter, which is actually an average of the velocity of each star, coincides with v_0.

DIFFERENTIAL GALACTIC ROTATION. Lindblad, with his theory of sub-systems rotating with velocities dependent on their flattening, had offered a very probable interpretation of the observations. It was left to Oort in 1927 to provide a direct proof.

If the Galaxy was rotating as a solid body, then the relative position of all stars would be unchanged and it would be impossible to observe this rotation unless the Galaxy was observed from the outside. It is very improbable, however, that this type of rotation would take place. If the majority of the mass of the galactic system is concentrated near the centre, then the outermost parts of the Galaxy must revolve in a manner similar to that of the planets around the Sun, namely the stars nearest to the centre should revolve faster than the furthest. If this effect does take place then it is possible to predict how it appears when seen from the Sun.

Let fig. 23 represent the system of stars near the Sun. Assuming that the revolution is similar to that in the solar system, stars at *A*, *B*, *H*, nearer to the galactic centre, will have greater velocities than those at *C*, *G*, and the Sun, while stars at *D*, *E*, *F*, further away, will have lower velocities. From the Sun, in such a case, the difference

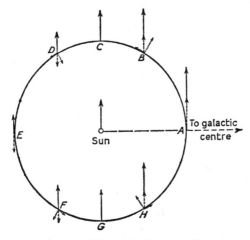

FIG. 23. Differential galactic rotation

between the stellar and solar velocities would be observed and these differences are represented in fig. 23 by dotted vectors.

From the Sun it is not possible to observe the spatial velocity of a star, but only the tangential and radial components of the velocity, namely the proper motion and radial velocity of a star. Its radial velocity (that is the component parallel to the line joining the star to the Sun) expressed in km./s. will be measured by means of the Doppler effect. The proper motion of the star, namely its angular displacement in a direction at right angles to the line joining the Sun to the star, will be observed. From fig. 23 it can be seen that if a 'differential' rotation does take place, then the radial velocities, as seen from the Sun considered at rest, will vary with the galactic longitude and will be zero in four positions. These are the directions of the centre and anti-centre, since in these directions the velocities with reference to the Sun are all tangential, and the directions of Cygnus and Carina since the Sun and stars at C and at G move with the same velocity. The velocities will have a positive value, that is to say they will be velocities of recession from the Sun for stars which are nearer to the galactic centre than the Sun and which have any longitude between the galactic centre (327°) and Cygnus. Stars further than the Sun, which have a longitude between the anti-centre and Carina, will also have a velocity of recession from the Sun. For distant stars between Cygnus and the anti-centre and for stars near to us between Carina and the centre, the velocities will have negative values, that is to say they will be velocities of approach. The amplitude of the curves which give radial velocities as a function of longitude will be greater the further are the stars under consideration since the difference between stellar and solar velocity increases with increasing distance from the Sun. Figure 24 shows the results of observations of radial velocities and these confirm the above predictions.

Proper motions too must vary with the galactic longitude. The maximum value will be found for the longitude of the centre and anti-centre while in the directions of Cygnus and Carina they will be zero. Since we are dealing with angular displacements, the motion will not depend upon the distance. Thus, for stars twice as far from the Sun, the tangential velocity with reference to the Sun will be doubled but the angle will not change.

From the analytical study of this effect Oort obtained two equations which bear his name. The first represents the law with which the radial velocity of a star, with reference to the Sun, varies according to the distance of the star from the Sun and according to the galactic longitude. The second represents the law with which proper motion varies according to galactic longitude. The mathematical expression of these laws is:

$$v_r = Ar \sin 2(l-l_0)$$
$$\mu = A \cos 2(l-l_0) + B$$

where v_r and μ represent the radial velocity in km./s. and the proper motion expressed in seconds of arc. A and B are two constants having the dimensions of an angular velocity, l_0 is the longitude of the galactic centre and r is the distance of the star from the Sun.

From the first equation it can be seen that the radial velocity becomes zero when $l-l_0 = 0°$; $l-l_0 = 90°$; $l-l_0 = 180°$ and $l-l_0 = 270°$; that is in the directions of the centre, of Cygnus, of the anti-centre, and of Carina. The radial velocity reaches a maximum positive value when $l-l_0 = 45°$ and $l-l_0 = 225°$, that is to say at B and at F, and a maximum negative value when $l-l_0 = 135°$ and $l-l_0 = 315°$, that is to say at D and at H. We can also see from the same equation that the radial velocity is proportional to r, that is to say its absolute value increases with increasing distances of the star from the Sun, therefore the amplitude of the curve will also increase with the distance. That A must be an angular velocity appears clear

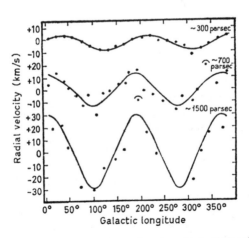

FIG. 24. Variation of radial velocities as a function of galactic longitude for three groups of stars at 300, 700 and 1500 parsecs respectively

149

from the fact that the radial velocity is a linear velocity, which is the result of the product of an angular velocity by a length, in our case r.

The second equation tells us that the proper motion reaches a maximum when $l-l_0 = 0°$ and $l-l_0 = 180°$ which are the directions of the centre and anti-centre, and a minimum given by $B-A$, in the directions of Cygnus and Carina. According to figure 23 the proper motions with reference to the Sun must be zero in the directions of Cygnus (C) and of Carina (G). This followed the assumption that the Sun was at rest, but actually the Sun moves in its orbit and the direction of the galactic centre, as seen from the Sun, changes. In other words, the longitude of the centre of the Galaxy changes when it is observed from the Sun. It follows, therefore, that the minimum value of the proper motions represents the angular motion of the galactic centre as seen from the Sun. The same quantity, with changed sign, that is $A-B$, represents the angular motion of the Sun as seen from the galactic centre or, in other words, the angular velocity of rotation of the Sun. Since the Sun has a velocity which is at right angles to the direction of the line joining the Sun to the galactic centre, the product of the angular velocity by the distance from the centre represents its spatial velocity and not the tangential component alone.

It is possible to obtain directly from observations the values A, B, and l_0. The two equations given above can be applied to a great number of stars of which the radial velocity, the distance from the Sun and the proper motion have been observed. We thus obtain as many equations as the number of stars observed, with the three unknowns A, B, and l_0. These unknowns can be determined by applying the method of least squares to the equations obtained.

The results obtained by several observers give values of A, B, and l_0 which are in very good agreement. So for the longitude of the galactic centre l_0 the value $325° \pm 2°$ is obtained. From the values of A and B and taking R, the distance of the Sun from the galactic centre, as being 30,000 light-years, we obtain for the velocity of revolution v of the Sun around the galactic centre:

$$\mathrm{v} = (A-B)\, R = 240 \text{ km./s.}$$

which is in very good agreement with the value obtained by taking as reference the system of galaxies. From this it follows that the period of revolution of the Sun, P is:

150

$$P = \frac{2\pi R}{v} = \frac{6\cdot 28 \times 30,000 \text{ light-years}}{240 \text{ km./s.}} = 237 \text{ million years}$$

From the knowledge of the law regulating the motion of our Sun, it is possible to estimate the mass of our Galaxy. Let us assume that the Sun is kept on its orbit by the balance between the gravitational attraction due to the part of the Galaxy contained between its centre and the orbit of the Sun, and the centrifugal force. Then:

$$\frac{G\,Mm}{R^2} = \frac{m\,v^2}{R}$$

where m is the mass of the Sun, M the mass of the central part of the Galaxy, G is the constant of gravitation, v and R the velocity and the distance of the Sun from the centre respectively. From the above we obtain:

$$M = \frac{v^2\,R}{G} = 2\cdot 4 \times 10^{44}g = 1\cdot 2 \times 10^{11} \text{ solar masses.}$$

This figure should be taken only to represent the order of magnitude of the mass of the Galaxy. It is in fact only a very rough approximation to assume that the part of the Galaxy inside the solar orbit should behave as a solid body of mass M. Moreover the mass of that part of the Galaxy further than our Sun has been neglected. The above figure, however, gives us an indication of the enormous mass of the galactic system. It also explains why the Sun must move at the great velocity of 240 km./s. in order to balance the gravitational attraction that this enormous mass exerts on it, notwithstanding the great distance of the Sun from the galactic centre. If all stars had the same mass as the Sun, then we could say that the number of galactic stars is 120 thousand millions. Statistical studies of the distribution of stellar masses and of the mass of interstellar matter, give as a result for the number of stars, a figure very near 100 thousand millions.

Recent investigations on the velocity of rotation of the Galaxy at various distances from the centre, confirmed the view that the laws regulating its rotation could not be the same as those pertaining to the solar system. They appear much more complex, because of the lack of a single predominant, central mass. Table 6 gives the velocity of rotation of the Galaxy at various distances. From this table we can see that starting from a distance of 20,000 light-years, the law of motion is similar to that of the solar system and that the velocity decreases with increasing distance from the centre. For distances between the centre and 20,000 light-years, the velocity increases with

TABLE 6

Distance (light-years)	Velocity (km./s.)	Distance (light-years)	Velocity (km./s.)
0	0	25,000	224
5,000	150	30,000	213
10,000	190	35,000	197
15,000	220	40,000	180
20,000	230		

distance, not in proportion to it, as would be the case for a solid body, but rather more slowly. We can deduce that the laws regulating the rotation of the Galaxy are in between those for a solid body and those for the solar system. We must add that this rotating model of the Galaxy is only a first approximation. We have assumed that it consisted of sub-systems of various degrees of flattening and all of them of an ellipsoidal shape. So far we have not taken into account at all the presence of spiral arms. We shall discuss this subject later on, after having learnt something about the physical constitution of the Galaxy which has a bearing on this question.

GALACTIC REVOLUTION AND BIRTH OF STARS. In the preceding pages we have found that the period of revolution of the Sun is of 237 million years. According to very recent data it is probable that this period is somewhat shorter, about 200 million years, since the rotational velocity is likely to be about 220 km./s. The orbit of the Sun is almost circular, this means that at the time of its birth, nearly 5 thousand million years ago, its distance from the galactic centre was the same as at present. The Sun, therefore, like all the stars physically similar to it, was born at the edge of the Galaxy.

Other stars, particularly those called 'high-velocity' stars like the RR Lyrae stars, which have a rotational velocity of the order of 150 km./s. were formed probably at a distance of 5,000 light-years from the centre and they happen to pass in our neighbourhood now because of the ellipticity of their orbits (fig. 21). When we deal with the physical constitution of the Galaxy, we shall see what significance the place of birth has for a star, whether this was in the galactic nucleus or at the extreme edge, namely in the spiral arms.

Let us now here resume what we have already found about the Galaxy. The form is that of a very flattened ellipsoid with the equatorial axes measuring approximately 80,000 light-years and the polar axis no more than 16,000 light-years. The Sun is situated very near to the equatorial plane, 27,000 light-years from the galactic centre. The stability of the system is due to the balance between the centrifugal force produced by its rotation and the gravitational force. The Galaxy, as a whole, rotates around its own centre in a clockwise direction as seen by an observer looking at the galactic plane from its north pole. The law regulating the rotation of the Galaxy is a law in between that of a solid body and that of our solar system. The velocity of rotation increases from zero to a maximum of about 230 km./s. as we proceed from the centre to a distance of 20,000 light-years. After this, the velocity decreases with increasing distance.

A given number of sub-systems, composed of objects having physical similarities, have the shape of smaller ellipsoids within the galactic ellipsoid. Their degree of flattening varies from a minimum for the globular clusters endowed with the lowest rotational velocity, to a maximum for stars of classes O and B having a maximum rotational velocity.

The existence of orbits highly elliptical, allows stars from the neighbourhood of the galactic centre, to pass temporarily near the Sun, the orbit of which is practically circular. Probably there are physical differences between these stars born in the dense galactic nucleus, and stars like the Sun born at the edge of the Galaxy. Interpretation of these differences may throw a certain amount of light on the question of the birth and evolution of stars. The study of the different physical characteristics of the various components of the Galaxy, together with the search for a link between these differences and their evolution, constitutes the physical study of the Galaxy.

VI.5   Physical constitution of the Galaxy.

The total mass of the Galaxy is almost all concentrated in stars. Recent radio astronomical observations of the hydrogen 21-cm. line have shown that interstellar matter contributes only 2%. In the neighbourhood of the Sun, however, the percentage is very different and almost a third consists of interstellar matter. We have already had the opportunity of discussing the latter in an earlier chapter. We have seen how it appears in the form of diffuse bright nebulae when there are stars embedded in it bright enough to produce excitation of the atoms, or produce reflection of their light, or else it appears as large dark clouds (the Coal Sack Nebula for example) when the exciting stars are not present. In the latter case the existence of interstellar matter is detected as it were in a negative way, by the sudden absence of all stars in a region of the sky with well-defined limits. We have also had the opportunity of seeing how interstellar matter reveals itself by a twofold absorption. The first, which is continuous and greater at short wavelengths, is probably produced by minute solid particles which are responsible for the observed 'reddening effect' of the remote stars in the neighbourhood of the galactic plane where the greatest part of interstellar matter is concentrated. The second absorption is discontinuous and is produced by free atoms in space which, in stellar spectra, produce the interstellar lines. These lines do not show the same radial velocity as the lines originating in stellar atmospheres, and have an intensity which increases with increasing distance of the star from us.

The heavy density of interstellar matter near the galactic plane, and particularly in the direction of the galactic centre, has been the cause of the mistaken interpretation of the observations of stellar distribution which led first Herschel and then Kapteyn to conclude that the Sun was very near to the galactic centre. Another proof of the existence of interstellar matter and of its distribution is found in the fact that galaxies can only be seen above a given galactic latitude. No galaxies are found in a belt (zone of avoidance) between $+10°$ and $-10°$ of latitude. A further confirmation of the existence and distribution of interstellar matter is given by the observation of the galaxies which can be reasonably assumed to be similar to our Galaxy in their structure, flattened shape and rotation. These galaxies, when seen edgeways, show the existence of a belt of absorbing dark matter, and when seen face on reveal dark bands crossing both the central nucleus and the spiral arms.

More difficult to prove is the existence in galactic space of a dark diffuse matter, similar to interstellar atmosphere. This matter, being very tenuous, produces only a very weak absorption and a reddening of the light from the stars, a reddening which is greater the further the stars are from us. The only possibility of determining the existence of this matter is to compare the spectral type of the star determined by the intensity of the lines, with the spectral type obtained from the distribution of the continuum modified by the absorption of this interstellar 'smoke'. This very tenuous gas too is particularly concentrated near the galactic plane. In fact no detectable reddening occurs even in very remote stars such as those in the globular clusters, when their galactic latitude is fairly high.

We have already dealt with the properties of the obscuring matter and we have described how it is possible to determine its power of absorption, its distance, its chemical composition and physical constitution. Now we propose to deal with the stars, in particular with their distribution in the Galaxy according to their physical characteristics and their evolution.

When studying the rotation of the Galaxy, earlier, we said that in it we can classify sub-systems according to their flattening and their rotational velocity. In particular we mentioned the globular clusters as having the least degree of flattening and the smallest rotational velocity; then the RR Lyrae stars which move in orbits highly elliptical and which are classified as stars of apparent high velocity. The bright blue stars of classes O and B form a very flattened system, since it is endowed with a high rotational velocity approaching the escape velocity of the Galaxy. It is only in recent years that it was discovered that the stage of evolution of a star is closely linked with the family to which it belongs and its distance from the galactic nucleus.

THE NEAREST AND BRIGHTEST STARS. THE HERTZSPRUNG–RUSSELL DIAGRAM. Since we wish to study the main stars populating our Galaxy, it is natural that we should be particularly interested in our Sun among all the stars and that we should ask ourselves several questions about it. What is its position among the stars? Is the Sun one of the brightest and biggest? Does the Sun occupy a medium position among the stellar classes?

Let us take the Sun together with the best-known stars, either because they are the nearest or because they are the brightest and therefore easily observed even from a great distance. If we plot the absolute magnitude of stars against their spectral type, or what amounts to the same thing, their surface temperature, we notice a very interesting fact, discovered in 1912 independently by Hertzsprung and Russell. Stars appear to have a preference for pairs of values of brightness and temperature, in other words the points in the Hertzsprung–Russell diagram are not distributed uniformly in the plane absolute magnitude-tempterature. The stars in the diagram (which for brevity we shall call the H–R diagram) occupy given positions along a line called 'main sequence' which starts from the top left-hand corner of the diagram, corresponding to great magnitude and high temperature, and ends at the bottom right-hand corner, showing that the brightness decreases with surface temperature. Another stellar sequence, which we will call the 'giant branch', is distributed along a horizontal line almost parallel to the abscissae axis. The stars in this branch are brighter although they have approximately the same temperature as the corresponding stars of the same spectral type belonging to the 'main sequence'. Since the luminosity depends on the energy radiated per square centimetre (therefore on the temperature) and on the area of the radiating surface, it follows that the stars occupying the 'giant branch' must

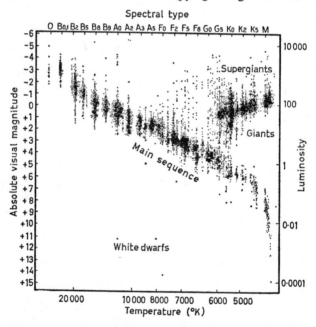

Fig. 25. H-R general diagram for all stars of which the absolute magnitude is known. Abscissae represent spectral types and the corresponding surface temperature. Ordinates represent absolute magnitude and luminosity. Luminosity of the Sun=1

have a greater radius than the stars of the same spectral type belonging to the 'main sequence', which we can therefore call the 'dwarf branch'. There are also rare stars, even brighter than the giants, and they are found on the 'supergiant branch'. Another small group of stars with a high surface temperature and low luminosity constitutes the 'family of white dwarfs' (fig. 25).

Let us now compare this diagram which we will call 'general diagram', with the one dealing only with stars which are near the Sun, namely stars which are included in a sphere of 17 light-years (fig. 26). One fact emerges at once and that is the altered numerical ratios between dwarfs, white dwarfs, giants and supergiants. These last two groups, which are fairly large in the general diagram, do

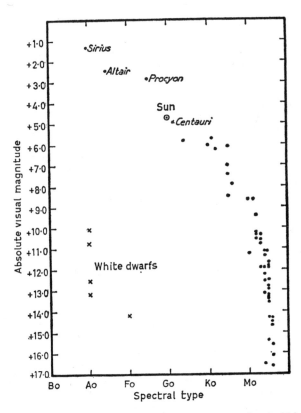

Fig. 26. H-R diagram for the nearest stars, that is, stars enclosed within a sphere of 17 light years

157

not even appear in the diagram for the nearest stars. The white dwarfs, on the other hand, which are so few in the general diagram, appear in larger proportion in the second diagram. Even the main sequence appears to increase in population as the absolute magnitude decreases. This behaviour is easily explained: it simply means that stars of low brightness are greater in number than the bright stars. These, however, can be seen at much greater distances, and when we consider all the stars, irrespective of their distance, the brightest have an advantage. It is sufficient to limit the space studied for the numerical ratio of the various classes of magnitude to revert to its real proportions.

When we examine the H–R diagram for the brightest stars of our sky, namely for stars of apparent magnitude between −1·6 (Sirius) and +1·3 (Regulus and Deneb), then we discover that the diagram has again changed in appearance. This time it is the white dwarfs and the lower part of the main sequence which are missing while giants and supergiants are well in evidence (fig. 27). This diagram

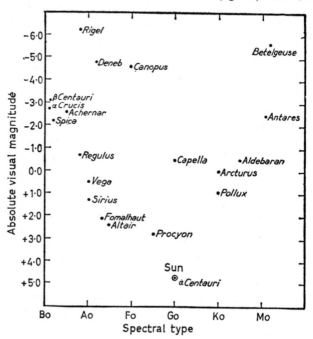

FIG. 27. H-R diagram for the brightest stars in the sky (apparent magnitudes between −1.6 and +1.3)

is a good representation of the top part, just as the previous one was a good representation of the lower part, of the H–R general diagram. In these three aspects of the same diagram, we see that the Sun occupies an intermediate position in the main sequence. The Sun is therefore a dwarf star, neither too faint nor too bright and very similar to α Centauri which is the star nearest to us. Apart from giving us some indication of the characteristics of the Sun compared with other stars, the H–R diagram enables us to carry out a census, as it were, of the physical properties of the stars populating the Galaxy. So we find that there are stars 160,000 times brighter than our Sun and others 25,000 times less bright than the Sun; stars with surface temperature greater than 100,000° K. (as is the case for the nuclei of planetaries) and red stars with a temperature which does not reach 3,000° K.; stars with a radius 100 times that of the Sun and others with a radius hardly $\frac{1}{100}$ of the Sun's radius.

It is not only information about radius, temperature and brightness which can be obtained from the H–R diagram. There exists a very important relation between brightness and mass of a star. According to this a star is the brighter the greater its mass (fig. 28).

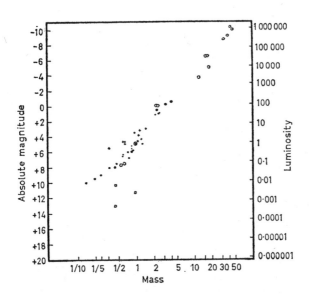

FIG. 28. Mass-luminosity relationship. Mass of the Sun=1; luminosity of the Sun=1

This relation, which was at first determined empirically from stars of which both the brightness and the mass were known, was later discussed theoretically by Eddington, who proved that a star of a given brightness, in a condition of equilibrium, must also have a determined mass. Therefore from the brightness of a star it is possible to determine what its mass ought to be. The white dwarfs, which

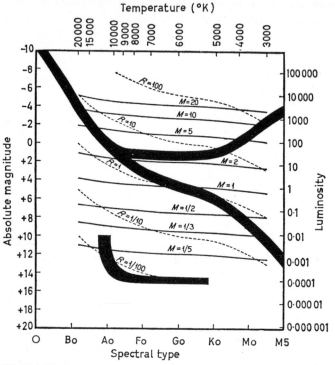

Fig. 29. Simplified H–R diagram (thick black lines) and corresponding values of radius R and mass M. Mass of the Sun=1; luminosity of the Sun=1; radius of the Sun=1

have a greater mass than their brightness indicates, are an exception to this law. Among the stars populating the Galaxy, some are found which have a mass 20 times that of the Sun and others with masses $\frac{1}{5}$ that of the Sun. In the simplified H–R diagram of fig. 29 we have given the corresponding values of the masses M and of the radii R, and from these it is possible to obtain the values of the density. The white dwarfs for which the mass-luminosity relation is not valid are excluded. It is worth noting that while the radii vary between very wide limits, from 100 to $\frac{1}{10}$ of the solar radius, the masses are within much narrower limits, the majority of stars having masses between 20 and $\frac{1}{5}$ of the solar mass. As a consequence the supergiants will have a density much lower than that of dwarfs. For a red supergiant the density is $\frac{2}{100000}$ that of the Sun, while for a red dwarf the density is 200 times the density of the Sun. In the case of white dwarfs we find that their density reaches exceptional values from 50,000 to 100,000 times that of the Sun.

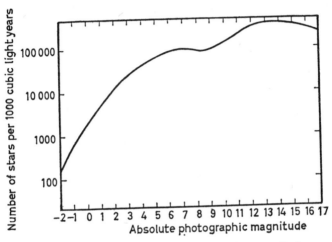

FIG. 30. Concentration of stars of given absolute magnitude

The comparison between the H–R general diagram and those for the nearest stars and for the brightest stars has already shown how the dwarf stars are much more common than the giants and even more than the supergiants. A more accurate census has been made by counting the number of stars of a given absolute luminosity per unit volume. The curve obtained by plotting the number of stars of a given absolute magnitude per unit volume against the absolute magnitude itself is called 'luminosity function' (fig. 30). From this curve we see that a maximum is reached for absolute magnitude between +13 and +15; these dwarf stars are more than 1,000 times more numerous than the giants of magnitude −2. The supergiants of magnitude between −4 and −8 are extremely rare.

For many years it was thought that the H–R diagram was common to all stars in whatever part of the universe they were to be found. This belief was strengthened by the fact that stars could be plotted in a diagram of similar form whether they belonged to extra-galactic systems (the Magellanic Clouds, for instance) or to the spiral arms of the nearest galaxies. Because of the great distance of the extra-galactic objects, it is reasonable to consider that the stars forming these systems are all the same distance from us, and therefore we can assume that their absolute magnitude differs from their apparent magnitude by a constant which is common to all the stars of the extra-galactic system under consideration. Moreover, since these stars are all too faint to enable us to obtain their spectra, it is usual, instead of the spectral type, to use the colour index in the diagram; this is the difference between photographic and visual magnitude. Both colour index and spectral type are closely related to the surface temperature, and therefore the result obtained will be the same.

Shapley, in his investigations on the globular clusters, had noticed some strange facts. The brightest stars in these clusters are red stars, about three magnitudes brighter than the white stars which are practically all RR Lyrae. Now an examination of the H–R diagram shows that among the stars near to us the brightest are the blue stars, which are not RR Lyrae, while the red giants are 3 to 5 magnitudes fainter. The general diagram contains mainly stars near to us

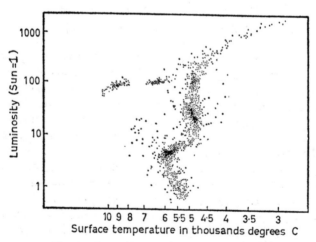

FIG. 31. H–R diagram for the globular cluster M.3

162

since it is only for these that it is possible to determine accurately their distance and hence their absolute magnitude. We must remember that with the instruments available at the time Shapley was carrying out this investigation, it was possible to study only the brightest stars of the globular clusters, so that the H–R diagram could not be complete. When in 1950 the 200-inch came into use at Mt. Palomar, it became possible to study more accurately the distribution of the apparent magnitude as a function of the colour index in the globular clusters nearer to us. The result was surprising. The H–R diagram took a very different form from that so far known (figs. 31, 32). The bright blue stars which are in the top part of the

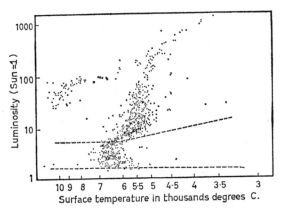

FIG. 32. H–R diagram for the globular cluster M.92

main sequence, do not exist in globular clusters. The region corresponding to absolute magnitudes −1 and 0 and to spectral types A and F, which in the previous diagram had very few points, is this time crowded with RR Lyrae stars. In the diagram for the globular clusters the upper part is very different from the classical diagram, but the lower part, namely the second half of the main sequence with stars of magnitude less than 5, is still the same. Later we shall see what interpretation can be given to the differences and similarities of these two diagrams. At present we shall concentrate on this second diagram which, originally valid for the globular clusters, was later found valid also for the galaxies. In this way the generalization which appeared to be lost with the discovery of two diagrams instead of one was shown to be still true and even more important.

The most interesting investigations on this subject are those made by Baade, and we will give briefly the important conclusions reached by him.

1. At the outer edges of our Galaxy, that is where our Sun is, as well as in the arms of spiral galaxies, there exists a population of stars which Baade called 'population I' with such physical characteristics as to satisfy the original H–R diagram.

2. In the central nucleus of our Galaxy, in globular clusters and in the central parts of spiral galaxies, the population of stars has such values for luminosity and temperature as to give rise to the second or newer type of diagram. This population Baade called 'population II'.

To Baade we also owe the discovery that not all galaxies have stars which belong to the two populations. So the galaxies of regular shape, devoid of spiral arms and interstellar matter, are only populated by population II stars, while the irregular galaxies, such as the Magellanic Clouds, rich in obscuring matter, are populated mainly by population I stars. Between these extremes are the spiral galaxies. The central parts of these have stars of population II, while the arms, rich in absorbing matter, are inhabited mainly by population I stars. Apart from any direct proof, the presence of stars of both populations in our Galaxy leads us to believe that it too belongs to the type of spiral galaxy. We have stressed the fact that where obscuring matter is found there we also find population I stars. From observations this seems to be generally true in all the universe known to us. In globular clusters as in regular galaxies without spiral, both obscuring matter and population I stars are missing. We ought to add here that this division between stars of population I and population II is only a simplification, since in reality there are several intermediate degrees between these two extremes.

Let us now go back to the H–R diagrams of population II. They refer to objects very far from us for which we cannot determine the distance nor, therefore, the absolute magnitude. Since these objects are so remote from us and have a very small apparent magnitude, it is not possible to obtain their spectrograms. By selecting individual objects which belong to one globular cluster or to one galaxy, the dimensions of which are negligible compared with their distance from us, we shall be able to draw the H–R diagram by plotting their apparent magnitude against their colour index. The difference between the apparent and absolute magnitude is a constant depending on the distance from us of the cluster or galaxy. Let us now compare the various diagrams obtained for the clusters with each other and with that for the region near to us. Before doing this we must, however, reduce the apparent magnitudes into absolute magnitudes, and we must therefore make some assumption about the unknown distances. Since the RR Lyrae stars so common in the clusters, have characteristics of colour, periods and light curves identical to those in our Galaxy, it is reasonable to assume that their physical charac-

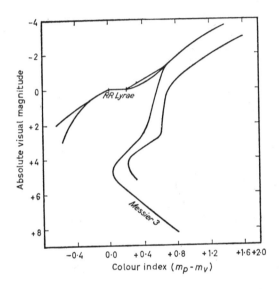

Fig. 33. H–R diagrams for M.3 and other globular clusters

teristics too are identical in whatever part of the universe they are found. We can then assume that they also have the same absolute magnitude, which for RR Lyrae stars in our Galaxy is zero. If we superimpose then the region of the H–R diagrams where the RR Lyrae are found, we see at once that the globular clusters have diagrams which have very similar forms, but are not identical (fig. 33). Moreover, the lower arm of the diagrams is very nearly the same as the lower part of the main sequence in the diagrams obtained for the nearest stars. This suggests that there is a certain relationship between the two types of diagrams.

STELLAR EVOLUTION. In the H–R diagrams we notice that stars can be found only for some given values of temperature and brightness; that bright blue giants are completely absent among stars of population II and that dwarf stars are in much greater number than giant stars. All these facts must have a particular meaning connected with the development of stellar evolution. We are indebted to theoretical studies for the interpretation of these peculiarities.

The enormous amount of energy radiated into space by the stars for millions of years is due to the nuclear transformation of hydrogen into helium, which, because of the high temperature required for the starting of the reaction, takes place only in the central nucleus of the stars where the temperature is greater than 20 million degrees.

In order to understand the evolution of a star, we proceed in the following manner. First we draw up a 'stellar model' which justifies observational data and at the same time satisfies some physical hypotheses which are necessary to explain the state of equilibrium of the mass of gas. The observational data refer only to the external layers of the atmosphere of a star, since this is a limitation imposed by our instruments. Several models could be suggested which satisfy the main requirements and are different from each other because of other hypotheses. For instance two stellar models are the 'homogeneous' and the 'non-homogeneous'. The first is one in which the chemical composition of a star is assumed to be the same throughout, namely in the interior as well as at the surface. The advantage of this is that the interior of a star will be the same as the observed atmosphere. The star would consist of 80% of hydrogen, 19% of helium and just under 1% of other elements.

For the 'non-homogeneous' models we assume that the central nucleus contains much more helium than other parts of the star. Once the stellar model is decided upon, its evolution is studied following the nuclear reactions taking place at the centre of the star.

According to theory, a 'homogeneous' model has the same physical properties as the stars of the main sequence. The values of brightness and temperature, hence the position in the sequence where this model is found, depend only on the original chemical composition and mass. Let us consider a group of stars having all the same chemical composition. Actually observations show that the nearest stars satisfy this condition. The higher in the sequence is the star, the greater is its brightness and therefore the emission of energy. We can suppose then, that the bright blue stars burn their supply of hydrogen much faster than the other stars. Theoretical considerations enable us to calculate the time required by a star of given mass and hence of given brightness, to convert a great part of its central hydrogen into helium (fig. 34b). At the end of this time we cannot consider this model any more to be homogeneous, since the nucleus will consist almost entirely of helium, while the more external parts, where the reaction does not take place, will have maintained the chemical

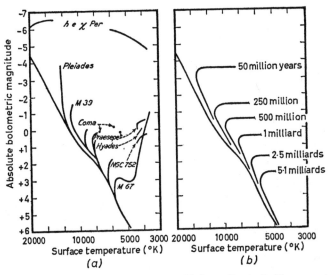

FIG. 34. (a) H–R diagram for open clusters. (b) According to the theory, a star of absolute magnitude +6 leaves the main sequence after 50 million years
A comparison between diagrams (a) based on observations, and (b) based on theory, enables us to evaluate the age of the clusters

ratios of elements very near to the initial value. This is true provided the star is not rotating rapidly, because then the layers would mix and a different type of evolution could take place. Theoretically, the equilibrium in these models, now become non-homogeneous, can be maintained only if the star expands, still maintaining its own surface temperature. It follows that we would have an increase in brightness, without any great changes in the spectral type to which the star belongs.

When the nucleus of helium reaches 12% of the mass, the surface temperature decreases and the star will change its place in the H–R diagram, decreasing in brightness and changing its spectral type. Progressing in its evolution, when the nucleus of helium reaches 20% of the mass of the star, a new expansion takes place. The temperature decreases slightly, but the radiating area increases so that a sudden increase in brightness takes place, and the star will once again change its place in the H–R diagram. When the helium nucleus reaches 50% of the mass of the star, then the star contracts so much that the central temperature reaches such a high value that the conversion of helium into carbon begins. Meanwhile the temperature of the star increases and its surface decreases so it may happen that the star moves to the left in the H–R diagram.

With these theories we can follow more closely the path of a star in the H–R diagram. We start with a group of stars all having the same chemical composition. These stars may be stars near to us which probably all originated in the same galactic region, or stars which belong to a globular or open cluster and which are all parts of a same group having a common origin. According to whether their mass is large or small, they will have a temperature and a brightness which will place them high or low in the main sequence. Meanwhile the hydrogen in their nucleus is being converted into helium. If the star is rotating rapidly it is probable that the matter in the nucleus will be mixed completely with that of the more external layers and the chemical composition of the whole stellar matter will change slowly. In this case the evolution of the star will cause it to shift a little out of the main sequence to the left and there will be an increase both in temperature and brightness. The interpretation of the two types of diagrams for the two populations and of the surplus of dwarf stars and the absence of blue giants in the diagrams of the globular clusters, agrees with the observations only if we assume that in the great majority of stars the mixing of the nuclear matter with the more external layers does not take place and the stellar model changes from homogeneous into non-homogeneous. In this case a time will be reached when the star begins to leave the main sequence. According to calculations this should happen after 50 million years for stars 100 times brighter than the Sun, after 1,000 million years for stars 5 times brighter than the Sun, and after more than 5,000 million years for stars 3 times less bright than the Sun (fig. 34). For the Sun this moment should be reached about 3,000 million years after its birth. According to recent views on the age of the Earth, and therefore of the Sun, this moment should be close at hand. The stellar model then can be represented by a central nucleus of helium in which no more energy is produced since the whole of the hydrogen has been exhausted, and the temperature is not high enough to set off the reactions capable of converting helium into carbon, neon and oxygen. There remains, however, inside the nucleus a slender layer in which hydrogen is still active. For this to take place it is essential that the temperature of the layer should increase, and that the other internal layers should contract upon the hydrogen layer. The radius of the star at first will not change but the surface temperature will increase. The star will move from L to M in fig. 35.

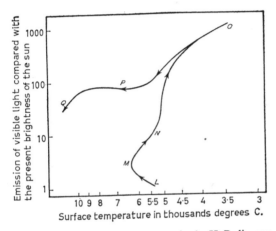

FIG. 35. Evolutionary path of a star in the H–R diagram

After this the radius too will begin to increase and so will the brightness, while the surface temperature decreases and the star will move from M to N and to O. When it has reached this point the star is 1,000 times brighter than it was at the time at which it left the main sequence. Up to this point the helium nucleus has been growing, while new thin layers, where the hydrogen reaction is taking place, replace those which gradually become part of the helium nucleus. In O, 50% of the stellar mass consists of the helium nucleus. The pressure of the external layers on the internal ones is such that the central temperature reaches about 100 million degrees and at this temperature helium can begin to be converted into carbon, oxygen and neon. The surface temperature increases while the radius decreases. The star moves from O to P and then to Q. A point is reached when helium and all other elements too are completely exhausted and the star begins to cool and to descend from Q to the stage of white dwarf. The conclusion we reach is that stars which are born in the main sequence in a, b, c, d (fig. 36) will all evolve following the path $L\ M\ N\ O\ P\ Q$, the brighter ones very fast and the others more slowly. According to calculations, after five thousand million years, stars from a and d will have reached A and D respectively, and the H–R diagram of that group of stars will have changed from the branch $d\ a$ of the main sequence to the branch $A\ B\ C\ D$. The comparison of the theoretical diagram $A\ B\ C\ D$ with the H–R diagrams obtained for the globular clusters (the diagrams we have called typical for population II) throws light on the whole question. Both diagrams, the theoretical and the observed one, have the same form (figs. 31, 32, 33, 36). The H–R diagram for population II is nothing more than the result of a transformation of the diagram for population I which has undergone an evolution more advanced in time. The stars nearest to us, and in general the stars found in the spirals of the galaxies and in the irregular galaxies, which follow the diagram for population I, are young stars, that is stars which have not yet reached the critical point of their evolution, the point L of fig. 35, where they begin to leave the main sequence. On the other hand, stars of population II belonging to globular clusters, to the nuclei of our Galaxy and of the spiral galaxies, and regular galaxies

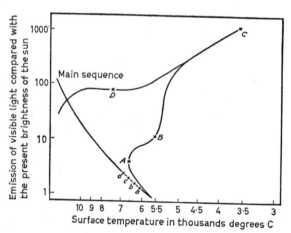

FIG. 36. Stars originally in the main sequence (d,c,b,a) will be in D,C,B,A after 5 thousand million years

without spiral arms, are stars in an advanced stage of development, that is to say stars that have already reached the critical point in their evolution. Only stars less bright than the Sun, which have a very slow evolution, are still found in the main sequence, and the H–R diagrams for the clusters show in fact the presence of this branch. The blue giants of population I have already long since completed their evolution cycle and there is no evidence any more of the upper part of the main sequence. The rapid evolution of the giants explains also their scarcity and the fact that dwarfs are in such greater numbers.

Comparisons of the theoretical diagrams of evolution, computed for different periods of evolution, with the diagrams obtained from the observations of the clusters, enable us also to estimate their age. The good agreement between the theoretical diagram calculated for a period of evolution of 5 thousand million years (fig. 36) and that observed for the two globular clusters M.3 and M.92 (figs. 31, 32) suggests that the age of these clusters must be of that order. Probably this is also the age of the Galaxy.

We have already had occasion to note that where there are stars of population II, interstellar matter is absent and that, on the other hand, we find a great abundance of this matter where blue giants of population I are very numerous. Since blue giants are young stars undergoing a rapid evolution which soon takes them out of the main sequence, and since observations show them constantly associated with dark matter, we are led to conclude that this must be the matter in which new stars are formed.

H–R DIAGRAMS FOR GLOBULAR CLUSTERS AND OPEN CLUSTERS. We have dealt first with the H–R diagram for stars near the Sun because knowing their distance we were able to use their absolute magnitude. This diagram which we have called 'general' is, however, not homogeneous. It contains stars having different origins and different ages and which are situated in different parts of the Galaxy. The diagram, although containing mainly stars near the Sun, contains also the high-velocity stars which, very probably, were born in the central nucleus of the Galaxy and happen to pass near the Sun only because of the high ellipticity of their orbit. While the red dwarfs, because of their slow evolution, are still found in the main sequence after 5 thousand million years, the blue giants forming the upper part of the main sequence were born only a few tens of million years ago, and there are stars which are still being born in the mass of dark matter found in the galactic plane. It seems probable that the chemical composition of stars born 5 thousand million years ago is very different from that of stars born in a more recent age. It is thought, in fact, that at one time interstellar matter consisted almost completely of hydrogen and that at a later stage, following the explosion of some ancient stars in the interior of which hydrogen had already been transformed into heavier elements, the interstellar matter had acquired these heavier elements. As a result stars of more recent formation will have a chemical composition containing more of these heavy elements than stars born 5 thousand million years ago. Not only the original mass but also the initial chemical composition determines the evolution of a star and the non-homogeneity of the H–R general diagram could complicate the interpretation of such evolution. For this reason, in order to understand the mechanism of evolution, it is more satisfactory to choose groups of stars all born in the same place and at the same epoch. Such groups are both the globular and the open clusters. The former present always a typical diagram of population II, have a spherical shape, are devoid of interstellar matter, and consist of the conglomeration of about a million stars; they form a spherical secondary system of the Galaxy. The open clusters are to be found always near the galactic plane. Their shape is irregular, they generally contain a great deal of interstellar matter, and they consist of a few dozen, or at most a few hundred, stars. Open clusters generally belong to population I.

The study of the H–R diagram for globular clusters and the comparison with the theoretical diagram of evolution have cleared several difficulties and have explained the greater age of stars of population II. If we are looking for a proof of the mechanism of evolution of blue giants it is sufficient to study the more recent open clusters rather than the globular clusters, because in the first the former blue giants are very near to the end of their life. We give in fig. 34a the H–R diagram for some of the open clusters. Comparing this with fig. 34b, in which are given the calculated values of the time required by a star of given mass to leave the main sequence, we see once again how theory and observations are complementary, and the theory allows us to determine the age of each cluster. So the double cluster h and χ Persei, still containing many blue giants, must be less than 50 million years old, while the Pleiades, partly consisting of bright whitish-blue stars which have already passed the critical point in their evolution and are out of the main sequence, must be about 50 million years old. The Hyades and Praesepe must be at least 1,000 million years old. M.67, which in its diagram has not only the lower part of the main sequence, but also one of the typical branches of a diagram for population II, is much older (probably 5,000 million years), and its former blue giants are already well advanced in their evolution, approaching the point where also the helium of the nucleus begins to burn.

VARIABLE STARS. We must deal here with variable stars because they have contributed so much to our knowledge of the Galaxy, both from the point of view of distance and type of stellar population.

In the H–R diagram for population II, there is a region near the point P of the evolution diagram (fig. 35) in which the star has such a structure that it is compelled to pulsate. This pulsation has a regular period of 8 hours for stars to the left of the point P and of 24 hours for those to the right of the same point. As a consequence of these pulsations, we have regular variations both in the temperature and luminosity of the star. We do not yet know the reason for these pulsations. What we do know is that stars contained in a limited region of the diagram pulsate while those outside this region do not show this phenomenon. These stars are known as variable stars of type RR Lyrae, from the name of the one first discovered. The position they occupy in the H–R diagram tells us that they are typical population II stars; they are found particularly in globular clusters. The few, like RR Lyrae, for instance, which are relatively near to the Sun, are all high-velocity stars. They originate in the neighbourhood of the galactic centre and are, at the moment, probably at the aphelion of their very elongated orbits.

There are also two more families of variable stars which are important; namely the 'classical' Cepheids and the Cepheids of type W Virginis. Both groups consist of supergiants with surface temperature lower than that of the RR Lyrae stars. While the latter belong to the spectral class A or F, the Cepheids are in classes between F and K and have therefore a colour between yellow and reddish-orange. Like the RR Lyrae these stars also pulsate, and their dimension, temperature and luminosity vary periodically. They differ from the RR Lyrae in the duration of their periods, which are between 1 and 50 days, and in their luminosity. The 'classical' Cepheids are distributed in proximity to the galactic plane and belong to population I. Their luminosity is between 4 and 100 times greater than that of the RR Lyrae stars and increases with increasing periods. On the other hand, the W Virginis Cepheids are high-velocity stars which are found in globular clusters and near the galactic centre, and are typical stars of population II. Like the 'classical' Cepheids, their period varies between 1 and 50 days but their luminosity is different, as for the same period they are 1·5 magnitude less bright. The spectrum, the form of their light curve, as well as the distribution of their periods, are very different from those of the 'classical' Cepheids. The majority of the latter have periods of 4 or 5 days, while the Cepheids of population II generally have periods between 10 and 25 days. Both the RR Lyrae and the two Cepheids families are out of the main sequence.

We have already said that stars of the main sequence with luminosity similar to or a little greater than that of the Sun (fig. 36) evolve towards the phase of RR Lyrae. It is not quite clear yet, which stars reach the phase of Cepheids and through what stages they pass. We could think that stars brighter than the Sun follow evolution diagrams of the usual form, but displaced towards greater luminosity. The phase corresponding to that of RR Lyrae stars would then be that of Cepheids of population I and II, according to the initial position of the star in the main sequence. So Cepheids of population I, although relatively younger, could represent a stage of evolution of stars which are very bright and have a very fast evolution. This would justify their belonging to such a population.

Characteristics of both the spectrum and the light curve enable us to decide to which of the three groups a variable belongs; namely RR Lyrae, Classical Cepheids or W Virginis Cepheids. This is extremely important because the presence of one type of variable rather than another in a cluster or in some part of our Galaxy or of galaxies, enables us to decide what type of population exists in the various parts of the universe. Therefore these variables are very important as 'population indicators', but they are even more important as 'distance indicators'. We have already mentioned that the few galactic RR Lyrae, the distance of which is known with a reasonable degree of accuracy, have an absolute magnitude which is near zero. Since the RR Lyrae belonging to globular clusters and galaxies have very similar physical characteristics (colour, spectrum, light curve and period) to those of the galactic RR Lyrae, it has been assumed that their absolute magnitude is also the same. In this case, if we know their absolute and their apparent magnitude, we can determine their distance from us.

Unlike the RR Lyrae, the Cepheids do not have a common absolute magnitude. They have, however, an important property which still enables us to use them as 'distance indicators'. The luminosity of Cepheids increases with their period according to a period-luminosity relation which it has been possible to study in clusters and in galaxies like the Magellanic Clouds. It has always been assumed that individual objects belonging to these groups can all be considered to be at the same distance from us, so that the uncertainty with which their distance is known does not affect the form of the

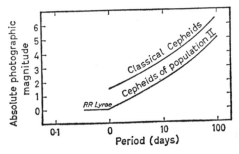

FIG. 37. Period–luminosity relation for classical Cepheids and for Cepheids of type W Virginis of population II

period–luminosity relationship. Figure 37 gives the period–luminosity relation for Cepheids of population I and II. The great advantage of using the Cepheids as 'distance indicators' is that they can be as much as 100 times brighter than the RR Lyrae stars, and this means that they can be seen even in the furthest clusters and galaxies when the RR Lyrae would not be seen by our telescopes.

COMPARISON OF THE 'MAIN SEQUENCE' OF VARIOUS CLUSTERS. When using the RR Lyrae or the Cepheids for the determination of distances, we can compare the H–R diagrams for various clusters both open and globular with each other and with the diagram relating to the nearest stars. We have already mentioned the results obtained; let us, however, study them again more closely. By superimposing the regions of the diagrams for the various groups containing the

RR Lyrae, we find that the 'main sequences' do not overlap perfectly, as already stated. For instance, the globular cluster M.3 distinctly deviates from the diagram relative to six other clusters. It is probable that this type of difference is due to various initial chemical compositions, from which the position of the main sequence branch depends. Since the H–R general diagram includes the nearest stars (born, that is, in the same part of the Galaxy) as well as stars which are near to us only temporarily because of the high ellipticity of their orbits round the galactic centre, it may be that the sequence is, in reality, the result of the overlapping of several various sequences composed of homogeneous groups. In fact if among all the stars of the diagram we select those having certain characteristics, apart from the dwarf sequence there also appear the sub-dwarf sequence. For instance, among all the high-velocity stars of the main sequence, a large majority appear to belong to the sub-dwarfs and are placed from 0·5 to 1 or 2 magnitudes, below the average sequence of all the stars. It is possible that these stars belonging to population II were born in the central regions of the Galaxy, probably from matter poor in metals, as their spectra seem to indicate.

THE BIRTH OF STARS. We have already mentioned the modern views of the birth of the stars with reference to the fact that younger stars are always found together with dark matter. Where this dark matter is absent, as is the case in globular clusters, the parallel absence of young blue stars shows that no more births take place. The fact that we may take blue stars as an indication of recent age does not mean that they are the only younger stars. A star is born with the characteristics which will define its position in the main sequence, the position being higher or lower according to the mass of the star. A star of medium brightness, like the Sun, can remain in the sequence practically in the same position for a period of 2 or 3 thousand million years, while a blue star will leave the sequence by evolution only after 50 million years. This means that the blue stars still in the sequence will certainly be young ones, while stars of medium luminosity could have any age below the age necessary to reach the critical point of evolution.

Although it is very probable that a star is formed from interstellar matter, it is not quite clear yet how such a birth could take place. In fact if the matter normally contained in a star was diffused in space so as to have the same density as the average density of the clouds of interstellar gas, the gravitational field of this matter would be far too weak to produce the necessary condensation to form a star. If, on the other hand, we consider a mass of gas a thousand times greater, or even more, than that of one star only, then the gravitational field of the cloud would be sufficient to keep the star together. Interstellar clouds happen to have masses of this order of magnitude. It is probable that they condense because of their gravitational force and that in the interior smaller condensations will form which will be the beginning of the life of a star. Bok has observed in some clouds of interstellar matter, the presence of small spherical 'globules' of dimensions between 0·06 and 0·5 parsecs. The mass of these globules has been estimated to be of the order of 2·5 times that of the Sun, and their gravitational field is capable of holding together the matter of which they are formed (Plate 22). We may therefore suppose that stars are born in groups from the same cloud. The existence of open clusters (Pleiades, Praesepe and ζ Persei), in which the component stars show a very close relationship, would confirm this hypothesis of a common origin. It remains to be explained why the majority of stars are not grouped in clusters but are isolated in space. The answer to this question is found in the study of the motion of the components of clusters which show that the individual star of a cluster has a velocity of recession from the common centre. Since the velocity of recession is of the order of 10 to 20 km./s., it can be foreseen that in a few million years or perhaps in a few hundred million years, the clusters will dissolve so that those we observe at present must be relatively young clusters.

From the study of open clusters we also have a confirmation of the hypothesis that stars can be born in any point of the main sequence. In several clusters, for instance in NGC 6231, or in the double cluster in Perseus, we find bright stars of type O and less bright stars along the main sequence, down to stars of type M. Since all the stars of the cluster, in all probability had a common origin, and since the presence of stars of class O implies that the cluster must be relatively young, the stars not yet having had time to evolve, it follows that we see the cluster as it was born, that is to say with stars of classes O and M.

OUR GALAXY IS A SPIRAL GALAXY. Observations of galaxies have led to the hypotheses on the structure of our own Galaxy, which were later confirmed by observations.

Baade discovered the existence of a close correlation between the shape of galaxies and the type of stellar population. Population I, recognizable by the presence of blue stars and interstellar matter, is found in irregular galaxies and in the arms of spiral galaxies, while very rare, or completely absent, in spherical galaxies, or in elliptical galaxies without arms. On the other hand, population II, recognizable by the presence of red giants, of RR Lyrae stars and by the absence of interstellar matter, is found in the nuclei of spiral, elliptical and spherical galaxies. There are three types of galaxies then, type one, type two and mixed, according to the type of population.

In the case of our Galaxy we find members of both populations. This leads us to think that our Galaxy is of a mixed type, with the nucleus of population II and with spiral arms of population I. We can establish to which type our Galaxy belongs with greater accuracy. As we shall see later, when we consider the galaxies, the spiral galaxies can be divided into a number of classes according to the relative extension of the nucleus and of the arms. The galaxies in which the spiral is predominant and the nucleus rather small in extension, are called *Sc*, then passing through *Sb* we reach type *Sa* where the nucleus is very extensive. Because the nucleus is much less flattened than the spiral, and is almost spherical, and because of the comparatively small dimensions of the nucleus, a galaxy *Sc*, when seen edgeways, will appear more flattened than a galaxy *Sa*, which, on account of the rather large dimensions of its nucleus, will appear as an almost round ellipsoid.

From the study of the relative importance that nucleus and arms have in the various types of spiral galaxies, and from a comparison with the data we have of our galactic nucleus, it is possible to decide to which type our Galaxy belongs. Baade reached the conclusion that our Galaxy is of type *Sb*. If it were of type *Sc* the nucleus would be too small and completely hidden from us by the clouds of interstellar matter. M.31, the galaxy in Andromeda, is probably the most faithful reproduction of our Galaxy that we can see, and it is a typical example of a galaxy of type *Sb*. The arms, which are such an important feature of its appearance, contribute only 20% of the total light emitted by the galaxy, the other 80% is due to population II of the nucleus.

The presence of stars of population II, such as RR Lyrae, at a great distance from the galactic centre, suggests that the nucleus of our Galaxy must be extensive. On the other hand the great quantity of dark matter, which hides large parts of the nucleus, the large diffuse nebulae, and the many bright blue stars surrounding us, all typical of the population of the arms of a spiral, suggest that the spiral arms of our Galaxy must be much more developed than what we would expect in a galaxy of type *Sa*.

There are direct proofs of the existence of these spiral arms. The first of them is due to the investigations of Morgan, Whitford and Code. We know that the blue stars of the main sequence have a definite brightness, identifiable by their spectrum, which allows us to establish what point of the main sequence they occupy. The investigations of these astronomers had as an aim:

1. The determination with the greatest possible accuracy, of the spectral type and hence the position and luminosity of blue stars in the H–R diagram.
2. The determination of the amount of interstellar absorption from the comparison between the observed colour of these stars, and the colour they would have if absorption did not take place.

Once these data were known, it would be possible to determine fairly accurately, the distance, and hence the distribution of these stars in the Galaxy. The investigations of Morgan, Whitford and Code showed that the blue stars belonging to the main sequence were not distributed uniformly in the galactic plane, but rather in three almost parallel arms. The furthest from the galactic centre passes through Perseus, the second through Orion and the third through Sagittarius. The Sun belongs to the arm passing through Orion. Observations show that the width of an arm is approximately 1,000 light years and the distance between the arms is about 5,000 light-years (fig. 38).

We owe the second proof to Münch. The light of a star in passing through interstellar matter, undergoes two different types of absorption. The first, continuous, greater in the violet than in the red, produces absorption of the light of the star and is due to solid particles forming the interstellar dust. The second, which is discontinuous and reveals itself by the presence of dark lines in the stellar spectrum, is produced by the atoms of the interstellar gas. The dark lines, due to absorption, are identifiable from those originating in the stellar atmosphere, by their Doppler displacement, which is due to the different radial velocities of the star and of the

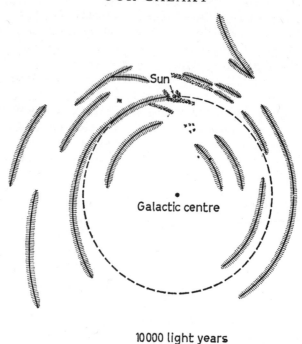

10 000 light years

FIG. 38. The Galaxy in plan. Dotted regions represent the result of optical observations by Morgan and Münch. Shaded regions represent the result of radio observations at Leiden for the northern hemisphere and at Sydney for the southern hemisphere

absorbing cloud. Münch, in studying the spectra of remote stars, observed that the interstellar lines, generally, are multiple lines, double or triple, as if the light from the star had travelled through two or three gas clouds which have different radial velocities. According to the observations of stellar motion, given rotational velocities correspond to given distances from the galactic centre. On the other hand, velocities obtained from the Doppler displacements of interstellar lines, show that the positions of the gas clouds coincide with the positions of the arms determined by Morgan, Whitford and Code. In this way we have a second confirmation, independent of the first, of the presence and of the position of spiral arms. In addition we have proof that the interstellar gas, as well, participates in the galactic rotation, and that blue stars and interstellar gases are almost always found near each other.

180

OUR GALAXY

Radio astronomy has now opened new fields. Radio waves are not absorbed by interstellar matter, and therefore they allow us to explore further into the galactic nucleus, beyond the thick clouds which stop the optical radiations. In this way we can have a more complete picture of the Galaxy than we have had so far. In the spiral arms, apart from stars of population I, there are large quantities of interstellar matter. We know that in the matter constituting a star, hydrogen is more abundant than the other elements, and we can suppose that the same is true for interstellar gas. This gas, however, is at such a low temperature that the hydrogen atoms are unable to emit optical radiations, and therefore cannot be detected spectroscopically. The Dutch astronomer van de Hulst predicted theoretically that the hydrogen atom could actually emit radiation, even at the very low condition of excitation in which it exists in interstellar space, at a wavelength of 21 cm., namely in the region of radio frequencies (*see also* p. 102). The reversal of the spin happens on average once every 11 million years, but given the great abundance of hydrogen there seemed to be a possibility that the 21-cm. line could be detected. This prediction has now been proved correct. The results obtained have given valuable information on the structure of the Galaxy. Van de Hulst, Müller and Oort have recorded the emission of interstellar gas at the 21-cm. wavelength, by pointing their radio telescope to the galactic equator, at every 5° of longitude (fig. 39). The line sometimes appears sharp and well defined, and sometimes with two or three separate peaks. Since hydrogen radiates at the wavelength of exactly 21 cm., every displacement from this wavelength is due to a Doppler effect. If we assume, as Münch observations appear to indicate, that the interstellar gas participates in the galactic rotation, and rotates with a velocity which depends only on its distance from the centre, then the two or three peaks can be related to the existence of two or three emitting clouds. Each one has its own radial velocity and these radial velocities will enable us to determine the distance of each cloud from the galactic centre. Figure 38 gives the position of the emitting gas clouds. Besides the radio observations we also have, in the same figure, the optical observations by Morgan and Münch. The agreement of the two sets of observations is obvious, but we ought to note how much more complete are the radio observations which can explore spiral arms almost diametrically opposite to our Sun. We hardly need to stress again that the superiority of the new method is due to the penetrating power of the radio waves. These can travel to a distance of about 50,000 light-years in the direction of the galactic centre, indeed they may even go beyond the galactic centre, almost reaching the edge of the Galaxy. The optical observations, on the other hand, cannot penetrate the dark matter, and the maximum distance we can reach with these in the direction of the galactic centre is no more than

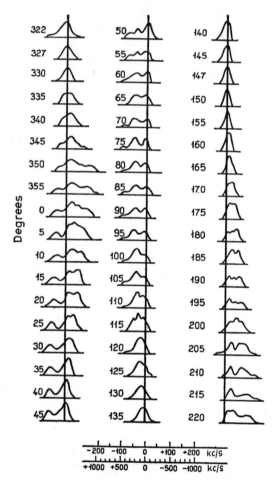

FIG. 39. Profiles of the 21 cm. hydrogen line obtained by van de Hulst, Müller and Oort at various galactic longitudes and 0° galactic latitude. Lines with two or three peaks indicate the number of arms which exist and which have different radial velocities with reference to the Sun

15,000 light-years. Furthermore, the radio waves have made it possible to determine with even greater accuracy than by optical means, the velocity of rotation of the Galaxy at various distances from the centre. The values given in Table 6 (p. 152) have been obtained mainly by observations of the 21-cm. line.

Recently Oort and his associates, while observing the 21-cm. hydrogen line emitted by regions very near to the galactic centre, discovered the existence of an expanding arm at a distance of 3,000 parsecs from the centre, as well as a central nucleus of HI which had a velocity of rotation of approximately 270 km./s. From these observations it was possible to establish that the law regulating the rotation of the Galaxy was more complex than it was at first thought. The velocity of rotation increases from 220 km./s. at a distance of 260 parsecs from the centre up to a maximum of 270 km./s. at a distance of 600 parsecs. It then decreases, reaching 220 km./s., and remains more or less constant up to a distance equal to that of the Sun from the centre, as had already been established. A similar behaviour, but on a different scale, had already been observed for the Andromeda galaxy (*see* p. 221).

An impressive picture of our Galaxy is given in Plate 36. This represents the Milky Way in the southern hemisphere, photographed with a special camera covering an angle of 140° of the sky. The similarity with many other spiral galaxies is really striking. Although the Sun is part of the Galaxy, it is placed so far from the galactic centre that the central regions of the Galaxy appear to us as they would appear to an extra-galactic observer.

VI.6 Magnetic field of the Galaxy.

In the chapter dealing with interstellar matter, we found that the light of the stars, which are affected by reddening, is also greatly polarized. One conclusion reached is that the particles of the interstellar dust must be of an elongated shape and all aligned in the same direction. In order to explain the orientation of these particles, the existence of a general galactic magnetic field has been postulated. There are, however, other indirect proofs of the existence of such a magnetic field. For example it could very well be responsible for the distribution of the clouds of gas and dust in the form of the spiral arms of the Galaxy, and could also explain, at least in part, the very great energy of cosmic rays. Fermi has put forward a theory which would explain, at least partially, the great energy of cosmic rays as being due to the presence of a galactic magnetic field.

Cosmic rays are particles reaching the Earth endowed with very great energy. Those of lowest energy have velocities 5 thousand million times greater than that of particles existing on the surface of the Sun and which move because of thermal agitation. Cosmic rays of higher energy reach the Earth with an energy even 10 million times greater than that of the rays of lower energy.

There are two questions which have to be answered, namely: what is the origin of cosmic rays and how do they acquire such enormous energy? With reference to the first question we know, from observations of the correlation between solar phenomena and cosmic rays, that the Sun also emits cosmic rays. Particularly important in this connection appears to be the increase of intensity of cosmic rays about an hour after the observation of a chromospheric eruption on the Sun. Moreover, more recently, it has been observed that the intensity of the cosmic radiation increases by $0 \cdot 5\%$ when small solar eruptions occur. Probably like the Sun, the stars too produce cosmic rays. It has also been suggested that the great explosions of super-novae could be powerful sources of cosmic radiation. However, this question of the origin of cosmic rays needs still to be investigated.

The second question also awaits solution. Following the suggestion that the Galaxy may have a magnetic field of its own, capable of producing the polarization of the light from the stars, Fermi put forward a theory which would explain why the particles of cosmic rays are endowed with such high energy. The theory assumes the existence of cosmic rays of low energy. The particles would follow a spiral path winding round the lines of force and would at times be accelerated and at others retarded, but the average final result would be an increase in energy. Assuming that the cosmic rays of low energy were produced by the stars, then the magnetic field of the Galaxy would act as an accelerator of these particles, and produce cosmic rays with high energy. Some recent investigations by Rossi show the existence of cosmic rays with energy of 10×10^{18} eV. In order to explain how particles could reach such a high energy, Rossi suggests that the dimensions of the Galaxy must be much greater than those so far attributed to it; for only then could the interstellar magnetic field produce particles with such a high energy. On the other hand, the radio emission reaching us from a vast galactic region and from a spherical halo surrounding it, could be explained

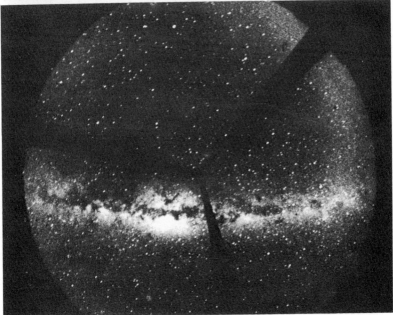

36. The Milky Way in the southern hemisphere. Above: in blue light; below: in infra-red light. Taken with the wide-angle Greenstein-Henyey camera.

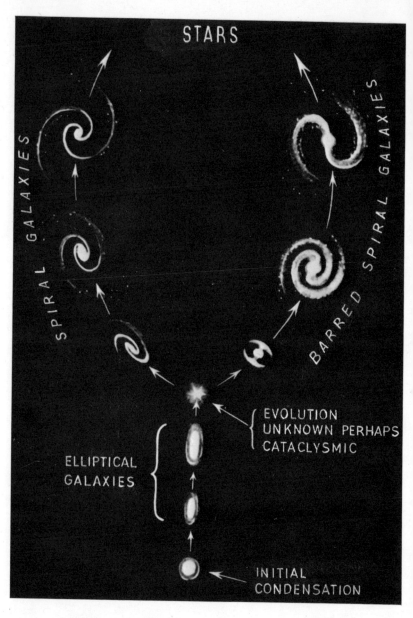

STARS

SPIRAL GALAXIES

BARRED SPIRAL GALAXIES

EVOLUTION
UNKNOWN PERHAPS
CATACLYSMIC

ELLIPTICAL
GALAXIES

INITIAL
CONDENSATION

37. Classification of galaxies according to Hubble

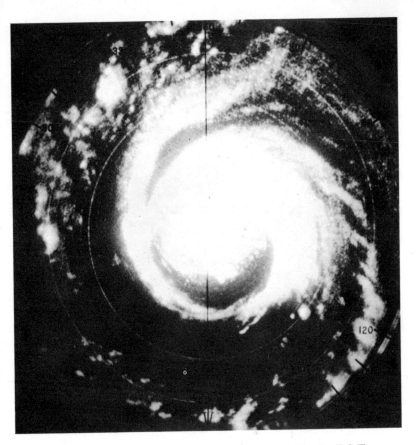

38. Hurricane of September 21, 1948 at 11 h 31 min E.S.T.

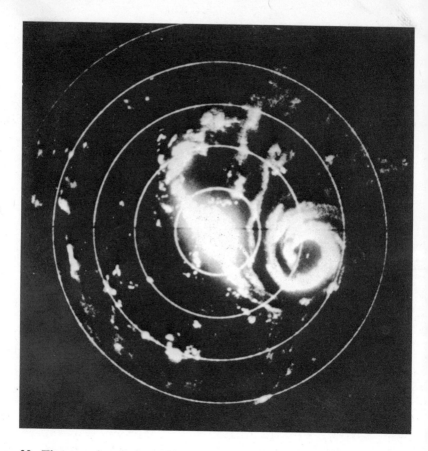

39. The same hurricane of Plate 38 at 16 h 10 min. E.S.T. The eye of the cyclone appears as a circular vacant spot surrounded by rain-cloud echoes

as being produced by synchrotron emission of relativistic electrons which have energy and density in agreement with the data supplied by the study of cosmic rays, and which are in motion in a magnetic field of the order of 10^{-5} to 10^{-6} gauss. Therefore, indirectly, the radio astronomical observations give further confirmation of the existence of a general magnetic field in the Galaxy. Direct measurements of the galactic field have been made successfully during these last years by measuring the hydrogen line at 21 cm (see also p. 126).

VI.7 Conclusion.

By now we have a fairly complete picture of our Galaxy. We have described and studied its dimension and shape, its motion and the physical characteristics of its components. In the Galaxy we have a large conglomeration of stars and of interstellar matter. The latter is composed of gas which consists mainly of hydrogen atoms and of very minute solid particles. We have seen that the shape is that of a very flattened ellipsoid surrounded by spiral arms. In order to maintain stars and gas in their orbits a very high velocity of rotation is required, which develops the centrifugal force necessary to balance the gravitational attraction exerted by the very great mass of the nucleus. A swarm of globular clusters surrounds the Galaxy and rotates slowly around it. In this great conglomeration, stars are born in groups in the clouds of dark matter. Their lives are of various length according to the rate at which they use their fuel, they pass through critical ages which can be very catastrophic and finally reach extinction. In their interior, during their lifetime, the hydrogen is converted into heavier elements. Part of this matter is ejected into interstellar space in the explosions which convulse the stars during their cycle of evolution. Stars of newer generations will be richer in heavier elements than the older stars belonging to population II.

The Galaxy was formed about 10 thousand million years ago. Even if we go back to the early beginning of historical times, our observations can only cover 8,000 years. But it is only for little more than a century that we have been able to study the Galaxy with instruments which enable us to overcome the obstacle created by the very limited power of our eyes. Our view of the Galaxy is therefore instantaneous, since one century compared with 10 thousand million years is like comparing one second with one year. From this ephemeral view, man tries to deduce a knowledge of the birth, development and death of the stars and of the galaxies; an extremely arduous task. In spite of this very short period of observations, astronomers have been able to develop plausible theories about the life of a star. The aspect of the Galaxy is changeable, stars are born and die continuously. From a statistical point of view, the development is very much like that of human population. The individual changes, old people die and are replaced by the newly born, but on the whole the population numerically and qualitatively, remains the same. Like a great city, the Galaxy also is in a state of dynamical equilibrium.

The Sun takes about 240 million years to perform a complete revolution around the galactic centre. During this period, sometimes called the 'cosmic year', many bright blue stars are born and have time to exhaust a great part of their hydrogen. In about one-fifth of a 'cosmic year' they reach the critical stage of their development, and following their evolution, they become stars which are dying. Other stars 100 or 1,000 times less bright than the former, as for instance our own Sun, have already performed several complete revolutions around the galactic centre, without having changed much their physical characteristics.

The small differences of orbital velocity (10 or 20 km./s.) between the Sun and the nearest stars are responsible for the fact that the appearance of our sky has remained practically unchanged for hundreds and even thousands of years. Today we still see the same constellations which were seen by the early inhabitants of the Earth and we use the same names which were given to them by the Greeks and the Romans. Gods and heroes of their mythology still live in the sky. However, a difference in velocity of only 1 km./s. over a million years produces a change in the distance between two stars of about 3 light-years. If this happens during $\frac{1}{200}$ of the 'cosmic year', it is clear that after a whole cosmic year, the sky we know will have changed considerably. New constellations will have taken the place of the old ones, while clouds of gas and interstellar matter will have changed shape and dimension.

And what will happen to the clusters? The globular clusters which are so thickly populated and so remote from the galactic centre are firmly held together by the attraction exerted by the nucleus of the cluster on all the components. This force will be strong enough to resist the tidal effect of the galactic nucleus.

The open clusters, on the other hand, sooner or later will break up. The parts nearer to the galactic centre are subject to a greater attraction than the parts which are further away. The velocity of the components will gradually change. In 10 to 100 cosmic years, these clusters will have dispersed completely, while new ones will be in process of formation.

In every region of the Galaxy, in the globular clusters and in the nucleus as well as in the spiral arms, the stars which are less bright than our Sun are still in the main sequence. They have not yet reached the critical turning-point of their existence. Since according to theory, these stars can remain in these conditions for up to 10 thousand million years from their birth, or even more, it follows that the Galaxy must be about this age. Were the Galaxy older than this, then in some parts of it we would find stars less bright than the Sun, already on the point of leaving the main sequence. In the older globular clusters the stars are still in their first phase of life, in the sequence where they were born.

These are the results of the study of a stellar system which covers about 80,000 light-years in space and at least 10 thousand million years in time; results which were collected in a century and a half of observations. These observations have been taken from our own Earth, a minute object travelling in space and belonging to the solar system, a system of less than $\frac{1}{800,000}$ of a light-year in diameter and situated at the periphery of the Galaxy.

CHAPTER VII

The galaxies

VII.1 Nomenclature.

THE name of nebula well suits those irregular masses of gas which are to be found scattered in the Galaxy. This word, however, was used also for other celestial objects, four of which are visible to the naked eye and have such an appearance as to justify the name.

William Parsons, with his giant telescope, discovered an object which has a magnificent whirlpool structure near the tail of Ursa Major. He was able to see in it a very delicate spiral structure of almost geometrical precision and with hazy outline. It was the first time that this type of object, consisting of stars and at the same time having a nebular appearance, was found in the sky. These, however, were very different objects from the irregular galactic nebulae as was shown by their distance from the Galaxy and by their spectra. Although the name of 'extra-galactic nebulae' was given to those objects, it is preferable to call them 'external galaxies' or, more simply, galaxies according to more recent conventions.

During the second half of the eighteenth century, Messier in France and Dreyer in England made a systematic observation of galactic and extra-galactic nebulae and of globular clusters, and classified them in catalogues. These catalogues are still in use today and the objects in them are represented by numbers. The Messier catalogue is abbreviated by M. followed by a number; for instance M.31 identifies the Andromeda galaxy, while Dreyer's catalogue is known as the New General Catalogue, and is abbreviated to NGC followed by a number. There are two supplements to this catalogue which include observations up to 1908 and they are known as the 'Index Catalogue' (IC). The majority of the NGC and IC objects are galaxies, and those listed in the NGC are generally brighter than those in the IC and include the objects observed by Messier. Since

1908, however, the increasing power of instruments has led to the discovery of countless galaxies. These are no longer listed in catalogues but their distribution and their characteristics are being studied. Whether these spiral and elliptical 'nebulae' were galactic or extra-galactic objects was still being debated as late as 1920. The 100-inch reflector of Mt. Wilson gave the final answer to this question, by showing that the Andromeda 'nebula' (M.31) and that in Triangulum (M.33) consisted, like our own Galaxy, of stars, clouds and globular clusters. Moreover the discovery of Cepheid variables in these galaxies made it possible to determine the distance of the galaxies and showed that their dimensions were at least ten times the probable dimensions of our own Galaxy.

VII.2 Description and classification.

The study of the various forms of the galaxies, which appear to us at various inclinations to the line of sight, leads us to the conclusion that they must all belong to one family of celestial objects in which we may see an evolution process. Let us say from the start that they all have a well-defined common appearance, symmetrical with respect to the central nucleus, around which they rotate. Only about 2 to 3% of the total number have an irregular shape without a well-defined nucleus. Two of the more common regular forms are the elliptical and the spiral, which seem to suggest a regular sequence from the more compact of the galaxies to the more open of the spiral galaxies, namely a progressive dispersion and expansion. One of the almost general characteristics of the spiral galaxies is that their bright matter is mixed with the dark. The former consists mainly of stars and, in less measure, of gaseous masses, while the latter consists of very small particles the size of which justifies the name of 'cosmic dust'. The mass of cosmic dust can be detected because it absorbs light, while the gaseous mass is identifiable by its typical emission spectrum.

When the principal plane of a spiral galaxy is seen edgeways, the cosmic dust appears as dark patches projected against the bright nuclear region. For other inclinations of the galaxies, the cosmic dust is identifiable by its relative absorption or by the reddening of the luminous objects embedded in it. The emission spectra, which can be observed at various points of these galaxies, enable us to detect not only masses of gas but also the presence in the same gas of stars at high temperature of the order of 30,000° K. These spectra are studied not only to determine the presence of gaseous masses, but also to determine radial velocities in various parts of the galaxies. This study, however, can be carried out only for the galaxies which are nearest and therefore sufficiently luminous, such as M.31 and M.33.

Hubble has suggested an empirical classification which is based on the study of several hundreds of galaxies, photographed with the large American reflectors. This classification starts from the elliptical and proceeds towards the spiral form.

The elliptical galaxies are classified starting from those of globular form (E_0) through the flattened ones of ellipsoidal form (E_5) and reaching, finally, those of lenticular form (E_7). Their luminosity decreases slowly from the stellar nuclei to the boundaries. It is for this reason that the size of the images which they make in astronomical photographs grows with increasing exposure but the shape of their photographic images remains approximately constant. To the E_7 class belong objects which seen edgeways appear lenticular in shape. The real existence of all forms, from globular to lenticular, can be deduced from the frequency distribution of the ellipticity of the projected images.

The sequence (Plate 37) goes from elliptical to spiral galaxies. The latter can be divided into two types, *normal* (*S*) and *barred* (*SB*). The barred are less in number than the normal and perhaps represent only a special case. Hubble, therefore, after E_7 divides the sequence into two branches, one for the normal galaxies and the other for the barred. The normal galaxies have a luminous nucleus and a nebulous unresolved region which is similar to the lenticular galaxy E_7. The arms which emerge from the edges are not yet resolved, they are still relatively undeveloped. Proceeding along the sequence, we find that the arms become thicker at the expense of the nuclear region, and they open gradually until they reach a stage in which they appear to us fully open while the nucleus has become less conspicuous. About the middle of the sequence, or perhaps even sooner, condensations begin to appear. Generally speaking, resolution into stars appears first in the external arms, then progresses gradually towards the interior, reaching the nucleus at the end of the sequence. The various types of galaxies in this branch of the sequence are identified by the letters *Sa*, *Sb*, *Sc*. In the other branch, the barred galaxies at first appear lenticular in shape, with the external regions condensed into a ring, concentric with the nucleus. A large bar of condensed matter crosses the nucleus diametrically, from one edge to the other of the galaxy. The shape is not unlike the Greek letter θ. As the sequence progresses the ring appears to detach itself from the bar at two opposite points (just above the bar at one end and just below it at the opposite end), and the arms of the spiral widen at the free ends of the broken ring. After this stage the galaxies have a development which is very similar to that of the normal galaxies. As before, the arms thicken at the expense of the nuclear region as they continue to open. The resolution into stars is first noticeable in the external arms and then gradually in the nucleus. In this branch the various types of galaxies are identified by the letters SBa, SBb, SBc. The position in each branch of the sequence is determined by the amount of matter present in the arms in relation to what is left in the nuclear regions, by the degree of opening of the arms of the spiral and by the degree of resolution into stars. The transition from E_7 to SBa presents almost a continuity, but this is less evident in the transition from E_7 to Sa.

The complete sequence, which we have described, shows several characteristics which vary systematically throughout from the beginning to the end. Colour index, spectral type and degree of resolution into stars change with continuity. In this general picture the Galaxy presumably is a type of normal spiral Sb or Sc. We ought to note here that Hubble did not give to the sequence a significance of evolution from type E_0 to the spiral type, but rather he limited himself to noting the apparent change of form. Only later many astronomers gave the meaning of evolution to the sequence established by him. There was, however, the possibility of considering the irregular galaxies to be the younger and the elliptical the older, and this is in fact the direction in which more recent opinion is moving. Today, however, a third possibility, which appears probable, is considered. We shall see that galaxies are always found grouped in clusters of galaxies which are more or less thickly populated. Observations have shown that in the denser clusters only elliptical galaxies are found. Indeed, according to Spitzer and Baade, collisions among neighbouring galaxies have the effect of expelling the gas so that these objects cannot develop their spiral arms. In less thickly populated clusters, on the other hand, there is a possibility that galaxies can develop spiral arms.

Morgan and Mayall have suggested an interesting classification of these galaxies, based on their spectra. This could be considered as a complement to the sequence which Hubble suggested and which is based on the form and degree of resolution into stars. The spectrograms which were used for this classification were obtained mainly by Humason at Mt. Wilson and Mt. Palomar and by Mayall at Lick.

Humason had already arranged these galaxies in a sequence from A_5 to G_8 related to Hubble's types. Generally the early spectral types are associated with Sc and SBc systems and the later spectral types with the elliptical systems. With the great progress achieved both in the construction of spectrographs and in the development of photographic emulsions, it is now possible to study the systems as a whole, either when the nuclear region is barely concentrated, or when it predominates over the rest of the system. A great deal of useful information on the spectra of galaxies has naturally been obtained by studying the largest and brightest galaxies such as M.31 and M.33. For fainter galaxies the study of the spectrum is limited to the region $\lambda\lambda$ 3850–4100 Å.

Systems which have on the whole a spectrum of class A are called '*systems A*'. Typical examples are NGC 1518 (*Scp*), NGC 4449 (irregular) and NGC 672 (*SBc*) in which the greatest part of the light comes from stars of class A. These systems show neither a central concentration of light, nor a well-developed structure.

Systems which have spectra between classes F_0 and F_2, still in the same region of the spectrum ($\lambda\lambda$ 3850–4100 Å.), are called '*systems AF*'. These are all spiral galaxies of type Sc (NGC 925, NGC 2976, NGC 4713, for example) and have as a main characteristic a very weak central concentration of light.

'*Systems F*' include spectral types which are a little more advanced. To this class belong M.33 and M.51, which are spiral galaxies with an intermediate central concentration of light. As examples of this class we mention the Sc systems: NGC 5194 (M.51), NGC 598 (M.33) and NGC 3810. In the $\lambda\lambda$ 3900–4400 Å. region the galaxies have spectra which belong to class F.

'*Systems FG*' belong to a stage even more advanced in the spectral sequence. Most of their total brightness is due to the central condensation of light. NGC 4666 (*Sc*), NGC 5055 (M.63, *Sb*), and NGC 7331 (*Sb*), are typical examples.

Finally '*systems K*' represent the largest group and have a great variety of appearance. In the blue-violet region, the greatest contri-

THE GALAXIES

bution to the total luminosity is due to giants of classes between $gG8$ and gM. The shapes of these systems can be classified in five groups: (1) large spiral systems Sb and Sa; (2) barred spirals with a strong central concentration of light; (3) giant elliptical systems; (4) systems devoid of dust which have the form of spiral Sa and Sb; (5) irregular systems.

Examples of typical systems of these classes are as follows: (1) NGC 4594 (Sb), NGC 2841 (Sb), NGC 224 (M.31, Sb), and NGC 3031 (M.81, Sb) among normal spirals which have the common property of large amorphous nuclear regions in which the greatest part of the light is concentrated; (2) NGC 5850 (SBb), NGC 1398 (SBb) and NGC 4643 (SBo) among the barred systems which have large and amorphous bright nuclei and spectral class K; (3) M.87, which is an example of giant elliptical systems and has a spectrum gK; (4) NGC 4486 (M.87, E_0), NGC 3115 (E_7) and NGC 4762 (Sa), which are examples of galaxies without regions of dust, that is to say without dark matter; (5) finally we can mention NGC 4762, which belongs to the irregular systems and which appears like an Sb galaxy without the spiral structure and without dark regions.

There is no denying a strong correlation between form and spectrum. Systems A have the common characteristic of a small central concentration of light; systems F have a central concentration of light which is stronger, while systems K have the strongest central concentration of light. The central nucleus, absent in systems A and F, begins to appear in the group FG.

The correlation between form and stellar population shown by Morgan and Mayall has been used by Morgan in 1958 to suggest a classification of form which would give an indication of the type of stellar population found in the majority of the classified galaxies. One class of systems has the greatest part of its light in the blue-violet region (spectral classes B to A and to F). At the other end we have a group of elliptical systems which, together with the internal parts of systems like M.31, owe the greatest part of their light to red and yellow giants. Systems occupying an intermediate position have populations which are intermediate between the two extremes. This classification may have some significance in the question of stellar evolution, both for individual stars and for those belonging to clusters.

THE GALAXIES

VII.3 Distribution and orientation of galaxies.

The further in space we explore the greater is the number of galaxies we discover. The problem of studying their distribution is therefore very similar to the problem of studying the distribution of stars with the same complication that galaxies have not all the same intrinsic brightness. There exist 'giant' and 'dwarf' galaxies, and galaxies which are between the two. Hubble, with the 100-inch and the 200-inch reflectors, has probed specially selected regions of the sky, reaching galaxies as faint as 20th magnitude, and he was able to find that the number of galaxies varied from region to region. At high galactic latitude the number of galaxies is greatest while between $+40°$ and $-40°$ of galactic latitude the number of galaxies decreases rapidly as the galactic equator is approached. Figure 40 gives the distribution of the galaxies on the celestial sphere according to Hubble and the total absence of galaxies between $+10°$ and $-10°$ is very noticeable. This is produced by the interstellar matter existing in this region, particularly near the longitude of the centre of our Galaxy ($325°$).

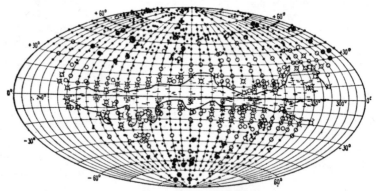

FIG. 40. Distribution of galaxies

According to Hubble's observations of galaxies as faint as 20th magnitude, the relation between the number of galaxies and the latitude l is given by:

$$\log. N = 2 \cdot 115 - 0 \cdot 15 \cos l$$

where N represents the number of galaxies per square degree.

If we take into account this distribution and the effect of interstellar matter which hides the galaxies, we have some indication of the true distribution of galaxies. This varies considerably from one region to another of the sky, although not in a systematic manner, so it is possible approximately to speak of a uniform distribution of galaxies on the celestial sphere. Taking the magnitude limit as magnitude 21, galactic systems are as numerous as the stars of our own Galaxy. The space of the universe, at least as far as the observable limit, is not only isotropic, but also homogeneous, that is to say it is the same everywhere and in every direction. Galaxies are scattered at an average interval of the order of one million parsecs, which is probably equal to 200 times their average diameter.

Galaxies often appear in 'groups' and in 'clusters'. Systems consisting of two or three galaxies are numerous, such as the Galaxy with the Magellanic Clouds, or the spiral galaxy in Andromeda and its satellites. In such systems all types of galaxies can be observed so that it is possible to learn something about their dimensions in relation to the various stages of the sequence. Groups of large dimensions can be compared with open star clusters, but it is the smaller groups which are more common. Clusters of galaxies are very similar to each other and they consist of about 500 components with luminosities which may differ by as much as 5 magnitudes. The concentration of the components near the centre is apparent but not conspicuous, and even in this respect the clusters of galaxies are comparable to open star clusters. All types of galaxies are represented but elliptical galaxies predominate. A correlation appears to exist between the characteristics of the type and the density of the cluster. This correlation becomes less as we proceed from the elliptical to the spiral galaxies. A recent hypothesis suggests that the frequent collisions in the very thickly populated clusters would produce the expulsion of gas, thereby preventing the formation of the spiral arms.

A recent investigation (1954) on the distribution of galaxies has been carried out at Lick Observatory by Shane and Wirtanen with a 20-inch astrograph. The number of galaxies photographed up to a limit of 18·4 magnitudes is of the order of one million. The galaxy counts have been performed on plates covering 36 square degrees, and the curves of equal density have been traced on a map. Three great clouds of galaxies exist between +40° and +50° of galactic latitude, with a maximum frequency of about 200 galaxies. The deficiency in other regions is noticeable, where only a few units are found. From these counts it can be concluded that in the equation given by Hubble (p. 194) different coefficients for every interval of 20° of longitude ought to be used. From the map the irregularities of distribution due to galactic absorption are evident. A considerable deficiency of galaxies is found for $L = 312°$ and $l = +34°$, and again for $L = 333°$ and $l = +35°$ (where L and l denote the galactic longitude and latitude respectively). This is probably due to the presence of absorbing clouds. Moreover we also notice that the galaxies are not distributed at random, but rather tend to congregate in given areas. Some clusters, such as the one in Virgo, can be considered as open clusters, while others, such as the one in Coma, for example, present a considerable central condensation and tend to have a spherical symmetry. Shapley had already observed that groups of galaxies may be double or even triple. The nearness of their components both in direction and distance, and their distribution in apparent magnitudes, suggest that these multiple groups must have some physical link. Counts confirm the aggregation of groups of two or more clusters of galaxies.

As for the orientation of the galaxies, until recently it was thought that the equatorial planes of galaxies were distributed at random in space. Wyatt Jr. and Brown have observed that 812 galaxies in a region of Cetus tend to have their major axis approximately in the same direction. This may have a cosmological significance which, so far, has not been explained.

VII.4   Distances.

In order to be able to decide whether the galaxies were systems related in any way to our Galaxy or quite independent 'island universes', it was necessary to find a method of determining their distances. This became possible when powerful telescopes enabled astronomers to resolve some galaxies, at least in part, into stars. In 1917, Ritchey at Mt. Wilson and Curtis at Lick discovered in a spiral nebula some novae having light curves similar to those of novae in the Galaxy. Since these stars appeared in the galaxies with an apparent magnitude of 15, they must have been very distant, perhaps a few hundred times the average distance of novae appearing in our Galaxy. This helped to confirm the view that spiral galaxies were independent systems, comparable to our own galactic system, in a universe where our observations could reach distances of the order of hundreds of millions of light-years. Many years later, the

100-inch reflector enabled astronomers to detect Cepheids in galaxies and to determine their periods. The Cepheids were thought to be of the same type as those nearer to us observed in our Galaxy. Moreover, white or blue stars of great brightness, irregular variables as well as novae and supernovae, could be identified in the galaxies. In the Andromeda galaxy (M.31), a typical Cepheid was discovered. This had a period of one month and at maximum an apparent magnitude of 18·2. By means of the period–luminosity relation its magnitude was found to be —4 (that is 4,000 times brighter than the Sun) and therefore its distance about 275,000 parsecs. In this way the distance of galaxies can be found by the same methods we adopt for our own Galaxy, that is the method for determining absolute magnitudes. This, however, only if we assume that stars belonging to galaxies are very similar to those of the Galaxy and of the Magellanic Clouds. With increasing distances the first stars we lose sight of are the Cepheids, then the irregular variables, then the blue supergiants, and finally only supernovae will be left. The various indirect methods used for the determination of the distance of the galaxies were not in good agreement. Mineur, in 1944, in discussing proper motions and radial velocities, and taking into account the rotation of the Galaxy, reached the conclusion that the 'classical' Cepheids found in the spiral arms must be four times brighter than had been thought until then, and the distances therefore had to be almost doubled.

Baade, with the help of the 200-inch of Mt. Palomar, was able to throw some light on this problem. The discovery of the existence of the two 'populations' of stars in the constitution of the galaxies led also to the discovery that Cepheids do not all follow the law formulated by Miss Leavitt. Cepheids must be divided into normal classical Cepheids belonging to population I; Cepheids of type RR Lyrae with a period of less than one day and those of type W Virginis with a period greater than one day, both belong to population II. From photographs of M.31, obtained with the 200-inch, Baade, in 1952, was able to establish that there must be two zero points for the period-luminosity relation of Cepheids. While for Cepheids of population II the zero point is the same as the one used so far for the determination of distances, for Cepheids of population I it is necessary to displace the zero point by about 1·5 magnitudes, which means an increase in the brightness of these Cepheids by a factor of 4. From this it follows that the Andromeda galaxy is at a distance of

630,000 parsecs and must therefore have greater dimensions than our Galaxy. The distance of the Magellanic Clouds increases from 25,000 to 50,000 parsecs. The new scale of distances has the effect of reducing considerably the size of our own Galaxy. While before, the Galaxy was a very large system indeed, now it has become normal, although it still ranks as one of the larger galaxies.

This general doubling of distances of galaxies has since received confirmation from other sources. Thackeray and Wesselink, at Pretoria, have found an average magnitude of 18·7 for some variables of type RR Lyrae in three globular clusters of the Magellanic Clouds. If we assume for these variables an absolute magnitude zero, the distance of the Magellanic Clouds agrees very well with that given by the new scale. This confirms that the absolute magnitude of Cepheids of population I is 1·5 magnitudes brighter than that of Cepheids of population II.

Hubble and Sandage have studied the light curve of five irregular variables in M.31 and M.33, based on observations from 1916 to 1953 and have determined their colour index. They have established the fact that variables of this type have not yet been found in our Galaxy. These variables are distinguished by their great brightness as they have an absolute magnitude of −8·4 in the new scale of distances. At their maximum they are blue in colour and belong to the spectral class F. Since the dispersion of the values of their luminosity is very small near the average value of their maximum, these stars must be suitable (according to Hubble and Sandage) for the determination of the distances of the galaxies in which they are found.

Further investigations by Baade on M.31 have led to the discovery of Cepheids concentrated in great numbers in the spiral arms, the shortest periods of which are of about 3 days. Their brightness indicates a difference of 24·25 between apparent and absolute magnitudes corresponding to a distance of about 630,000 parsecs for M.31.

The great improvements in the measurement of magnitudes, due to the use of photo-electric photometers, have made it possible for astronomers to investigate objects at ever-increasing distances. Baade, still using the 200-inch, was able to discover in M.31 five planetaries, which do not appear as a disc as is the case for the planetaries of the Galaxy, but which can still be identified from the fact that the greater part of their light comes from bright lines in the green region of the spectrum. On plates taken in this region of the spectrum the new planetaries appear of magnitude 22, to which corresponds an absolute magnitude of $-2\cdot1$. This magnitude is in good agreement with that of the planetaries of our Galaxy.

VII.5 Absolute magnitudes and spectral types.

Hubble has determined the mean value of the absolute photographic brightness for the various types of galaxies. For all the various types, faint objects excepted, he obtained a magnitude of -14, corresponding to the absolute luminosity of 85 million suns. There are, however, strong deviations from the average value, especially in the case of elliptical galaxies, for objects are found of absolute magnitude -11. It is not yet possible to determine the luminosity function or to give definite values for the mean absolute magnitude of galaxies and their scatter around this mean. For galaxies which can be observed spectroscopically, the luminosity function of each type is nearly a gaussian distribution with the mean photographic absolute magnitude of $-16\cdot5$. The main group of dwarf galaxies could be represented by a gaussian luminosity function with an average magnitude of -14, which includes the faint elliptical, some lenticular as well as some more advanced spiral and irregular Magellanic galaxies. In the spiral galaxies the luminosity of the background decreases regularly and against it are projected the bright spiral arms. The colour of the background is nearly the same as that of the nucleus and very similar to that of stars of classes G and K. The spiral arms, on the other hand, are white, like stars of classes B and A, and so are the little diffused condensations which can be detected in various parts of the spiral arms. The yellow colour of the nucleus is in agreement with Baade's observations, that the individual bright stars in the nucleus are red giants. The white colour of the spiral arms and of the condensations agrees with what we observe in the corresponding regions of the Galaxy where stars belonging to classes B and A are very common and where the former tend to collect in clusters. In the elliptical galaxies no difference of colour in the different parts is noticeable, since, as far as colour is concerned, they are all similar to the nucleus of spiral galaxies. This too is in agreement with Baade's observations of the brightest stars contained in these objects.

In these galaxies spectral class G predominates, although occasionally we find also classes F and K. According to Hubble there exists a spectral sequence from the elliptical to the spiral type:

THE GALAXIES

$E_0 - E_9$	G4
$Sa - SBa$	G3
$Sb - SBb$	G2
$Sc - SBc$	F0

The average type of the dark line spectra belongs to class *G3*. In the galaxies of irregular type and in the external regions of open spirals, emission lines too are observed, but these are localized in the condensations within the galaxies themselves. The spectra are very similar to those observed in gas clouds in the vicinity of very hot stars like those in Orion.

In low dispersion spectra of the galaxies, only one bright line is found, λ 3727 Å., which is due to forbidden transitions of singly ionized oxygen atoms (OII). This emission takes place in conditions of very low density and when a large volume of gas is present, and this is actually typical of the gaseous masses of spiral galaxies.

Generally speaking, the emission of the OII doublet is related to the abundance of population I and it is often present and intense where this population is abundant, as for instance in the advanced spirals or in the Magellanic type of galaxies. Other bright lines which appear are those of the Balmer series and the forbidden lines N_1 and N_2 of OIII. The frequence of the λ 3727 Å. is 20% in galaxies of type *E* and reaches 80% in those of type *Sb* and *Sc*. Sometimes the bright lines appear very wide because of dispersion of large radial velocities which may reach several thousand km. per second. It is extremely difficult to explain how these velocities are produced and maintained. From micrometric measurements taken at Mt. Stromlo in Australia, of the diameters of 200 southerly galaxies, it appears that the *E*-type galaxies, on average, have a diameter of 1·2′ and this increases slowly when we proceed along the sequence towards the *Sa* and *Sb* types. The average diameter for the *Sc* type is 2·2′. These are the measurements of diameters, when the unit of distance is taken as 10 million parsecs approximately. They correspond to 3,500 parsecs for galaxies of type *E*, to 6,500 parsecs for galaxies of type *Sc* and 5,500 parsecs for the Magellanic spirals of type *Sm*.

VII.6 Rotation and internal motions.

Galaxies, whether seen edgeways or face on, appear as objects which are elongated in the direction of their galactic equator, very flattened at the poles and endowed with rotational motion as their

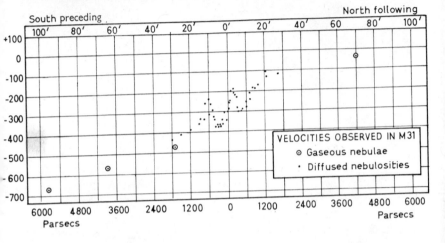

40. M.31 (above). The circles mark the nebulosities used for the measurements of the radial velocity in the diagram below. The distances from the centre (abscissae) must be multiplied by 2·6 according to the new scale of extra-galactic distances. The curve which represents the radial velocity as a function of the distance from the centre is symmetrical with respect to a line corresponding to a velocity of nearly −300 km/s. This line represents the velocity with which the galaxy as a whole moves with reference to us. The difference between the observed velocities at various points, and the velocity of the galaxy as a whole, gives the velocity of rotation. The difference must be corrected because of the inclination of the equatorial plane with respect to the line of sight

41. Spiral Galaxy in Andromeda M.31—NGC 224. Satellite nebulae NGC 205 and 221 also shown. 48-inch Schmidt Mt. Palomar

42. Central region of the Great Spiral Galaxy in Andromeda M.31—
NGC 224. 100-inch Mt. Wilson

43. Region of a spiral arm of the Andromeda galaxy M.31—NGC 224,
resolved into stars. 100-inch Mt. Wilson

spiral form shows. This is also true for our Galaxy. For systems relatively nearer to us having an apparent dimension which is not too small, it has been possible to determine the radial velocity. This was measured by means of a spectrograph by setting the slit parallel to the major axis of the galaxy, or at right angles to their equator, at various distances from the nucleus.

If we assume in a first approximation that a spherical stellar system has a constant density ρ, the velocity of rotation v on a circumference of radius r internal to the system, is obtained by taking the gravitational attraction as being equal to the centrifugal force:

$$\frac{v^2}{r} = \frac{G\,4\pi\,r\rho}{3}$$

and from this we have:

$$v = \sqrt{\frac{4G\pi\rho}{3}}\quad r \qquad [1]$$

Outside the system, if we call M the total mass of the system, we have:

$$v = \sqrt{\frac{GM}{r}} \qquad [2]$$

Measurements taken by Mayall and Aller on the spiral galaxy of Triangulum (M.33; fig. 41) show that the above equations are true. From the centre up to a distance of about 15′, v increases with

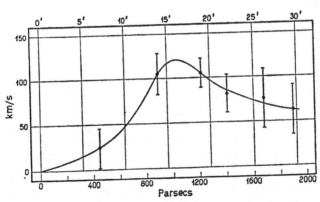

FIG. 41. Velocity of rotation of M.33 at various distances from the centre. Distances from the centre should be multiplied by 2.6 according to the new scale of extra-galactic distances

increasing *r*. For greater distances v begins to decrease. It is probable that this happens for other galaxies, although on account of the difficulty of such measurements there are very few similar observations so far obtained.

If we look at a galaxy which is face on and which has a well-developed spiral, we note the existence at the centre of a relatively small spherical nucleus. From two opposite points of this nucleus, two distinct spiral arms originate. Let us join any point of one arm with the centre of the galaxy and then draw the tangent to the spiral at the same point. Measurements of the angle made by these two lines, show that it may vary from one spiral to another, but that for

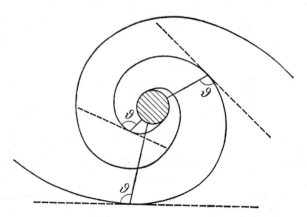

FIG. 42. Logarithmic spiral

a given spiral the angle has always approximately the same value, whatever point is chosen (fig. 42). This angle may vary between 126° and 94°, but on average it is 106°. It can be said that a logarithmic spiral represents approximately the shape observed in spiral galaxies. The spiral shape of galaxies, in addition to the spectroscopic evidence, leads us to think that they are rotating. We ought to be able to confirm this rotation by observing the proper motion of stars and of condensations belonging to the spiral arms on photographs taken at long intervals of time. Measurements made for this purpose have not given satisfactory results because of the distance of these objects and the relatively short interval of time since the earliest photographs were taken. An interesting and important problem arises when for some galaxies which appear at a suitable angle, it is possible to

THE GALAXIES

measure the radial velocity at various distances from the nucleus. The problem, very important from the point of view of the dynamics of these systems, is to establish whether the material which forms the arms is moving towards or away from the nucleus, that is whether the spiral is winding or unwinding. The interpretation of the observational data which will lead to the solution of this problem is not at all easy and still leaves room for doubt. This will be so until such a time when the observations obtained will be sufficiently numerous and reliable.

Let us suppose that we observe with a spectrograph a spiral galaxy seen edgeways at an angle, for example, of 15° as is nearly the case with the Andromeda galaxy (M.31). By setting the slit of the spectrograph on the edge of the spiral or along the major axis, we find from the Doppler displacements that the left-hand edge is receding from us, while the right-hand edge is approaching us (fig. 43). As in the case of the orbits of spectroscopic binaries, we do not know whether the inclination angle of the plane of the spiral is positive or negative, or, in other words, we do not know whether it is the upper or lower part of the object, as seen projected against the sky, that is nearest to us. Should the upper part be the furthest, then the observed motion corresponds to B in fig. 43a. If, on the other hand, the upper part is nearest to us, then the direction of rotation is that given in C of fig. 43a. In B, the spiral is winding round the nucleus, in C it is unwinding. It would appear to be an easy thing, from the examination of the appearance of many galaxies, to judge the orientation in space. In actual fact only a few allow us a plausible estimate. This is based on the fact that when we observe a galaxy edgeways, we see a dark band along its equator, and this absorbing mass has the appearance of being in front of the bright matter which constitutes the main part of the object. Generally, however, in similar objects, it is difficult to identify the arms of the spiral and their direction. Slipher and Hubble studied several galaxies and were among the first to determine clearly the direction of their rotation. They assumed that the asymmetry of the darkening gives a definite criterion for the definition of the direction of inclination. According to their observations, the arms of the spiral are winding themselves around the nucleus as shown in B of fig. 43a.

On the other hand, theoretical investigations by Lindblad on the dynamics of these systems leads to an opposite conclusion for what concerns the direction of motion of the arms of the spiral. This

203

conclusion has been confirmed by the study of the colour index of the various galaxies made by Lindblad himself. The colour index shows that the edge of the spiral which is towards the observer is bluer than the opposite edge which is further away. Further investi-

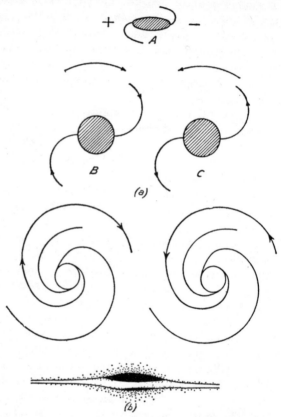

FIG. 43. A galaxy seen edgeways A and (b) and the two possible directions of rotation of the spiral arms (a)

gations of this problem were carried out by Mayall. He determined the radial velocity of the galaxy NGC 2146, which appears as a well-defined, left-handed spiral with an arm inclined approximately 20° to the fundamental plane of the system, and he studied the orientation of its arms, an orientation which is clearly indicated. These investigations of Mayall confirm Slipher and Hubble's conclusions, namely that the spirals are winding around the nucleus.

THE GALAXIES

Irvin has studied the direction of rotation of the spiral galaxies with the 36-inch reflector (90 cm.) of the Goethe Link Observatory at the University of Indiana. He was able to show that for 16 of these galaxies the position of their central point is asymmetric with reference to the brighter regions of the nucleus and, moreover, one edge of this is always better defined than the opposite. It is reasonable to assume then that the nuclei of these galaxies are partially obscured by absorbing matter and that the well-defined edge belongs to the spiral arms which are in the same plane. These criteria, combined with measurements of radial velocities, confirm the direction of rotation of these systems.

Recent measurements of the radial velocity of the spiral galaxy NGC 253 made by Evans at Pretoria, together with what can be deduced from the orientation of the spiral arms, show again that the spiral is winding. If, as seems likely, these spiral galaxies can be compared with our own Galaxy, then we can make a comparison of the direction of rotation between our Galaxy and the others.

From the study of the motion of stars of classes O and B contained in two arms of the spiral and from the study of radio waves emitted by hydrogen, the direction of rotation of the Galaxy appears to be right-handed for an observer from the north pole, that is the spiral advances with its convexity leading. This confirms what probably is happening for the galaxies (fig. 44).

In order to have a better understanding of the internal motions of the galaxies, many more observations are required. As Lindblad points out, we may think that the motion of the individual formations, that is stars and nebular matter which constitutes the arms of the spiral, is the result of a rotation superimposed on an expansion. In this way we would have an undulating motion around the system so that the points where an arm begins to detach itself from the central part of the system remain apparently fixed in space. The displacement of a point of the central system, relative to a point of a neighbouring arm of the spiral, would follow an arc, which in its development is determined by the law of areas. In time it will be possible to determine this relative motion comparing photographs of these galaxies taken at long intervals of time. Measurements of this type have been made by van Maanen at Mt. Wilson, but the interval of time which he was able to use was far too short (only about 25 years) to give reliable results.

Hypotheses on the formation of these systems can be put forward.

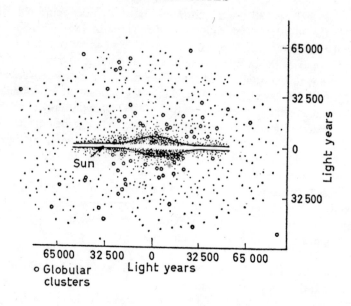

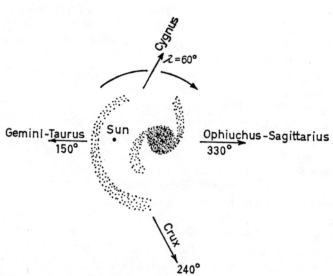

Fig. 44. The appearance of our Galaxy seen edgeways (above); direction of rotation of the spiral arms (below)

If the matter of which they are composed has been ejected by explosion along the major axis of the ellipsoid, the difference of the velocities of the ejected matter may produce the spiral form and determine the direction of rotation so that the spiral is winding. We could also suppose that the interstellar matter scattered in the universe condenses into a supra-galactic cloud which begins to rotate forming stars around the nucleus. With increasing velocity of rotation, the system will become increasingly flatter, until it takes the shape of a disc from which new stars of very high temperature, namely of population I, begin to be produced. The first stars formed in the nucleus would be the red giants of population II.

As a matter of interest we may recall what happens in the condensation of water vapour when cyclonic formations develop on the Earth. Plates 38 and 39 show the eye of the cyclone photographed by radar at Key West in Florida. The first photograph was taken at 11h 30m and the second at 16h 10m. The bright areas represent echoes produced by precipitation, the circles are 16 km. apart. The clouds have a spiral form around the centre, with a left-handed rotation in the northern hemisphere, that is to say the spiral is winding.

With reference to the formation of spiral arms, Jeans, in 1928, wrote in *Astronomy and Cosmogony*:

'. . . the only result that seems to emerge with some clearness is that the spiral arms are permanent features of the nebulae. They appear to have been formed in the process of shrinkage, two convolutions or thereabouts being formed by each nebula, and to have been perpetuated in static form ever since. Their further interpretation forms one of the most puzzling, as well as disconcerting problems of cosmogony.

'Not only so, but until the spiral arms have been satisfactorily explained, it is impossible to feel confidence in any conjectures or hypotheses in connection with other features of the nebulae which seem more amenable to treatment. Each failure to explain the spiral arms makes it more and more difficult to resist a suspicion that the spiral nebulae are the seat of types of forces entirely unknown to us, forces which may possibly express novel and unsuspected metric properties of space. The type of conjecture which presents itself, somewhat insistently, is that the centres of the nebulae are of the nature of "singular points" at which matter is poured into our universe from some other, and entirely extraneous, spatial dimensions so that, to a denizen of our universe, they appear as points at which matter is being continually created.'

VII.7 Masses.

The velocity curves obtained for the rotation of galaxies give us information about the density distribution in their various parts. If we look at the data obtained for M.33 (fig. 41) we find that the density of its more internal parts must be almost constant. At a distance of about 16' from the centre, corresponding to approximately 2,600 parsecs, according to the most recent scale of distances, the density diminishes very rapidly. For instance, at 25' corresponding to a distance $r = 4,200$ parsecs, the measured velocity being $v = 75$ km./s. we obtain for the total mass of the system $M = 4 \times 10^9$ solar masses, using equation 2, page 201. The data obtained from observations are still too few to enable us to calculate the mass of the various systems and the distribution of the density in them. Systems M.31 and M.33 appear to be characterized by the absence of an appreciable concentration of matter towards the centre. The velocities of rotation of these two galaxies increase in the main part of the system as the distance from the nucleus increases. In the more external regions the velocity of rotation decreases when regions of relatively low density are reached. From observations of the motions of the Galaxy, it has been found that the velocity of rotation in the neighbourhood of the solar system, decreases towards the exterior. Therefore if the distribution of density in the Galaxy is somewhat similar to that obtained for M.31 and M.33, we must infer from this that the Sun is placed at a great distance from the centre of our stellar system. As we shall see later when we describe M.31, this galaxy, which belongs to the class of giants, has a much greater mass than M.33 and than galaxies of medium brightness. We can deduce, at least as a first approximation, that the masses must vary in direct proportion to their brightness.

With various methods we find that we can take $2 \times 10^{44} g = 10^{11}$ solar masses as the average value for the mass of the galaxies. So far very little is known of the difference in mass between the various types of these galaxies.

Schwarzschild has studied the distribution of the masses and the mass-luminosity ratio for the galaxies. For M.31, M.33, NGC 3115 and M.32 and for the cluster in Coma, he finds that the distribution of masses and of luminosity is identical. For the elliptical galaxies in which stars of population II predominate, a greater value for the ratio mass-luminosity is obtained, while for the neighbourhood of the Sun, for M.33 and for the Large Magellanic Cloud, where stars of population I predominate, a smaller value is obtained. For M.31, which is composed of a mixture of stars of population I and II, the value obtained is between the two.

We can therefore conclude that a high mass-luminosity ratio in a galaxy shows that it is composed of many stars of a mass smaller than that of the Sun and of low brightness, that is to say of dwarf stars generally of type dK and dM and occasionally of sub-dwarfs or white dwarfs. A low mass-luminosity ratio, on the other hand, shows that the system is rich in supergiants of population I, like those which are observed in systems of Magellanic type.

VII.8 Radial velocities.

Slipher, in 1912, had already begun at the Lowell Observatory (Flagstaff, Arizona) the measurement of the radial velocity of M.31 and other galaxies. He found in the dark line spectra a displacement of the lines towards the red which meant a strong velocity of recession. In 1916 de Sitter, in developing his theory on the structure of the universe based on the theory of relativity, foresaw that the recession of galaxies would increase with increasing distances. Confirmation of this theory by observations could only be obtained once the distances of galaxies had been determined. This became possible when Hubble, in 1923, discovered, in some of the nearest systems, Cepheids and other objects the absolute magnitude of which could be evaluated. So Hubble himself was able to establish a linear relationship between velocity and distance in regions of space where even faint and remote galaxies could be photographed first with the 100-inch and later with the 200-inch.

In order to increase the accuracy of the observations, Hubble and Humason measured the radial velocities of galaxies belonging to various clusters, assuming that each group of galaxies was at the same distance. The results so far obtained are summarized in Table 7.

If the displacement towards the red in the spectra of these galaxies interpreted as a Doppler displacement, is $\Delta\lambda/\lambda$, and if r is their distance, v the velocity of recession and c the velocity of light, then:

$$v = c\Delta\lambda/\lambda = Hr$$

THE GALAXIES

TABLE 7

Clusters of galaxies	Distances in thousands parsecs	Velocity km./s.
Virgo	2,300	1,200
Ursa Major	30,700	15,000
Corona Borealis	40,000	21,500
Bootes	70,600	39,300
Hydra	107,000	60,900

(The distances in the second column are given according to the old scale.)

where H is 'Hubble's constant' and its reciprocal $T_0 = 1/H$, represents the time, expressed in years, since the beginning of a uniform expansion of the universe from a relatively small volume. A galaxy which is now at a distance r and has velocity v, would have covered this distance in a length of time which is the same for all galaxies:

$$T_0 = r/v = 1/H$$

T_0, the reciprocal of Hubble's constant, can be taken then to represent the age of the universe.

The constant H, given originally by Hubble, was 520 km./s. for every million parsecs and the reciprocal T_0 was 1.9×10^9 years. However, the correction to the zero point for the period–luminosity relation for the classical Cepheids, found by Baade, which doubles the extra-galactic distances, reduces this constant to nearly half.

According to Sandage, the distances ought to be multiplied by 2·5 and he concludes that Hubble's constant ought to be:

$$200 \text{ km./s. } \times 10^6 \text{ parsecs}$$

and its reciprocal would then be:

$$4.9 \times 10^9 \text{ years}$$

Humason's observations with the 200-inch reveal that the 'red shift' is linear over the whole observable region, from the cluster of galaxies in Virgo which is receding at a velocity of 1,140 km./s. to the cluster in Hydra receding with a velocity of 60,960 km./s. This confirms the isotropy of the law of red shift. With the 200-inch it is

210

possible to reach even further in space extending the observable regions up to 150 million parsecs. Just to give some indication of the red shift we may mention that for a velocity of 61,000 km./s. the H and K lines of ionized calcium are shifted by 804 Å. and will therefore be near the region of λ 4750 Å., that is in the green region of the spectrum.

Humason, Mayall and Sandage have collected and discussed all the measurements of red shift for 800 galaxies observed from 1935 to 1955 at Lick, Mt. Wilson and Mt. Palomar Observatories. From the discussion of these data the most probable value for the parameter of expansion is 180 km./s. $\times$ 10⁶ parsecs with the uncertainty of 20%, and the reciprocal will be:

$$5 \cdot 4 \times 10^9 \text{ years}$$

A further correction to the scale of distances has been made in recent years. This correction must be applied to all objects external to our Local Group of galaxies. It follows that the distances have to be almost doubled with the exception of those relating to the members of the Local Group. The parameter of expansion is equal to 100 km./s. $\times$ 10⁶ parsecs or perhaps to 80 km./s. $\times$ 10⁶ parsecs and the reciprocal or the time T_0 becomes $9 \cdot 8 \times 10^9$ years and 12×10^9 years respectively.

Up to the present, the question whether the red-shift observed is to be interpreted wholly or partially as an effect of velocity of recession is still unsolved. The red-shift may be due to other causes so far unknown. In order to try to find an answer to this question, efforts have been made to search for effects of the second order, which could be revealed only by probing space to the limits reached by the 200-inch reflector. Hubble suggested that we could study the effect on the apparent luminosity of very remote galaxies, of increasing displacements towards the red. It is well known that a source of light which is rapidly receding will appear fainter than a stationary source of light at the same distance, at a given time. The flux of the quanta of light coming from the source in motion is diminished by the effect of recession, thus only a smaller number of quanta per second can reach the observer. Since the measure of luminosity is based on the number of quanta, it is obvious that the source which is receding will appear fainter. The actual reduction of the apparent brightness is represented by a factor which is equal to v/c, where v is the velocity of recession and c the velocity of light. A recession with a velocity v = 3,000 km./s. reduces the apparent brightness by 1%. When the velocity is v = 30,000 km./s. we have a reduction of 10% and so on. The effects of the recession of galaxies will therefore be negligible until a velocity of several thousand km./s. is reached. These effects will become conspicuous for velocities which are measurable with the 200-inch. If therefore the red-shift is really produced by recession of the galaxies, the factor of reduction of their apparent magnitude should be easily measurable on photographs taken with the 200-inch. At the limit of its power the factor should be of the order of 40 to 50%: such values should leave no doubt of its existence. By these observations it will be possible to decide whether the red-shift can be taken as a proof of the expansion of the universe or whether it is due to some other new natural cause so far unknown.

VII.9 Radio emission from the galaxies.

Many investigations and observations have been carried out in recent years in order to determine the flux of radio-waves emitted by the galaxies. Generally speaking, with the exception of a few well-defined cases, like M.31, for instance, the radio sources do not coincide with galaxies.

Mills, at Sydney, has studied ten galaxies, including the Magellanic Clouds, with a radio-telescope consisting of two arrays of dipoles arranged in the shape of a cross (Mills Cross), and working on 86 Mc./s. (3·5 m.). He found that the radio-frequency emission from these galaxies shows two different distributions of radiation; the first, similar to that of stars of population I, while the second has the shape of a halo and does not correspond to any distribution of known stars. Neither radio emission is of a thermal character and the relative contribution of each appears to be different for the various types of galaxies. It is certain that in the not too distant future, with improvements in technique, with the greater power of radio-telescopes and their greater resolving power, it will be possible to increase our knowledge in this field.

Some spiral galaxies relatively near to us, such as M.31, M.33 and M.81, have been definitely identified as being radio sources. Although radio sources have been identified with well-developed spiral galaxies of types *Sb* and *Sc*, this has not been possible as yet in the case of elliptical galaxies. In Table 8 we compare the photographic magnitude of some spiral galaxies with their radio-electric magnitude obtained from observations at 158·5 Mc./s. (1·9 m.).

TABLE 8

Galaxy	Type	Radio-electric magnitude	Photographic magnitude
M.31	Sb	6·0	5·0
NGC 3031	Sb	8·9	8·7
NGC 5194–5	Sc	9·7	9·7
NGC 2841	Sb	10·4	10·5
NGC 891	S	9·0	12·2

Coutrez finds that the agreement between these magnitudes is good and that we can therefore assume that the ratio between the optical and the radio-frequency flux is constant for the normal spirals and of the order of 10^6. Observations of the radio emission from normal galaxies of type *Sb* show that their flux is more intense compared with the optical flux of systems like NGC 891, in which the nucleus is relatively less important, than in systems like NGC 4594. This suggests that the radio emission from normal galaxies is not related to the stars of population II, but rather to the spiral structure.

Radio emission is particularly intense from peculiar galaxies and from pairs of galaxies which were once thought to be colliding galaxies. Cygnus A is one of the most intense known sources (57×10^{-24} wm^{-2} (c./s.)$^{-1}$) at 158 Mc./s. The optical identification of this object has been extremely difficult and was obtained finally with the 200-inch. With its help it has been possible to show that the galaxy in question has a double nucleus and this suggested a collision between separate galaxies. It has also been possible to find in the spectrum of this object the existence of wide, bright lines produced by interstellar gas which is in a condition of high excitation. These lines could be produced in this collision. They are lines of NeIII, NeV, OI, OII, OIII, NII and $H\alpha$. The width of the lines corresponds to a velocity of dispersion of 4,000 km./s. The bright lines are responsible for half of the total luminosity of the object and the temperatures must be of the order of $10^{8\circ}$ K. Its distance is estimated to be 90 million parsecs.

By comparing the optical and the radio-frequency flux emitted by galaxies, it appears that two classes exist; namely the 'normal' galaxies for which, as we have already mentioned, the ratio between the optical and radio-frequency flux is of the order of 10^6, and galaxies generally identifiable by optical anomalies which can be observed. To the latter class belongs the peculiar galaxy in Cygnus, coincident with the very strong radio source Cygnus A; the flux ratio for these objects is much smaller, i.e. between 1 (in the case of Cygnus A) and 1,000. At first, most astronomers accepted the collision hypothesis—that most of these objects were actually two gravitationally linked galaxies in collision.

Further investigation, however, has strengthened a number of objections which can be levelled against this hypothesis. In the case of Cygnus A, for instance, in order to explain the intensity of the radio emission, the relative velocity of the two objects should be 3,000 km./s. If that were so the spectral lines of the two objects should be distinctly separated as a result of the Doppler effect, and this is not confirmed by the observations. Besides, it is not very probable that the two objects should move exactly in a tangential direction.

On the other hand, all the radio galaxies which have been identified with optical objects are very bright systems. While the probability of collision is fairly high among the numerous small galaxies, the probability of collision among the more rare giant galaxies is extremely low, so low, in fact, as not to account for the number of radio galaxies observed.

Šklovskij, Hoyle and Burbidge, independently, out forward another hypothesis. Since supernovae explosions almost certainly produce the strongest non-thermal galactic radio emissions, it is possible that the radio galaxies are systems of comparatively recent formation, very rich in interstellar matter, where many massive stars are formed, which end their short life as supernovae. The great number of remnants of supernovae could then explain the exceptional intensity of radio emission for these galaxies.

VII.10   The Local Group and clusters of galaxies.

When we were discussing the distribution in space of the galaxies, we mentioned that they may appear not only as isolated objects but also often as groups consisting of two or more galaxies, like systems of double or multiple stars. Our Galaxy, for instance, is a member of the 'Local Group' which consists of about 20 galaxies, if we consider only those that are visible. It is possible that others may exist invisible to us because they are in the zone of obscuration near the galactic equator. The Local Group is a system having an elongated ellipsoidal shape, the major axis of which is 800,000 parsecs. The minor axis is about half this value and the thickness is between 160,000 and 290,000 parsecs. Its centre is located towards the Andromeda galaxy, which is at one end of the group together with the two satellites; i.e. the Magellanic Clouds. In Table 9 are given the characteristics of the components of the Local Group.

TABLE 9

Components of Local Group	Type	Distance 1,000s parsecs	Apparent Magnitude	Absolute Magnitude	Diameter 1,000s parsecs
Galaxy	Sb			− 18·6	24
M.31 Andromeda	Sb	630	4·3	− 19·6	55
M.33 Triangulum	Sc	580	6·2	− 17·6	14
Large Magellanic Cloud	Irr	52	1·2	− 17·4	11
Small Magellanic Cloud	Irr	52	2·8	− 15·8	7
NGC 6822	Irr	415	9·2	− 13·9	2·4
IC 1613	Irr	550	10·0	− 13·7	3·7
NGC 205 Andromeda	E	630	8·9	− 15·0	4·8
M.32 Andromeda	E	630	9·1	− 14·8	2·2
NGC 147	E	480	10·5	− 12·9	2·5
NGC 185	E	480	10·2	− 13·2	2·0
Sculptor	E	76	8·8	− 10·6	1·0
Fornax	E	150	9·1	− 9·4	2·3
Leo I	E	430	—	—	1·9
Leo II	E	400	—	—	1·7
Draco	E	61	11·1	− 7·9	0·6
Ursa Minor	E	70	—	—	1·0

The Local Group contains two giant spirals (The Galaxy and M.31), an Sc spiral (M.33) of dimensions a little greater than half of those of the Galaxy, some dwarf systems and some irregular galaxies. Neither spirals type Sa nor barred spirals exist in this group. The absolute magnitude varies between −8 and −19·6, from dwarfs to supergiants with a luminosity ratio ranging from 1 to 50,000, while the diameters range from 600 to 55,000 parsecs. Probably not all the members of this Local Group are known, but it is the only cluster of galaxies which we can study in detail. As far as the individual masses are concerned M.31 has the greatest mass (2×10^{11} solar masses), followed by the Galaxy (10^{11} solar masses), M.33 (4×10^9 solar masses), and the Large Magellanic Cloud with a mass 2×10^9, that of the Sun.

Generally the spiral galaxies are rather large and bright, while the elliptical are smaller and of faint luminosity. Within the Local Group we can notice a tendency to further clustering. The Galaxy is relatively nearer to the Magellanic Clouds, and M.31 has two elliptical companions. The galaxies belonging to this Local Group are the ones which can be resolved into stars, and therefore the possibility of determining the distance of more remote galaxies depends solely on them.

The largest cluster that can be reached with the more powerful telescopes is that in Virgo. This cluster extends for about twenty degrees in Coma. If its distance is nearly 6 million parsecs, its major axis is 2·3 million parsecs. Although the galaxies forming this cluster of magnitude 10 have been studied in great detail, its total population is still not well known as it is very difficult to separate the dwarf galaxies of the system from the more remote (hence apparently faint) galaxies, situated beyond the cluster. It may well be that we see only the central part of the cluster. In fact a great number of galaxies can be observed almost as a continuation of the cluster, reaching Ursa Major and Lynx. This would imply that the cluster actually has greater dimensions. We are therefore in the presence of a majestic 'super-galactic' system composed of several hundreds of galaxies and which appears flattened like the Galaxy. The velocities of the galaxies in the cluster are of the order of 1,500 km./s. This would suggest that the total mass of the system is of the order of 10^{14} times that of the Sun and that the average mass of its component is 2×10^{11} times that of the Sun.

Other clusters, apparently of similar dimensions, are observed in Corona Borealis, in Perseus and in Leo. Data about these are given in Table 10. An examination of this table shows that the total population of the clusters consists of some hundreds of components. These have a spherical symmetry and a high central density which at first decreases rapidly with increasing distance from the centre and then a little more slowly.

We can conclude that these galaxies have the particular characteristic of being grouped in clusters, and that therefore they are not distributed at random. They are very numerous and the counts

THE GALAXIES

carried out by Shane at Lick show that on average there are more than two per square degree. Often two or more clusters are joined together in groups, to form, as it were, clouds of galaxies. The most conspicuous clusters are similar to that in Coma, but there exist also clusters devoid of strong central condensations like those in Virgo and Ursa Major.

TABLE 10

Clusters	Apparent diameter in degrees	Distance 1,000s parsecs	Radial Velocity (km./s.)	Approximate number of galaxies
Local Group	—	—	—	16
Virgo	12	6,000	1,200	2,500
Pegasus	1	18,000	3,800	100
Perseus	2	28,500	5,200	500
Coma	3	32,000	7,400	1,000
Ursa Major I	0·7	70,000	15,000	300
Leo	0·6	94,000	20,000	300
Corona Borealis	0·5	85,000	21,000	400
Gemini	0·5	78,000	23,000	200
Boötes	0·3	170,000	39,000	150
Ursa Major II	0·2	170,000	42,000	200
Pisces	1·0	18,000	4,700	30
Cancer	1·0	23,000	4,900	150
Ursa Major III	0·7	35,000	—	90
Centaurus	2·0	64,000	—	300

VII.11   Description of the most important galaxies.

GALAXY IN ANDROMEDA. M.31–NGC 224. R.A. 0h11m; Decl. +41° 3'.

This very well known celestial object, which for a long time was thought to be a nebula, had been observed by the Persian astronomer Al-Sufi (A.D. 903–986) who mentioned it in his 'Book of the fixed stars'. It was first observed with a telescope by Simon Marius (A.D. 1612) and later by Halley, Messier and the Herschels.

Its appearance in the sky is that of an elongated ellipse. In actual fact it must be a spheroid or a very flattened disc, inclined at an angle to our line of sight. Since the ratio of the axes of the apparent ellipse is about 3 or 4 to 1, Hubble estimated that the inclination of the equatorial plane of the spiral to the line of sight, was approximately 15° and that the major axis of the apparent ellipse has a position

217

angle of 36° 7'. Its diameter measures 150' but photo-electric measurements have shown that in actual fact it is about 300'. The central region, which appears like a nebular mass, measures approximately 10' × 30' and at its centre we observe a brilliant almost star-like nucleus. The region surrounding the nucleus has a radius of 4' to 5' and appears spherical in shape. From this the spiral arms evolve, arms which can be resolved into stars of various brightness, into star clusters and into hazy patches. The arms of the spiral can be traced from about 1' from the nucleus, and can be followed for two revolutions, up to a distance of 1° 30' or even more. Using Hubble's classification, this galaxy is of an intermediate type of spiral *Sb* and its spectrum is of class G.

In M.31, 200 globular clusters have been detected, very similar to the 100 of the Galaxy. These globular clusters are distributed almost symmetrically around the nucleus, and their apparent density, namely their number per unit area, decreases rapidly with increasing distance from the centre, so that, for instance, at 20' from the centre they are less than half of the original number. The majority of them are projected against the regions enclosed by the spiral arms. Outside the known limits of the galaxy, we find 10 clusters, the furthest being at about 3° 5' from the centre of the galaxy. This is very similar to what happens in the case of the globular clusters of the Galaxy. Dark masses appear in elongated regions or lanes which follow side by side the bright spiral formed of stars. We can imagine that these dark clouds seen from a star in the interior of the galaxy, would appear very much like the great fork of our Milky Way in Cygnus and in Aquila. The absolute magnitude of M.31 is −19·6 and its distance is 630,000 parsecs. Its total diameter is more than twice that of the Galaxy and measures 55,000 parsecs. On one side of the nucleus we detect four arms and five on the other, thus each arm describes two or three complete turns. The spiral arms contain bright blue stars, Cepheids, clusters and emission nebulosities about a thousand of which have been detected. The Cepheids have periods between 10 and 48 days and magnitude between 19·3 and 18·1. The brightest stars in the arms have absolute magnitude −7 and −8 and many of them appear to be supergiants of class F.

The 200 globular clusters surrounding M.31 consist of stars similar to those forming its central part. From the reddening produced by absorbing matter present in the arms, Baade was able to conclude that the southern rather than the northern part of M.31 is nearer to us. Bearing in mind the results obtained when the radial velocity at the two ends of the spiral is studied, it is possible to say that the convex part of the spiral arm is leading, that is to say the spiral is unwinding.

M.32 overlaps one of the arms of M.31 and is very near to NGC 205. With the 200-inch, Baade succeeded in photographing individual stars in these systems, showing that M.32, like the nucleus of M.31, appears to consist of red stars of absolute magnitude −1. The absolute magnitudes of NGC 205 and M.32 are respectively −15·0 and −14·8.

Schwarzschild has compared the stellar populations of M.31 and of its elliptical companion NGC 205. The stars in both systems were counted and their surface brightness was determined photographically. The ratio between number of stars and brightness is much higher for NGC 205 than for M.31 and agrees with the results obtained for the globular clusters. Actually for M.31 this ratio is in good agreement with that for stars near the Sun. This shows that the greater part of the light of M.31 is not due to stars of population II, but probably to more advanced stars of population I.

Already in 1914, Slipher had discovered that the spectral lines of M.31 were inclined when the slit of the spectrograph was set along the major axis of the galaxy. From measurements made by Pease at Mt. Wilson, up to a distance of 2′ 30″ from the nucleus, it can be deduced that the galaxy, in the central part, rotates with a constant angular velocity. If x represents the distance from the centre in seconds of arc, and y represents the radial velocity measured in km./s., we have:

$$y = -0\cdot48\,x - 316$$

Similar measurements of radial velocities have been made by Babcock to the extreme limit of the spiral arms, that is up to 1° 35′ from the nucleus. From these measurements anomalies in the rotation appear at the limit of the central region.

In the spiral arms of the Andromeda galaxy it is possible to photograph small irregular nebulosities which are faint and which are gases emitted by the stars. In fact bright lines, typical of gaseous nebulae, can be seen superimposed on a faint continuum. These objects, therefore, can be used, with the help of large telescopes, to measure radial velocities in various regions of the galaxy. They appear to concentrate along the spiral arms, and from their distribution and association with stars already formed in the spiral they would appear to belong definitely to this system. Spectra of five objects distributed along the major axis of the galaxy are very similar to the spectrum of the Orion Nebula. The most intense line is the λ 3727 Å. (OII), followed by $H\alpha$ and the other lines of the Balmer series. The main nebular lines are N_1 and N_2 (OIII). The photographic magnitude of the objects measured (Plate 40) range from 14·5 to 17. From the observations given in Plate 40, it can be seen that the most probable value for the radial velocity of the galaxy as a whole, is —300 km./s. In a first approximation it can be assumed that these observations, made along the major axis, show the velocity of rotation in the equatorial plane, once they are corrected for the inclination of this plane to the line of sight. The observed velocities must therefore be added to the velocity of the nucleus and multiplied by sec. 15° which obviously is a negligible correction. In figure 45 we give the average velocities of rotation in the plane of the spiral according to the observations carried out by Babcock. The most interesting features of this curve are the progress towards a constant

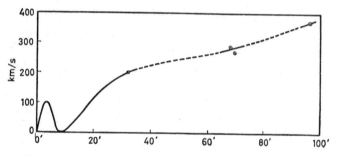

FIG. 45. Rotation of M.31 according to observations by Babcock

angular velocity for the internal arms of the spiral and the sudden rise at zero velocity, or when velocity is negligible, in regions 8′ to 10′ from the nucleus. The fact that this minimum occurs in a region of lesser density, between the nucleus of the galaxy and the first turn of the spiral, may be significant. It may be due to a non-uniform mass distribution along the radius vector of the spiral. We can therefore conclude that the nucleus has a period of rotation of approximately $1·1 \times 10^7$ years, while the period for the external arms is approximately $9·2 \times 10^7$ years. The fact that starting from a radius of 20′ towards the exterior, the angular velocity is almost constant shows that a very great part of the mass of the galaxy must be in the external regions. Supposing that in the more internal regions of this galaxy the centrifugal force balances the gravitational attraction of the mass, the mass within a central sphere of an apparent diameter of 5′ is found to be approximately 3×10^8, while the mass of the system as a whole reaches the value of 2×10^{11} solar masses. This is double the value for the Galaxy.

The circular velocities of stars in a large region around the Sun decrease with increasing distance from the centre, therefore, although both the Galaxy and the Andromeda galaxy have some common characteristics, it would appear logical to suppose that important differences exist in the rotation. Recent measurements, made by Humason and Mayall, have made it possible to determine the radial velocities of various clouds which are at distances between 60′ and 114′ from the centre. The results of these investigations show that from a distance of 65′ or 70′ the line representing a uniform angular velocity, or a velocity of rotation proportional to the distance from the nucleus, changes direction and the slope is opposite to the original, indicating that for greater distances the rotational velocity decreases (fig. 46). In M.31 then, as in the Galaxy and in M.33, the rotational velocity reaches a maximum and then decreases with increasing distances from the nucleus. It is interesting to note here that in M.31, which has a diameter nearly double that of the Galaxy, a maximum of the velocity of rotation is reached at a distance of 15,500 parsecs from the centre. This is about twice the corresponding distance for the Galaxy. The form of the two curves (fig. 46) is very different, at least according to the observational data so far available. The maximum for the Galaxy is much flatter than for M.31 and this may indicate the existence of differences in the law of distribution of the masses in the two objects.

The spiral arms of M.31 can be traced only within a radius of 1° 6′, corresponding to 13,000 parsecs. Beyond this radius, no bright stars are found comparable to those near the Sun. Observations made by Stebbins and Whitford show the existence of a faint and diffuse luminosity around the galaxy.

In order to establish how far the rotation is similar to that of a solid body we need further determinations of radial velocities of spiral galaxies, or alternatively we need to know of what nature are the deviations from the uniform angular velocity. It would be interesting, for instance, to discover whether the gaseous masses

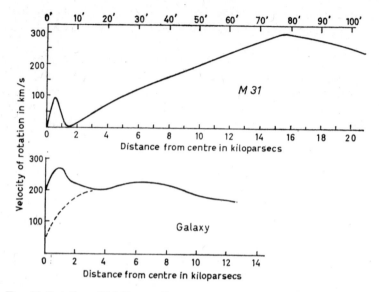

FIG. 46. Rotation of M.31 according to recent observations by Humason and Mayall (above). Rotation of our Galaxy according to recent observations of the 21 cm. hydrogen line by Rougoor and Oort (below). The dotted part of the curve represents the part which was unknown before these observations and was obtained by extrapolation. The distances from the centre are given according to the new scale

have a component along the radius vector, starting from the nucleus as well as a general rotation, namely whether the spiral is approaching or receding from the nucleus. This would, no doubt, give us valuable information on the theory of the spiral structure.

Baade, with the 100-inch at Mt. Wilson, has photographed the central region of M.31 and its two companions M.32 and NGC 205, and he succeeded in resolving them into stars. M.32 is superimposed on the more external arm of the main spiral, at about 24′ south of the nucleus. M.32 is not a spiral, but is rather a typical example of an elliptical galaxy (E_2) with the ratio of its axes between 1 and 1·5. It presents no definite structure except a continuous decrease of intensity from the nucleus towards the exterior to the rather indistinct limits. NGC 205 is 37′ north of the nucleus of M.31, almost exactly along its minor axis. This galaxy too is of the elliptical type (E_5) with a ratio of its axes of 2 to 1. The central concentration is very faint and mixed together there are dark clouds, several indivi-

222

dual stars and small hazy objects which are possibly globular clusters. The brightest stars in both the systems and in the nucleus of M.31 are of photographic magnitude 21·3 and the colour index is +1·3. The absolute photographic magnitude of the brightest stars in these systems is −1·1, therefore very bright blue stars are completely absent. This would indicate that the nucleus of the galaxy has a stellar composition similar to that of the globular clusters and totally different from that of open clusters, which instead contain blue supergiants.

Concerning the constitution of M.31, we can conclude that the spiral arms in the main body of the galaxy and the external parts consist evidently of many emitting objects and of hot blue stars. As we approach the nuclear region, the population changes considerably. Bright stars and emission nebulosities gradually disappear, and the arms continue towards the interior (together with the well-defined channels of gas and dust), almost reaching the nucleus. It is probable, therefore, that the fundamental material of the spiral structure is interstellar gas and dust, which reach a relative high density in the spiral arms and in the dark channels. Moreover, the appearance of the very bright stars in the spiral arms and their absence in the regions limited by the arms, suggest the existence of a close link between dust and supergiant stars.

Photographs of M.31, taken by Baade with the 200-inch at Mt. Palomar, show the existence of an evolutionary cycle when we follow one of the spiral arms from the interior to the exterior. In the inner part of the arm we find dust but no very hot blue stars of class B, which are thought to have originated in the clouds of dust. Further along the arm we find stars of class B and regions of HII and finally, in the outer parts of the arm, we find only stars of class B but no dust.

Baade points out that in this galaxy it is possible to study both population I and II. He photographed an area $5° × 1° 5'$ in blue and red light (Plates 41, 42, 43). The comparison of these photographs shows a very surprising feature. Stars of population II, which are present in great numbers in the nucleus, are also found at a great distance from the nucleus, beyond the spiral structure. It seems as if stars of population II form a disc rather than a halo, and the spiral is embedded in the disc. More than 80% of the light comes from the disc and an even higher proportion of the mass must be composed of stars of population II. Presumably the majority of these stars were

223

formed 6 thousand million years ago. We can put forward the hypothesis that the arms of the spiral produce stars continually and we can ask ourselves how many stars have been produced in this way since the initial formation of population II. Van de Hulst, by means of radio observations of the 21-cm. hydrogen line, has determined the total mass of neutral hydrogen in M.31 and has found that only 1 or 2% of the total mass of M.31 is still in a gaseous state. In the Magellanic Clouds, as we shall see later, this proportion is 30%. Since the total mass of M.31 is 3×10^{11} solar masses, the quantity of matter still left to produce stars is of the order of 10^9 solar masses.

M.31 is also a radio source. The optical galaxy is surrounded by a large, almost spherical, 'corona' of radio emission, which extends for a considerable distance in an east–west direction, as appears from the isophotic contours drawn by Brown and Hazard from observations with the 220-ft. paraboloid at Jodrell Bank operating on a wavelength of 1.89 m. From these measurements and from others made on wavelengths of $3 \cdot 7$ m. and $1 \cdot 2$ m., it appears that on average the galaxy emits a flux density of $1 \cdot 5 \times 10^{-24}$ wm^{-2} (c./s.)$^{-1}$.

GALAXY IN TRIANGULUM. M.33–NGC 598. R.A. 1h 31m; Decl. $+30° 25'$.

This stellar system is also similar to our Galaxy. It appears to us with the plane of the spiral almost at right angles to the line of sight and its dimensions are approximately $83' \times 53'$. Its spiral form was first observed by Lord Rosse who also made a sketch of it in 1849. In appearance the nucleus of this galaxy is very like a large globular cluster (Plate 44), although there is no evidence of resolution into stars. The nuclear region shows a hazy, unresolved, nebular background with several black patches, and many stars can be seen on this background. As we proceed away from the nucleus, the nebulosity becomes fainter and the arms of the spiral become more evident. The arms are wide and populated with stars, clusters and clouds. Some small clusters are very similar to those in M.31 in appearance and in colour but are systematically one or two magnitudes fainter.

The distance of M.33 is about 580,000 parsecs, approximately the same distance as M.31. An appreciable percentage of the total luminosity of this galaxy is produced by blue supergiant stars. The corresponding percentage in M.31 is much smaller and in the ellipti-

44. Spiral galaxy in Triangulum M.33—NGC 598. 200-inch Mt. Palomar

45. The Large Magellanic Cloud

46. The Small Magellanic Cloud

47. Spiral galaxy NGC 891 in Andromeda. 60-inch Mt. Wilson

48. Barred spiral galaxy NGC 1300 in Eridanus. 200-inch Mt. Palomar

49. Spiral galaxy NGC 2841 in Ursa Major. 200-inch Mt. Palomar

50. Spiral galaxy NGC 2903 in Leo. 200-inch Mt. Palomar

51. Spiral galaxy M.81—NGC 3031 in Ursa Major. 200-inch Mt. Palomar

52. Spiral galaxy NGC 4565 in Coma Berenices. Photographed on a red-sensitive plate without filter. 200-inch Mt. Palomar

53. Spiral galaxy in Virgo M.104—NGC 4594. 200-inch Mt. Palomar

54. Spiral galaxy in Canes Venatici M.94—NGC 4736. 200-inch Mt. Palomar

55. Spiral galaxy M.51—NGC 5194 in Canes Venatici and satellite NGC 5195. 200-inch Mt. Palomar

56. Spiral galaxy M.101—NGC 5457 in Ursa Major. 200-inch Mt. Palomar

57. Cluster of galaxies in Coma Berenices. 200-inch Mt. Palomar

58. Cluster of galaxies in Corona Borealis. 200-inch Mt. Palomar

59. Cluster of galaxies in Hercules. 200-inch Mt. Palomar

cal galaxies these stars are completely absent. The nucleus has an absolute magnitude of -8 and is of spectral type F_5, but the total absolute magnitude is approximately $-17\cdot5$. Several Cepheids and a few novae which reach $-6\cdot4$ absolute magnitude have been identified in this system. Moreover, small nebular condensations in emission surrounding blue stars, which have been listed as separate individual galaxies, have also been detected. The most conspicuous is NGC 604 which is slightly elongated and has a diameter of about 230 light-years. Its spectrum is very similar to that of the Orion Nebula. Radial velocities of 25 of these condensations, well distributed in the spiral, have been measured by Mayall and Aller at Lick. The velocity of the system is -320 km./s. and the inclination of the principal plane of the spiral to the line of sight is $33°$. The rotational velocity of the individual condensations has been calculated assuming that a simple circular motion existed in the plane. Then combining these velocities an approximate curve for the velocity of rotation of the system as a whole was obtained. From these results (fig. 41) we can conclude that the main body of the galaxy, within a radius of 16′, seems to rotate almost like a solid body (the velocity of rotation increases fairly uniformly with distance), while the external parts, in a region between 16′ and 30′, seem to rotate like a planetary system (that is with a velocity of rotation which decreases with distance). The transition between the two types of motion occurs at approximately 16′ (about 1,000 parsecs) from the centre. At this distance the rotational velocity reaches a maximum of 120 km./s. According to Schwarzschild the total mass of M.33 is 5×10^9 times that of the Sun.

Voroncov-Velijaminov has investigated the distribution of supergiants and of dust in M.33. In the spiral arms of this galaxy there are numerous groups of supergiants distributed in irregular chains or in clusters in a cloud-like shape. Filaments or channels of matter are also concentrated in the spiral arms. The shape of the dark arms suggests to us that the dust is distributed along lines of magnetic force, as happens in the Galaxy, where filaments of matter often end in very hot stars. All this would tend to show that supergiants must be born in groups, where gas clouds and channels divide into many parts giving rise to condensations.

Šajn has discovered about 80 diffuse emission nebulosities and about 200 objects of high luminosity, by means of photographs taken in limited regions of the spectrum around $H\alpha$ and around λ 3727 Å.

(OII) and in the yellow region. Stars of population I are very common and the emission nebulosities are mostly distributed in the spiral arms.

The comparison between M.33 and M.31 gives useful information on the systematic variation of the stellar content along the sequence of the classification. For instance in M.33 (Plate 44), unlike M.31, the resolution into stars extends to the interior of the nucleus.

A comparison between the spectra of M.31 and M.33, made by Mayall and Aller, reveals that in M.33 the distribution of the star population, according to the H–R diagram, is completely different from that in M.31. The ultra-violet region of M.33 shows a considerable absorption in the lines of the Balmer series, while CN bands, which are well defined in the spectrum of M.31, do not appear at all in M.33. The spectral type of M.33 changes rapidly with wavelength, as it passes from the violet to the yellow, from class F to class G. Notwithstanding the fact that the data available are not yet complete, we can say that the percentage of stars of classes A and F is much higher in the central part of M.33 than in that of M.31. Moreover in M.33 there is no evidence of a central, bright and amorphous nucleus as vast as in M.31.

The determination of proper motion carried out by van Maanen at Mt. Wilson, for M.33 and other galaxies seen face on, has not given reliable results, because of the very short interval of time between the photographs. With greater time intervals it ought to be possible to show the rotation or expansion of this and similar systems.

MAGELLANIC CLOUDS—Large Cloud R.A. 5h 22m; Decl. −69° 5′; Small Cloud R.A. 0h 53m; Decl. −72° 6′.

The two galaxies described in 1521 by Pigafetta during Magellan's voyage round the world, and also called *Clouds of the Cape of Good Hope* or *Nubecula major* and *Nubecula minor*, are at about −70° of declination. The Large Cloud, covering a field of approximately 12°, is in Doradus while the Small Cloud, covering a field of approximately 8°, is in Tucana. The detailed study of the Magellanic Clouds, which was practically the starting-point of the study of galaxies, began when the Southern Stations of Harvard and Lick in South America and South Africa were set up.

In 1906 Miss Leavitt discovered a large number of variable stars in photographs of the Magellanic Clouds which led her in 1912 to the discovery of the period–luminosity relationship for the Cepheids.

Shapley and Miss Cannon made extensive investigations on the photographs and spectra of these objects. From these investigations it was possible to establish that the two Clouds were independent galaxies and not simply condensations within our Galaxy. Both have a mass smaller than M.31 and M.33 and are also fainter. The masses of the Large Cloud and Small Cloud determined by various methods are 2×10^9 and 2×10^8 solar masses respectively, that is they are in a ratio of nearly 3 to 1.

The Large Cloud contains blue stars, red supergiants of absolute magnitude -10, absorbing dust and much ionized hydrogen in the form of bright nebulosity. It is mainly composed of stars of population I mixed with a small number of stars of population II (Plate 45). The Small Cloud, on the other hand, does not contain any dust and has many stars of population II, which probably represent the majority of stars (Plate 46). In the Large Cloud we can establish an axis and guess at the shape of a barred galaxy with the beginnings of a spiral structure. The Small Cloud has no definite structure, but extends in the direction of the Large Cloud, perhaps because of a tidal effect produced by it.

At the Southern Station of Harvard Observatory, several novae were discovered in both the Clouds. These novae, however, are not as common as in our Galaxy or in the Andromeda galaxy. Two dozen objects have also been detected which appear to be planetaries. They are apparently associated with the central regions of the Clouds and the surrounding regions. The distribution of these objects, which certainly belong to population I, such as blue supergiants of classes O and B, bright diffuse nebulae, stars with emission lines, is concentrated on what looks like the bright arms of the barred spiral forming the Large Cloud.

In the Small Cloud are found several Cepheids with periods of two or three days, which are not common in the Galaxy, while in the Large Cloud the distribution of periods is nearer to that of the Galaxy. Both Clouds, but more especially the Large Cloud, contain a great number of bright blue stars. Nebulosity and dust contain Cepheid variables which in the Galaxy belong to population I. The two Clouds contain clusters which appear to be globular clusters in one of which it is possible to detect also RR Lyrae stars. In each of the Magellanic Clouds three novae have appeared, probably belonging to population II. Both these galaxies, which are visible to the unaided eye, are typical irregular galaxies which can be resolved into stars, without nucleus and without any evident symmetry of rotation. Their stellar content is very similar to that of the Galaxy, namely they have many varieties of stars, nebulae of the Orion type, a few globular clusters and several clusters of the type of the Pleiades. In the Large Cloud we find a large irregular cluster; NGC 1910 of Dreyer's catalogue. This cluster has a diameter of 200 light-years and is composed of a hundred or more giant and supergiant objects, among which is the star S Doradus, one of the brightest stars known to us, although not visible to the unaided eye, because of its distance. S Doradus is an irregular variable of the spectral type of P Cygni, and its magnitude varies between 8·2 and 9·4, while its luminosity is nearly a million times that of the Sun.

The apparent photographic magnitudes of the two Clouds are 1·2 and 2·8 respectively. The main parts of the two galaxies are almost circular and have diameters of 11 and 7 million parsecs. Variable stars and clusters are found also far away from the main parts. The majority of variables are Cepheids, but long-period and irregular variables as well as eclipsing binaries are present. More than thirty clusters have been detected in the Large Cloud, but only a few in the Small Cloud. Those detected in the Small Cloud are similar to the clusters in M.31, but appear systematically fainter than the globular clusters of the galactic system.

By means of the Cepheids the distance of the two Magellanic Clouds has been determined and this is about 50,000 parsecs for both of them. In reality the two Clouds, which are 21° apart from centre to centre, are much nearer than they appear to be. In fact with special photographic plates and by means of a star count of faint stars, it is possible to extend considerably the limits of both systems. Each Cloud seems to be surrounded by envelopes containing very few stars. The central part, which contains the majority of the mass of the system, is surrounded by a haze of stars. The total absolute magnitude of the Large Cloud is −17·4 and of the Small Cloud −5·8. According to Shapley it is possible that the two Clouds are two irregular massive nuclei surrounded by one large single envelope of stars. What is almost certain is that these galaxies are within the boundary, or at most at the limit of the haze of stars of our own Galaxy. The Magellanic Clouds can be considered as satellites of our Galaxy and they certainly are within its gravitational field.

So far it has not been possible to measure any proper motion of either Cloud, but the radial velocity of the Large Cloud is +280 km./s., while that of the Small Cloud, which is further away, is +170 km./s.

By means of radio observations of the 21-cm. line, the distribution of neutral hydrogen in both Clouds and its motion along the line of sight has been determined. The neutral hydrogen is found scattered in a volume much greater than that occupied by the stars, so that the two galaxies are in contact and a filament directed towards the Galaxy seems to exist. The radial velocities of many small areas scattered in both Clouds have been measured by means of radio observations and show that the Large Cloud is receding from the centre of the Galaxy with an average velocity of 37 km./s., while the Small Cloud is approaching with a velocity of 16 km./s. There is no doubt that both Clouds are subject to the gravitational field of the Galaxy and that they move around its centre like two planets or comets move around the Sun.

Mills has drawn the isophotic contours of the radio waves emitted by the Magellanic Clouds on a wavelength of 3·5 m. There is very little similarity between the photographic appearance and the distribution of radio-frequency emissions of the Clouds, perhaps because the regions emitting radio waves are much larger. We must however remember that photographs with a long exposure show that the Large Cloud extends over a much greater area and even beyond the limits of the radio-frequency emission regions. Mills concludes that the radio waves from the Magellanic Clouds on the 3·5 m. wavelength must originate mainly in a non-thermal process and must have a distribution which is closely linked with the interstellar gas and the brightest stars.

As we have already mentioned, the Magellanic Clouds together with M.31, M.33, a few other minor objects and our Galaxy form the Local Group. If we suppose that near the galactic longitude 55° the orbital velocity of the Sun with respect to the centre of the Galaxy is 250 km./s., then the relative velocities of the galaxies belonging to this group are rather small.

GALAXY IN ANDROMEDA. NGC 891. R.A. 2h 20m; Decl. +42° 2′.
This is a spiral galaxy seen edgeways (Plate 47) with a region of absorbing matter across its equatorial plane. Its dimensions are 12′ × 1′ and its approximate distance is 10 million parsecs.

THE GALAXIES

GALAXY IN ERIDANUS. NGC 1300. R.A. 3h 18m; Decl. —19° 33'.

The galaxy in Eridanus is a barred spiral galaxy of type *SBb*, very extensive and brighter at the centre. The spiral arms, partly resolved in chains of stars, originate from the bar (Plate 48).

CLUSTER OF GALAXIES IN CANCER. R.A. 8h 18m; Decl. +21° 14'.

This cluster is distributed over an area of nearly one square degree. With the 48-inch Schmidt at Mt. Palomar, 300 galaxies have been counted in it, with photographic magnitudes between 13·8 and 18. The brighter galaxies, perhaps having greater masses, tend to concentrate towards the centre, while the fainter, or smaller, masses predominate in the external regions.

GALAXY IN URSA MAJOR. NGC 2841. R.A. 9h 20m; Decl. +61° 9'.

This is a spiral galaxy of type *Sa* endowed with many arms. It has a strong central concentration in the nucleus, which increases rapidly in intensity towards the centre (Plate 49).

GALAXY IN LEO. NGC 2903. R.A. 9h 30m; Decl. +21° 41'.

The galaxy NGC 2903 is a spiral galaxy of type *Sb*. It is very large with arms resolved into stars and an irregular nucleus which is very bright at the centre (Plate 50).

GALAXY IN URSA MAJOR. M.81–NGC 3031. R.A. 9h 52m; Decl. +69° 16'.

This typical spiral galaxy is of type *Sa*. Its dimensions are 10' × 16' and its distance is approximately 2 million parsecs. The arms of the spiral are resolved into stars and its nucleus is very compact and bright with dark well-defined filaments where it decreases in intensity to open up into the spiral (Plate 51).

GROUP OF GALAXIES IN LEO. NGC 3185, 3187, 3190, 3193.

The average co-ordinates of this group are: R.A. 10h 15m, Decl. +22° 1'; galactic longitude 180° and galactic latitude +56°. This group consists of a great variety of types: NGC 3193 is a type E_2; NGC 3190 is a type *Sa*; NGC 3185 is a type *SBab*; and NGC 3187 is a type *SBc*. The apparent magnitudes vary from 12 to 13·5. The distance of this group is approximately 6 million parsecs. In the case of NGC 3193 Humason measured a red-shift corresponding to a velocity of 1,300 km./s.

THE GALAXIES

GALAXY IN CANES VENATICI. NGC 4449. R.A. 12h 26m; Decl. +44° 19'.

This irregular galaxy has often been considered as a duplicate in the northern hemisphere of the Magellanic Clouds. It has no definite symmetrical structure and its main characteristics are the existence of large regions of gaseous emission which have some resemblance to the HII regions in the Galaxy and in M.31.

From the spectra of the system we deduce that either it is embedded in a gaseous medium, or that it consists of many unresolved HII regions in which the bright lines of the Balmer series originate. The main nebular lines (OIII) are well defined and the emission spectrum is very similar to that of a vast region of HII. The absorption spectrum has intense bands in the ultra-violet. The spectral type is A_7 in the region $\lambda\lambda$ 3850 to 4100 Å. and approximately F at λ 4340 Å.

It is interesting to compare this galaxy with M.33 and M.31. From this comparison it would appear that NGC 4449 has a general spectrum produced mainly by stars of population I. In the arms of its spiral, M.33 has a spectrum and structure which are intermediate, and M.31 has a well-defined central nucleus, which contains a considerable number of giants of population II.

GALAXY IN VIRGO. M.87–NGC 4486. R.A. 12h 29m; Decl. +12° 37'.

This is one of the brightest elliptical systems of type E_0, and its absolute magnitude -15.5. Its distance is 13 million parsecs. The appearance of this galaxy is that of a giant globe of stars belonging to population II, completely amorphous and presumably free from interstellar dust. It is surrounded by a halo of luminous objects of absolute magnitude probably between -6 and -8, which must almost certainly be globular clusters too distant to be resolved into stars. This galaxy belongs to the Virgo cluster and is characterized by a 'jet' which has a continuous spectrum which is bluer than that of the spectrum of the rest of the galaxy. Forbidden lines, due to oxygen and with radial velocities of 300 km./s. with respect to the nucleus, suggest that the 'jet' is emitted from it.

NGC 4486 is also a powerful radio source (12.5×10^{-24} wm^{-2} (c./s.)$^{-1}$) at the frequency of 100 Mc./s. Since the blue 'jet' has a much smaller extension than the radio source, it is possible that the whole of the galaxy participates in the radio-frequency emission.

THE GALAXIES

GALAXY IN COMA. NGC 4565. R.A. 12h 34m; Decl. +26° 12'.

This is a spiral galaxy which is seen almost exactly edgeways. The dark equatorial belt, which is very conspicuous, is studded with luminous globules (Plate 52). The nucleus is very intense and appears more developed in the northern part of the galaxy, perhaps because of a small inclination of its equatorial plane to the line of sight. Its dimensions are 1' × 15' and the radial velocity is +1,100 km./s.

CLUSTER OF GALAXIES IN VIRGO. M.100–NGC 4321. R.A. 12h 21m; Decl. +16° 3'.
NGC 4567, 4568. R.A. 12h 34m; Decl. +11° 29'.
M.90–NGC 4569. R.A. 12h 35m; Decl. +13° 23'.

With the exception of the members of our Local Group, this cluster is the nearest to the solar system. It contains about 500 galaxies and is at a distance of approximately 6 million parsecs. More than a hundred of its members are brighter than magnitude 13, nearly 75% are spiral galaxies (*Sc*), and the remainder are elliptical galaxies. The cluster is receding with a velocity of 1,200 km./s. and it has internal relative velocities of 1,500 km./s. This cluster gives us the opportunity of comparing stars contained in the galaxies in various stages of their evolution. Generally, the components of the cluster of elliptical type cannot be resolved into stars. NGC 4567, 4568 are both spiral galaxies, the northern one is seen face on and the southern is more inclined to the line of sight.

GALAXY IN VIRGO. M.104–NGC 4594. R.A. 12h 38m; Decl. −10° 44'.

The galaxy in Virgo is a spiral galaxy which is seen edgeways and measures 1' × 7' (Plate 53). Its nucleus, which is amorphous, bright and very diffuse, is surrounded by the spiral, and cannot be resolved into stars. A very dark and intense band crosses both the nucleus and the spiral. NGC 4594 belongs to the spectral type F_5 and has a radial velocity of +1,100 km./s. From the photographic examination of the bright points which are seen in this galaxy, Lindblad was able to obtain the orientation in space of this object. If we combine this with the measurements of the radial velocities made by Pease, we find that this galaxy is not rotating in a right-hand direction. In this case, therefore, we will have a galaxy which, contrary to most galaxies, has an unwinding spiral.

THE GALAXIES

GALAXY IN CANES VENATICI. M.94–NGC 4736. R.A. 12h 49m; Decl. +41° 20′.

This spiral galaxy is seen face on. It is of type *Sa* and has arms which are closed with few stars scattered in them (Plate 54). The nucleus is very compact, with dark bands intermingled with bright matter.

CLUSTER OF GALAXIES IN COMA. R.A. 12h 55m; Decl. +28° 17′.

The two brightest components of this cluster have an apparent photographic magnitude of between 13·2 and 13·5. The apparent diameter is 12°, but since its distance is 36 million parsecs, the real diameter of the cluster is 7·2 million parsecs. A preliminary examination shows that in the cluster there are about 9,000 galaxies up to the apparent magnitude limit of 19 within a circle of 6° radius.

GALAXY IN CANES VENATICI. M.51–NGC 5194. R.A. 13h 28m; Decl. +47° 24′.

This is a classical and beautiful spiral galaxy with its equatorial plane at right angles to the line of sight (Plate 55). The stellar condensations clearly resolved in its arms are outstanding. The nucleus, of star-like appearance, and surrounded by a bright nebular mass with dark matter between the coils of the spiral, has a diameter of 41″. From the nucleus evolve four concentric coils. The galaxy measures 6′ × 12′ and its distance is approximately 18 million parsecs. To the north we have the galaxy satellite NGC 5195, joined to the other by a bridge of matter which is linked with one of the spiral arms.

GALAXY M.101–NGC 5457. R.A. 14h 2m; Decl. +54° 32′.

This is a galaxy of type *Sc* with a very open spiral seen face on (Plate 56) and it measures 16′. There are dark filaments in the arms and stellar condensations at the end of the arms which are clearly resolved and reach out far from the nucleus. The nucleus itself is rather small, round, very bright and not resolved into stars. Bright nodules of emission nebulosity surrounded by stars of early types have been identified. Here we have all the characteristics of spiral galaxies *Sc* and of irregular galaxies.

CLUSTER OF GALAXIES IN SERPENS. R.A. 15h 18m; Decl. +20° 53′.

The cluster in Serpens consists of a very compact group of six

233

galaxies covering a circular field of 120″ diameter. Its brightest component is NGC 6027 and the apparent magnitude of the six galaxies ranges from 14·7 to 16·9. According to Humason the radial velocities of the two brightest components of the group are +4,415 km./s. for NGC 6027 and +4,031 km./s. for NGC 6027b. He remarks that the difference of nearly 400 km./s. between the two is not exceptional since several other similar cases can be found in other groups of galaxies. From these radial velocities, the distance of the cluster is calculated to be approximately 20 million parsecs. The various components belong to types *Sa*, *Sb* and *Sc*. The group is possibly the densest among those known.

GROUP OF GALAXIES IN PEGASUS. NGC 7317, 7318, 7319, 7320. R.A. 22h 34m; Decl. +33° 46′.

Here we have four small galaxies one of which is elliptical (or rather of intermediate spiral type) and the others three barred spirals. The distance of the group is of the order of 26 million parsecs. NGC 7317 is almost round, with a bright nucleus and a diameter of 0·4′. NGC 7318 is a faint open spiral with two arms, a nucleus of star-like appearance and a diameter of 1′. NGC 7319 is moderately bright, oval in shape and 0·8′ long—it may possibly be a spiral. NGC 7320 is a faint spiral with a patchy appearance and a hazy nucleus and it measures 1·8′ × 0·8′.

VII.12 The evolution of galaxies

The existence of a continuous sequence of galaxies classified by morphological criteria has suggested a connection with galactic evolution. There are various interpretations. The Hubble sequence can represent an evolutionary sequence, starting from irregular masses, passing through the spiral stage and ending with elliptical galaxies. If all galaxies follow this path they probably have different ages. We can also imagine that the galaxies were formed at about the same time but now have different evolutionary ages. Galaxies rich in interstellar matter can keep themselves young, continuously generating new stars, while galaxies which have little interstellar matter must age. Recent researches have shown that other possibilities do exist. Observations disclosing the existence of galaxies with extremely strong radio emission suggest that great internal galactic explosions could have affected their evolutionary ages.

CHAPTER VIII

Origin and evolution of the universe

VIII.1   Introduction.

COSMOLOGY can be defined as the study of the nature of the universe, in space and in time, as it is now, what it was like in the past and what it will probably be in the future. In this way Gamow defines a science which can be considered as the final goal to which all our astronomical and astrophysical knowledge is directed.

The cosmological problems relating to the structure of the universe could perhaps be summarized in a few questions. Is the universe in a steady state or is it in a state of evolution? Is the universe finite or infinite? Is it curved?

There exists one important observational datum which all possible theories must take into account and that is the red-shift observed in the spectra of galaxies. This red-shift is greater the further is the distance of the galaxy observed. As we have already mentioned in an earlier chapter, this phenomenon has been interpreted as a Doppler effect, hence as an expansion of the universe.

Here perhaps we ought to explain what we mean by expansion. When talking of the expansion of the universe or of velocity of recession of the galaxies from us, we tend to think of ourselves as being at the centre of a universe the radius of which expands. Actually this is not the case. On whatever galaxy we found ourselves, we would always have the same impression. Every galaxy recedes from all the others. An example which may explain this is the following. Suppose we have a small balloon filled with gas, on the surface of which small dots are marked. When the balloon is inflated further the surface increases and the distance between the various dots increases too. Every dot appears to run away from all the others. The further two points are from each other, the faster they recede.

The velocity is given by the distance covered divided by the time taken to cover it. Thus if in a given instant two points A and B are 6 yards apart and the point A is 10 yards from the point D and after a given time t the two pairs of points are 12 and 20 yards apart, the velocity of A with respect to B (or of B with respect to A) is $6/t$ and that of A with respect to D (or of D with respect to A) is $10/t$; that is to say that the velocity is proportional to the distance between the points considered. A similar reasoning applies to a three-dimensional space for the molecules of gas contained in an expansible container. When the surface expands, every molecule moves away from the others and the density of the gas diminishes.

Let us now return to the problem of the expansion of the universe.

We have said that such expansion 'has been interpreted' as a Doppler effect. The astronomer, unlike the physicist, the chemist and other scientists in general, cannot perform direct experiments upon the objects he studies and cannot even examine them closely. He must limit himself to collect the radiation that these objects emit and then interpret the information contained in it. How does this interpretation take place? Generally by analogy with our experience and with terrestrial phenomena. Thus the displacement of a spectral line towards the red or the violet according to a given law, is due to motion of the light source with reference to the observer. This phenomenon at least has been proved by direct experiments. It is very probable that it is true in the whole of the universe, and therefore our interpretation is justified that similar displacements observed in the lines of spectra of celestial objects are due to a Doppler effect. The fact remains that we still have to make an extrapolation and the impossibility of a direct check of the generalization leaves us with the doubt that a law valid for short distances may not be still valid when the light reaches us after travelling for millions or thousands of millions of years. We do not have the absolute certainty that the only possible interpretation of the red-shift is that of a velocity of recession. However, up to now the most plausible interpretation of the red-shift is still the expansion of the universe, and the cosmological theories must take into account such expansion.

Two conflicting theories exist today. One maintains that the universe is in a steady state and the other that it is in a state of evolution. We shall try to describe briefly the fundamentals of both theories and

ORIGIN AND EVOLUTION OF THE UNIVERSE

the observational tests which have been suggested to prove their validity.

The steady state theory of the universe is upheld by Bondi, Gold and Hoyle. The expansion of the universe would appear to be irreconcilable with its steady state, but they formulate the hypothesis that although the universe is expanding continuously, its density nevertheless remains constant in time, because matter is being created continuously. The older galaxies disappear in space, receding with increasing velocities, while the newly created matter produces new galaxies and new stars.

According to the other theory, supported by many astronomers, the universe, as we see it at present, is the result of an explosion which occurred a few thousand million years ago when matter was in a state of very high concentration, and the flight of the galaxies would simply be the result of such an explosion. The universe evolves towards decay, when all sources of energy existing in the stars would be completely exhausted, and its density would diminish.

Besides this we could ask ourselves whether the universe is finite and unlimited, like the surface of a sphere, or rather infinite and Euclidean, or again infinite and with a negative curvature like the surface of a hyperboloid which has nearly the shape of a saddle. We shall return to this subject later on.

What are the observations that we can take as basis for the answers to these questions? The concentration of galaxies must vary with distance, according to a given law depending on the curvature of the universe. Unfortunately we do not yet know the distance of the furthest galaxies with the accuracy required to reach a definite conclusion. We see the furthest galaxies as they were millions of years ago, since that is the time taken by the light to reach us. If the physical properties of these remote galaxies are substantially different from those of galaxies nearer to us this could be a proof that evolution has occurred with time and therefore it would be an argument in favour of the evolution theory. But the information that the light from remote galaxies gives us on their physical properties is, so far, very scanty and such as not to allow us to reach definite conclusions in favour of either theory.

VIII.2   The Steady State Theory.

The postulate on which this theory is based is that continuous creation of new matter maintains the universe at a constant density, in spite of expansion. The principle on which Bondi and Gold base this conclusion is the physical principle of symmetry, which requires that an observer on any of the galaxies should have always the same view of the universe as a whole. If the universe changes with time, then we must postulate that these various observers would compare 'simultaneous' views of the universe. But what meaning has the word 'simultaneous' in a universe which as a whole is a collection of objects not only in different positions in space, but also in different epochs of time? Bondi and Gold avoid this difficulty by assuming that the principle of symmetry is valid not only for space but also for time. Wherever an observer may be and in whatever epoch, he would always have the same over-all picture of the universe. This postulate implies that the universe must be in a steady state.

The primal element which is being continuously created is hydrogen, and although it may change into heavier elements by nuclear reactions in the interior of stars, it is still by far the most abundant element, because we can assume that the region of the universe which we can investigate is still relatively young. We have several proofs that the age of the Galaxy is approximately 10 thousand million years. Probably heavy matter is concentrated in the oldest galaxies, but expansion would scatter it out of our field of observation, while creation of new hydrogen forms new galaxies.

Calculations show that the ratio between expansion of the universe and creation of new matter is such that the average density of the matter formed 200 thousand million years ago is only $1/10^{43}$ of that of the matter formed recently. A steady state universe which is expanding must necessarily be infinite in space and time. The continuous creation of matter may at first appear as a violation of the principle of conservation of energy, but Hoyle argues that the 'balance sheet', as it were, of energy cannot be completely balanced in one part of the universe, because no part of the universe is closed and limited. Moreover, in an infinite space in infinite expansion, according to the theory of relativity, the local concentrations of energy are closely linked to the energy of expansion of the whole universe. That the energy of expansion could assume forms which could create new matter cannot be excluded.

VIII.3 The Evolution Theory.

As we have already said, there are many proofs which indicate that our Galaxy has an age of about 10 thousand million years. More-over, if we imagine a reversal of the motion of receding galaxies, we find that 8 thousand million years ago they must have all been con-tained in a restricted space. This has led to the theory of evolution, according to which the universe is the result of an explosion which occurred 8 or 10 thousand million years ago.

One question which presents itself is why should all galaxies have extremely low densities and no denser galaxies exist? If they were formed by an explosion of an extremely dense universe, then we would expect to find at least some galaxies with greater density. Gamow argues that in the early stages of the explosion the tempera-ture of the universe was so high that the density of the energy was predominant and it had the effect of dispersing the gas uniformly in all directions. With decreasing temperature a time was reached when the density of matter was greater than the density of energy. It was at this stage that matter could begin to gather into extremely large and cold masses of gas called the 'supragalactic clouds'. These, in their turn, divided and condensed in smaller and smaller masses of gas. The condensing of these masses would increase their temperature until the stage was reached when nuclear reactions could begin to take place and then stars were born.

In order to clarify the concepts we have just been discussing, we shall have to remember that Einstein's equation $E = mc^2$ indicates the equivalence between mass and energy. When, therefore, we talk of average density of the universe, we must include not only density of matter, but also the density equivalent to all radiation existing in space. Generally speaking, the density of energy is always much lower than that of matter. In cosmic space, however, matter is so rarefied, that in relation to it, the density of radiation is no longer negligible. The density of energy is obtained by dividing the radiated energy per unit volume by the square of the velocity of light. The energy radiated per unit volume is given by the Stefan-Boltzmann law $E = \sigma T^4$, where σ is a constant equal to $7 \cdot 6 \times 10^{-15}$ and T is the absolute temperature. At the normal terrestrial temperature of ap-proximately 300° K., the density of energy is $6 \cdot 5 \times 10^{-26}$ g./cm.^{3}. In interstellar space, on the other hand, where the temperature is lower than 100° K., the density of energy is 10^{-27} g./cm.^{3}. But in interstellar space in the vicinity of the solar system, the density of matter is approximately 10^{-24} g./cm.^{3}, and therefore, the density of radiation is a small quantity (one per thousand), but by no means a negligible part of the total density. In normal conditions, however, the density of matter is much higher. For instance, the density of water is 1, that is to say, one cubic centimetre of water weighs one gramme, and this means that at our temperatures, the density of radiation is approximately 10^{25} times smaller.

When the universe was concentrated in a small space, its temperature must have been much higher. Gamow calculates that 200 thousand years after the explosion, the temperature must have been 6,000° K. But in an expanding universe, the density of energy diminishes more rapidly than that of matter. In fact, if the radius is multiplied by a factor l, the volume will be multiplied by l^3, and the density of matter will be divided by l^3. The temperature, on the other hand, is divided by l, and therefore, the density of energy will be divided by l^4. Therefore, even if initially because of the high temperature, the density of energy were greater than that of matter, there must have been a time when the situation was reversed. As long as the density of energy was predominant, the radiation was diffusing the gas irregularly in all directions in space; when, however, matter became predominant gravitationally, the gas began to break up and to collect into spheres, which became the supragalactic clouds. The research done by Jeans in this field has shown that a gas which fills a large volume tends to break up in separate masses, the dimensions of which depend upon the density and the temperature of the gas itself. Gamow calculates that this transition from the 'energetic' to the 'material' period occurred 250 million years after the explosion.

From what we have said so far, it appears that in contrast with the steady state theory which postulates a universe infinite in time and space, the theory of evolution conjures up a vision of a universe which could be either finite or infinite. Expansion can go on to infinity and the universe lapse into decay represented by an increasing rarefaction or, alternatively, expansion and contractions may follow each other and the universe can be 'pulsating' rather than expanding. The first will occur if the velocity of expansion is greater than the escape velocity, which is the velocity required to overcome the gravitational attraction which galaxies exert upon each other. In the other case, the pulsating universe, the velocity of expansion must be smaller than the escape velocity. What would happen here would be something like launching a rocket into space from the Earth with a velocity which is smaller than the escape velocity. The rocket would end by falling back on to the Earth, and if there were no friction produced by the atmosphere, and if the two bodies, Earth and rocket, were perfectly elastic, then the rocket would bounce up and down indefinitely.

With regard to the form of the universe we shall see that it is possible to formulate a hypothesis. A Euclidean universe is one in which Euclidean geometry is valid, that is to say a universe in which the shortest path between two points is a straight line. A positively curved universe is analogous in a three-dimensional space, to the surface of a sphere which is defined, as a positively curved surface, because a plane tangent to it at any point, leaves the whole sphere all on one side of the plane. A negatively curved space, on the other hand, is analogous to a surface of a hyperboloid; in fact a plane tangent at a point of the surface divides the hyperboloid into two parts. The surface of the sphere or of the hyperboloid curves in a three-dimensional space. The space of our three-dimensional universe must instead curve in a four-dimensional space, which our perceptions of three-dimensional beings cannot grasp. We shall therefore try to reason by analogy.

A two-dimensional being would be able to perceive whether his universe is Euclidean and unlimited or curved positively or negatively, by studying some of its geometrical properties. For example in a plane triangle, the sum of the internal angles is 180°. On a spherical surface, the spherical triangle has three internal angles the sum of which is greater than 180°. On the other hand, on a hyperbolic surface the sum of the internal angles of a triangle is less than 180°.

The geometrical property, which could help to solve the question of the form of the universe, is the manner in which the ratio between the volume and the radius of a sphere varies. In Euclidean space, the volume is proportional to the cube of the radius ($V = $ const. $\times R^3$). In the negatively curved space, the volume increases more rapidly than the cube of the radius ($V = $ const. $\times R^{3+\epsilon}$, that is to say the volume is proportional to the radius raised to a power a little greater than 3). In the positively curved space, the volume increases more slowly than the cube of the radius ($V = $ const. $\times R^{3-\epsilon}$, that is to say the volume is proportional to the radius raised to a power a little less than 3). Observations will tell us whether the volume of given spheres of space, which have the observer at the centre, increases proportionally to the cube of the radius or more slowly or more quickly. Let us assume that N is proportional to the volume, when N is the number of galaxies present in a given sphere. Galaxy counts will have to tell us whether N increases proportionally to, or more slowly or more quickly than, the cube of the distance of the furthest galaxies under consideration, the distance being the radius of the sphere.

In figure 47 we see that the galaxies, here represented by dots, are uniformly distributed on both the spherical and hyperbolical surface.

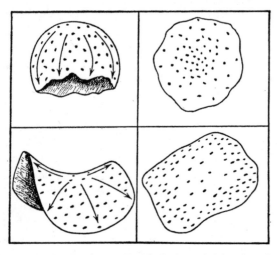

FIG. 47. Two-dimensional universe. Positively curved (above) and negatively curved (below)

If, however, we flatten these surfaces into plane surfaces, we notice that the distribution of the dots is no longer uniform. In both cases the number of dots increases when the area of the surface under consideration increases, but in the case of the spherical surface it increases more slowly because the dots thin out as the area becomes larger, while the opposite occurs for the hyperbolic surface. This test, however, is not conclusive, because of the uncertainty of the distance of the furthest galaxies. Hubble carried out this test by assuming that the distances of the galaxies could be evaluated from their apparent magnitude. It is approximately true to say that the fainter a galaxy is the further it is from us. This would be true if all galaxies had the same absolute magnitude. If we take a very large number of galaxies, we can assume that on average the variations of absolute magnitude will be compensated. The result of Hubble's investigation was that the universe must be finite and have a radius of a few thousand millions of light-years. This method, however, is also based on the fundamental hypothesis that the intrinsic brightness of a galaxy does not change with time; instead the opposite is more probable because galaxies, like individual stars, are evolving continuously. Therefore the question is complicated by the fact that we see galaxies in different epochs of time, according to their distance from us. If we assume that galaxies decrease in brightness with age, then the further galaxies, which we see, as it were, earlier in time, and which therefore are of more recent formation, will have greater intrinsic brightness than galaxies which are nearer to us. Their distance will be greater than that previously estimated when it was assumed that the brightness of galaxies did not diminish with age. The result of this correction is such that will lead us to conclusions which are exactly the opposite to those given above, that is to say our universe must be infinite and negatively curved. This test therefore, theoretically possible, has no meaning unless we know how the luminosity of galaxies changes with age. A test based on the study of the red-shift can give a decision in favour of either the steady state or the evolution theory and at the same time also give a decision on the curvature of the universe. We know that the red-shift is greater the further a galaxy is from us. It is very important to know whether between the velocity of recession and the distance exists a relation of close proportionality.

If the steady state theory is true, then the universe has been expanding since infinite time at a constant rate. On the other hand, if the evolution theory is true, then expansion is the result of an explosion. In this case the velocity of expansion has been diminishing constantly, because of the brake applied by the gravitational attraction of matter. Then the galaxies which are further away and which we see 'in the past' must have a velocity of recession greater than the one they would have with a constant rate of expansion. Moreover, since the law governing the expansion of a Euclidean universe is different from that regulating the expansion of a positively or negatively curved universe, the relation between velocity and distance must also give an answer to the question of the curvature of the universe. Once the laws are defined which regulate the variation of velocity with distance in the various hypotheses (steady state or evolution, Euclidean, positively or negatively curved universe) then the comparison with the observations may give an answer. But the relation between distance and velocity is practically the same in all the various hypotheses, until we reach distances near one thousand million light-years. Only at these distances do the theoretical relations which are valid for the various models of the universe deviate enough to be submitted to experimental tests.

Humason, with the 200-inch, has carried out such a test and he has found that six clusters of galaxies, at a distance of approximately one thousand million light-years, show a velocity of recession 10,000 km./s. greater than that we would expect in a strictly proportional relation between velocity and distance. We reach therefore the conclusion that a thousand million years ago the universe was expanding at a faster rate than at present. This would confirm the evolution theory. Moreover everything is in favour of a positive curvature of the universe. Having said this we must however bear in mind that the errors of measurements are considerable and therefore the test cannot, for the time being, be taken as decisive.

It is indeed to be hoped that much more information will be given to us by radio-telescopes and electron-telescopes, both being able to reach further in space than optical telescopes. Only by probing further in the universe, and hence further back in time, can we hope to be able to give an answer to this fascinating cosmological problem.

Appendix

IN THIS appendix we shall recall some of the main definitions used in astronomy and which we have used in previous chapters.

1. Co-ordinates: Equatorial and galactic.

The sky appears to us as the surface of a very large sphere of which we occupy the centre.

Because of the terrestrial rotation from west to east, the whole sky appears to move from east to west, rotating on an axis which is parallel to the terrestrial axis and directed to a point near the Pole Star. This point is the 'celestial North Pole'. In order to identify the position of a star in the sky, we use a method which is similar to that adopted on the Earth to mark the position of a point on its surface. The geographical latitude measures, in degrees, the distance of a place from the terrestrial equator, similarly *declination* measures the distance of a star from the *celestial equator*, which is the imaginary line on the celestial sphere where the plane of the Earth's equator, extended, cuts the sky. As the longitude measures the distance, in degrees or hours, of a place from the Greenwich meridian, so the *right ascension* measures the distance, in degrees or hours, of a star from a selected point which is that of the position of the Sun on March 21st (vernal equinox). On this date the Sun is on the celestial equator at a point which is called the *first point of Aries* and is denoted by γ (fig. a).

In the study of the galactic structure it is more convenient to use a different set of co-ordinates, which determines the position of a star with reference to the plane where the majority of stars and interstellar matter are found. This place is the *galactic equator*. By analogy with the geographical co-ordinates the *galactic latitude* measures, in degrees, the distance of a celestial object from the plane of the galactic equator. The *galactic longitude* is the arc on the galactic equator which measures, in degrees, the distance of a galactic meridian from a selected zero point on the galactic equator. This point, which is the equivalent to the one where the meridian of Greenwich cuts the terrestrial equator, is one of the two points where the celestial equator cuts the galactic equator. The one with right ascension 280° has been selected as zero point.

The galactic equator intersects the celestial equator at an angle of 63° (fig. a).

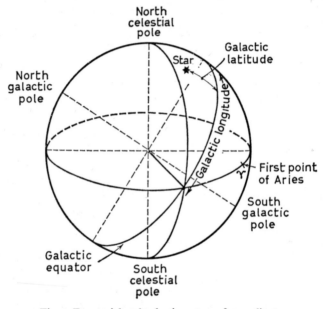

Fig. a. Equatorial and galactic system of co-ordinates

2. Unit of measure of distances.

Because of the great distances in astronomy a suitable unit had to be chosen. The Astronomical Unit (A.U.), which is equal to the distance between the Earth and the Sun, is 93,005,000 miles. This unit, which is useful in the solar system, is too small when dealing with objects outside the solar system. For interstellar distances we use the *parsec*, which is the distance from which the radius of the Earth's orbit is seen under an angle of 1 second of arc. The parsec is equal to 1.9×10^{13} miles, nearly 20 million million miles.

APPENDIX

Another unit which is also used is the *light-year*, which is the distance light travels in a year. Remembering that light travels at the speed of 186,000 miles per second, one light-year is equal to $5\cdot88 \times 10^{12}$ miles, nearly 6 million million miles. The parsec is equal to $3\cdot26$ light-years.

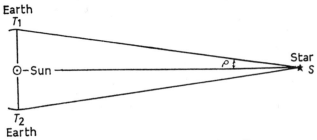

Fig. b. Parallax of a star or annual parallax

Direct measurements of stellar distances can be made by determining the *parallax* of a star. This is the angle under which the semi-diameter of the orbit of the Earth is seen from a star. In practice the position of a star is determined at a given time and is determined again six months later, when the Earth is occupying the opposite position in its orbit. With the aid of trigonometry it is a simple matter to determine the parallax.

In the triangle T_1T_2S (fig. b) the distance T_1T_2 is known and the two angles ST_1T_2 and ST_2T_1 can be determined. We have, therefore, enough information to enable us to obtain the value of the angle T_1ST_2. Half this angle is the parallax p. This angle, however, is very small as it does not exceed 1 second of arc even for the star nearest to us (Proxima Centauri). It follows that the errors of measurement can be considerable.

The parallax p can be determined trigonometrically only for stars which are relatively near to us. For p smaller than $0''\cdot01$, the measurements become very uncertain and for values approaching $0''\cdot001$ they have no meaning.

3. Stellar magnitudes.

In order to measure the energy radiating from a star we measure the quantity of energy which is received by a detector per unit time.

APPENDIX

A detector is some sort of equipment which is sensitive to radiation; it may be the retina of the human eye, a photographic plate, the cathode of a photo-cell or the junction of a thermocouple. In other words any instrument in which the radiation received is able to cause changes which can be felt and measured. So the radiation arriving on the retina will excite the optical nerve, which will transmit to the brain the sensation of light; on the photographic plate it will produce a darkening of the emulsion, on the cathode of a photo-cell or on the junction of a thermocouple, it will produce an electric current which will flow in the circuit of which they are part. In photometric terms, the energy per unit time is called *flux*.

Since very early times stars have been divided into classes of magnitude according to their brightness. Ptolemy divided them into six classes, placing in the first the brightest stars and in the sixth those which were just within the limit of visibility of the unaided eye.

In modern times the historical scale of Ptolemy has been kept but some necessary modifications and adjustments have been introduced to bring it into line with the accuracy of modern methods of measurements. These have shown that the difference between any two consecutive classes of magnitude corresponds to an almost constant ratio of fluxes. Two stars having a difference of 5 magnitudes have relative fluxes which have a ratio of 1 to 100. That is to say we receive from a star of magnitude 1 a flux 100 times greater than that received from a star of magnitude 6.

The relation between magnitude and flux is given by Pogson formula:

$$m_1 - m_2 = 2 \cdot 5 \log \frac{F_2}{F_1}$$

where m_1 and m_2 are stellar magnitudes and F_1 and F_2 their relative fluxes. For $F_2/F_1 = 100$ $m_1 - m_2$ is 5. This means that if F_2 is 100 times greater than F_1 then m_1 is 5 magnitudes greater than m_2. This agrees with Ptolemy's scale according to which the greater the magnitude the less bright is the star.

If $m_1 - m_2 = 1$ then $\log(F_2/F_1) = 1/2 \cdot 5 = 0 \cdot 4$, so that $F_2/F_1 = 2 \cdot 512$. Therefore a star of magnitude m radiates $2 \cdot 512$ times more than a star of magnitude $m + 1$.

These magnitudes directly linked to the flux we receive, depend not only on the quantity of energy radiated into space, every second by a star, but also on its distance from us and therefore they are called *apparent* magnitudes. If we want to make our measurements independent of the distance, we must introduce the *absolute* magnitude, that is the magnitudes the stars would appear to have if they were all placed at a standard distance from us. We shall now consider what is the relation between apparent magnitude m and absolute magnitude M.

Since the flux we receive is inversely proportional to the square of the distance, between the flux F of a star at a distance r and the flux F_1 which we would receive from the standard distance r_1 there exists the following relation:

$$F_1/F = r^2/r_1{}^2$$

but $m - M = 2\cdot5 \log(F_1/F)$ and therefore:

$$m - M = 2\cdot5 \log(r^2/r_1{}^2) = 5 \log r - 5 \log r_1$$

The standard distance r is taken to be 10 parsecs, and therefore the relation between apparent and absolute magnitude becomes:

$$m - M = 5 \log r - 5$$

The above is true as long as we consider the interstellar space to be empty, otherwise the absorption due to interstellar matter will reduce the flux. The reduction will be greater when the absorbing layer, through which the flux travels, and the absorbing power are greater. Assuming an absorption a for every 1,000 parsecs, then the above relation becomes:

$$m - M = 5 \log r - 5 + \frac{ar}{1,000}$$

All this means that a star of apparent magnitude m will have an absolute magnitude $M = m - 5 \log r + 5$ if the absorption is zero, otherwise the absolute magnitude will have to be decreased by a magnitudes for every 1,000 parsecs of absorbing matter having a coefficient of absorption a.

4. Point objects and extended objects.

The dimensions of a star are always very small in relation to its distance from us. While therefore the measurement of distance is better expressed in light-years or parsecs, the radius of stars can easily be expressed in miles. It follows that the angle under which we see the diameter of the stars is so small that it is almost always non-measurable or, in other words, the stars appear as points.

The stellar magnitudes we have just defined are related to the flux, a quantity which is independent of the unknown dimensions of the light source, and therefore it is particularly suitable in this case when we are dealing with point sources. When, however, we are, as in this book, dealing with nebulae and galaxies, the dimensions of which are so great that they are not negligible compared with their great distances from us, they will appear with measurable dimensions and we shall be able to measure their angular diameter a as seen from the Earth. The angular diameter is given by the ratio of two quantities, generally unknown, D (linear diameter) and r (distance):

$$a = \frac{D}{r}$$

where a is expressed in radians. In such cases we shall be able to measure not only the flux, but also the flux per unit solid angle. When looking at a surface S from a distance r, the solid angle is $\omega = S/r^2$. Therefore for a circular object of angular diameter a, linear diameter D at a distance r, besides the flux F we shall measure also:

$$\frac{F}{\frac{\pi D^2}{4r^2}} = \frac{F}{\frac{\pi a^2}{4}}$$

We can then define a magnitude m which corresponds to the flux and a magnitude μ which corresponds to the flux per solid angle. From Pogson's formula we then have:

$$m - \mu = 2 \cdot 50 \log \frac{4F/\pi a^2}{F} = 2 \cdot 50 \log \frac{4}{\pi a^2}$$

While for the great majority of stars the fact that we do not know their angular diameter makes it impossible to determine the energy emitted per unit time, by the unit area, in the case of the galaxies —the diameters of which can easily be measured—this is possible.

5. Temperature.

When we speak of stellar temperature, we must remember that the word has no precise and absolute meaning. The temperature of a star varies from about 10 million degrees at the centre to a few thousand degrees at the surface.

Since the radiation which we receive and measure comes only from the more external layers of the star, it can only give us direct information about the surface temperature and it is this that we mean when we talk of stellar temperatures.

The distribution of energy at the various wavelengths is strictly linked with the temperature. For instance we know that as we heat a piece of metal it will assume first a red colour and as the temperature increases it will change into orange and then white. In a similar manner the hotter stars radiate mainly in the violet and blue and appear to us of a whitish-blue colour. As the temperature decreases the colour changes from white to white-yellow, from yellow to orange and from orange to red. The 'colour index' is an objective measure of the colour and hence, indirectly, of the temperature of a star. The colour index is defined as the difference between the photographic and the visual magnitude of a star:

$$c = m_p - m_v$$

The magnitude of a star depends also on the detector we use to measure it, because in general a detector is not equally sensitive to all radiations. For instance, the eye has a maximum sensitivity in the yellow-green, that is in the region of λ 5700 Å. The common photographic emulsion, on the other hand, is sensitive in the blue-violet, in the region of λ 4000 Å. As a result of this, a blue star, which radiates mainly in the violet and very little in the yellow region, will appear brighter to the photographic emulsion than to the eye. The opposite will occur for a yellow star. If we use a detector which is equally sensitive to all radiations, such as a thermocouple, then we have the *bolometric* magnitude.

It has been agreed to take as zero the colour index of white stars, then blue stars will have a negative colour index, while yellow and red stars will have a positive one.

6. Spectra.

The atoms in the atmosphere of a star can absorb radiations originating in deeper layers, at some particular wavelengths rather than others, according to the surface temperature of the star.

In the very hot blue stars, the helium atoms which require high

APPENDIX

temperatures in order to be excited, produce absorption lines which are not present in colder stars. In the spectra of the latter, instead, the lines of metals predominate which can be more easily excited even at low temperatures. Therefore the variation of the energy distribution in the continuum, which can be identified as a variation of colour, is accompanied by a variation in the characteristics of the line spectrum.

Astronomers have divided stellar spectra into a number of classes closely related to the surface temperature, according to colour, intensity and the presence of given absorption lines. In Table A are given the main spectral classes of 'Draper's classification'.

TABLE A

Class	Colour	Colour index	Surface Temperature (° K.)	Main absorption lines
O	blue	−0·30	> 30,000	HeII, CIII, NIII, OIII, SiIV
B	blue-white	−0·15	30,000–10,000	HeI, CII, NII, OII, SiIII
A	white	0·00	15,000–10,000	H, SiII, MgII
F	white-yellow	+0·40	10,000– 7,000	H, ionized metals
G	yellow	+0·80	7,000– 5,000	neutral and ionized metals
K	orange	+1·20	5,000– 4,000	neutral metals
M	red	+1·80	< 4,000	molecular bands

The values given in the above table are mean values, in the sense that each spectral class is further subdivided into 10 subdivisions. These are denoted by: *A*0, *A*1 . . . *A*9; *F*0, *F*1 . . . *F*9 and so on.

7. Doppler effect.

When a source of light or of sound waves *S* is in motion with reference to an observer *O*, the frequency of the waves received by the observer is different from that originally emitted by the source. More precisely, when the motion of the source is away from the observer, the frequency diminishes.

If at a given time the source *S* emits radiations of a given frequency, in a second, a given number of wavelengths travels the

APPENDIX

distance *SO*. If *S* approaches *O*, the distance *SO* diminishes, but in it the same number of wavelengths must be included, corresponding to the frequency at which the source is emitting. It follows that the number of wavelengths must be compressed and the observer will receive waves of higher frequency. The opposite will take place if *S* is receding.

If we call v the velocity of the source along *SO*, c the velocity of light, λ the wavelength of the radiation under consideration, and △λ the difference between the wavelength of the radiation emitted by the source and that of the radiation received by the observer, we have:

$$\triangle\lambda = \frac{\lambda v}{c}$$

Since △λ is positive when the velocity is of recession and negative in the opposite case, v will be positive when the source is receding. When this happens the lines, in the spectrum of the source, will be displaced towards the longer wavelengths, or as we say, towards the red (red-shift). Therefore for positive values of △λ the stars recede from the Earth and for negative values of △λ the stars approach.

Bibliography

GENERAL BOOKS

G. ABETTI. *Le stelle e i pianeti* (Einaudi, Torino, 1956). (English translation in preparation. Faber & Faber, London.)

G. ABETTI. *L'Unità del Cosmo* (Bompiani, Milano, 1964).

L. H. ALLER. *Gaseous Nebulae* (Chapman & Hall, London, 1956).

G. ARMELLINI. *Trattato di astronomia siderale*, vol. 3, 'Le nebulose' (Zanichelli, Bologna, 1936).

E. E. BARNARD. *A photographic Atlas of selected regions of the Milky Way* (Carnegie Institution, Washington, 1927).

W. BECKER. *Sterne und Sternsysteme* (Steinkopff, Dresden, 1950).

B. J. and O. F. BOK. *The Milky Way* (Harvard University Press, Cambridge, Mass., 1957).

G. CECCHINI. *Il cielo*, vols. 1 and 2 (U.T.E.T., Torino, 1952).

J. DUFAY. *Nébuleuses galactiques et matière interstellaire* (Albin Michel, Paris, 1954).

P. EMANUELLI. *Il cielo e le sue meraviglie* (Hoepli, Milano, 1934).

M. HACK. *La radioastronomia* (Laterza, Bari, 1960).

M. HACK. *L'Universo* (Feltrinelli, Milano, 1963).

E. HUBBLE. *The realm of the nebulae* (Yale University Press, New Haven, Conn., 1936).

C. PAYNE GAPOSHKIN. *Introduction to Astronomy* (Prentice Hall, New York, 1954).

H. SHAPLEY. *Galaxies* (Blakiston, Philadelphia, 1943).

M. WALDMEIER. *Einführung in die Astrophysik* (Birkhäuser, Bale, 1948).

K. WURM. 'Die planetarischen Nebel' (*Scientia Astronomica*, vol. 1, 1951).

VARIOUS AUTHORS. *The Structure of the Galaxy* (Publ. Ast. Obs. Univ. Mich., vol. 10, 1951).

BIBLIOGRAPHY

Chapter II

A. LALLEMANDE and others. *Sur des spectres des nébuleuses obtenus par photographie électronique* (Publ. Obs. Haute Provence, vol. IV, No. 18, 1958).

Chapter III

L. H. ALLER. *Gaseous Nebulae* (see above).
L. H. ALLER. *Astrophysics*, vol. 2 (Ronald Press, New York, 1954).
I. S. BOWEN. *Astrophysical Journal*, vol. 67, 1 (1928); vol. 81, 1 (1935).
J. DUFAY. *Nébuleuses galactiques et matière interstellaire* (see above).
D. H. MENZEL and others. 'Physical processes in gaseous nebulae' (*Astrophysical Journal*, 1937).
R. MINKOWSKI. Publ. Astr. Obs. Univ. Mich., vol. 10, 25 (1951).
I. S. ŠKLOVSKIJ. *Non-stable Stars* (Symp. I.A.U., Univ. Press, Cambridge, p. 83, 1957).
B. VORONCOV-VELJAMINOV. *Gasnebel und neue Sterne* (Verlag Kultur und Fortschritt, Berlin, 1953).
VARIOUS AUTHORS. Publ. Lick. Obs., vol. 13 (1918).

Chapter IV

W. BAADE. *Astrophysical Journal*, vol. 96, 188 (1942).
J. C. DUNCAN. *Astrophysical Journal*, vol. 51, 5 (1920); vol. 57, 146 (1923).
R. MINKOWSKI. *Astrophysical Journal*, vol. 96, 199 (1942).
R. MINKOWSKI. Publ. Astr. Soc. Pacif., vol. 61, 151 (1949).
L. ROSINO. *Coelum*, vol. 16, 46 (1948).
G. A. ŠAJN and V. F. GAZE. *Atlas of diffuse nebulae*. Acc. of Sc. USSR (Moscow, 1952). *Mitt. Astr. Obs. Krim*, vol. 8, 3 (1952).
O. STRUVE. *Sky and Telescope*, vol. 11, 187 (1952); vol. 16, 322 (1957).
A. D. THACKERAY. *Monthly Notices*, R.A.S., vol. 110, 350 (1950).
L. VOLTJER. Bull. Astr. Inst. Netherlands, No. 483 (1958).

Chapter V

B. J. BOK. In *Vistas in Astronomy*, vol. 2, 1524 (Pergamon Press, London, 1956).

BIBLIOGRAPHY

A. COLACEVICH. *La materia interstellare Atti Convegno Milano-Merate* (Soc. Astr. Ital., September 1951).

J. DUNCAN. *Astrophysical Journal*, vol. 53, 392 (1921); vol. 57, 137 (1923).

J. GREENSTEIN. 'Interstellar matter' in *Astrophysics*, edited by J. Hynck (McGraw-Hill, New York, 1951, p. 526).

M. HUMASON, N. MAYALL and A. SANDAGE. *Astrophysical Journal*, vol. 61, 97 (1956).

Chapter VI

W. BAADE. Publ. Astr. Obs. Univ. Michigan, vol. 10, 7.

B. J. and O. F. BOK. *The Milky Way* (see above).

G. CECCHINI. *Il cielo* (see above), vol. 2.

P. COUDERC. *L'Univers* (Presses Universitaires de France, Paris, 1955).

M. HACK. *Esplorazioni Radioastronomiche* (Boringhieri, Torino, 1964).

F. HOYLE. *Frontiers of Astronomy* (Heinemann Ltd., London, 1955).

O. STRUVE. *Stellar Evolution* (University Press, Princeton, N.J., 1950).

Chapter VII

W. BAADE. *Sky and Telescope*, vol. 14, 371 (1955).

W. BAADE and N. MAYALL. *Problems of Cosmical Aerodynamics*, p. 165 (1957).

W. BAADE. *Observatory* 119 (1957).

W. BAUM and M. SCHWARZSCHILD. *Astrophysical Journal*, vol. 60, 247 (1955).

W. BECKER. In *Vistas in Astronomy* (see above), vol. 2, 1515.

R. BROWN and C. HAZARD. *Monthly Notices*, R.A.S., vol. 11, 357 (1951).

R. COUTREZ. *Radioastronomie* (Mon. Abs. Roy. Bruxelles, No. 5, 1956).

G. DE VAUCOULEURS. *Astronomie*, vol. 64, 380 (19 . . .).

G. DE VAUCOULEURS. *L'exploration des galaxies voisines* (Masson, Paris, 1958).

M. HACK. *Esplorazioni Radioastronomiche* (Boringhieri, Torino, 1964).

BIBLIOGRAPHY

E. HUBBLE and A. SANDAGE. *Astrophysical Journal*, vol. 118, 353 (1954).

J. B. IRWIN. *Astrophysical Journal*, vol. 57, 15 (1952).

B. LINDBLAD. Publ. Astr. Soc. Pacif. (1951).

B. MILLS. *Austr. J. Sc. Res.*, vol. 8, 368 (1955).

A. SANDAGE. *Astrophysical Journal*, vol. 59, 180, 273 (1954).

G. A. ŠAJN. *Mitt. Astr. Obs. Krim.*, vol. 11, 3 (1955).

M. SCHWARZSCHILD. *Astrophysical Journal*, vol. 59, 273 (1954).

C. SEYFERT. Publ. Astr. Soc. Pacif., vol. 63, 72 (1951).

C. D. SHANE. In *Vistas in Astronomy*, vol. 2, 1574.

C. D. SHANE and C. WIRTANEN. *Astrophysical Journal*, vol. 59, 285 (1954).

O. STRUVE. *Sky and Telescope*, vol. 14, 52 (1955).

A. THACKERAY and A. WESSELINK. Radcliffe Obs. Rep. No. 1 (1955).

H. VAN DE HULST, E. RAIMOND and H. VAN WOERDEN. Bull. Astr. Inst. Netherlands, No. 480 (1957).

B. VORONCOV-VELJAMINOV. *Astrophysical Journal*, vol. 55, 487 (1951).

F. ZWICKY. Publ. Astr. Soc. Pacif., vol. 62, 196 (1950); vol. 63, 61 (1951).

Chapter VIII

H. BONDI and T. GOLD. *The Steady State Theory of the Expanding Universe* (*Monthly Notices* R.A.S., vol. 108, 252, (1948)).

P. COUDERC. *L'expansion de l'Univers* (Presses Universitaires de France, Paris, 1950).

G. GAMOW. *The Creation of the Universe* (Viking Press, New York, 1952).

F. HOYLE. *Frontiers of Astronomy* (see above).

E. HUBBLE. *The Realm of the Nebulae* (see above).

H. SHAPLEY. *Galaxies* (see above).

VARIOUS AUTHORS. *Sci. Amer.*, vol. 195, No. 3 (1956).

Index

INDEX

260

INDEX

263